LARRY D. UNDERWOOD
THE Butternut Guerillas

WITH FOREWORD BY DEE BROWN

Dageforde Publishing

ISBN # 0-9637515-8-1
Library of Congress Catalog Card Number: 94-68459

Cover Art by Angie Johnson Art Productions

Printed in the United States of America.

Dageforde Publishing
941 'O' Street, Suite 728
Lincoln, NE 68508-3625

Contents

Grierson's Raid had many heroes who risked their lives in courageous deeds, audacious dashes, and reckless diversions on horseback, but the most daring of all were the Butternut Guerillas. From the day Lieutenant-Colonel William Blackburn conceived them in his bold imagination and entrusted them to his Canadian-born sergeant, Richard Surby, the Butternut Guerrillas were the forward eyes and ears — and tricksters — for that southbound cavalry column commanded by the former music teacher, Benjamin H. Grierson.

Surby of course claimed that he thought up the whole scheme, and perhaps he did, but without the ill-fated Blackburn's enthusiastic creativity and support, the Butternut Guerrillas would never have come to fruition, nor likely would such a rare group of Illinois derring-doers have been so shrewdly chosen from the ranks. Their first names reveal their hardy frontier heritage — Isaac, Lycurgus, Samuel, Uriah, and so on.

There was nothing these young daredevils flinched from doing. Dressed in their confiscated "Secesh" apparel — slouch hats, gray shirts, and butternut jeans — they became a band of military confidence men capable of outwitting their shrewdest adversaries with amazing nonchalance.

In this book, Larry Underwood has given the Butternut Guerrillas their full due, presenting a much broader picture of their activities and their personalities then was possible in *Grierson's Raid.*

Although he has introduced dialogue and other devices of fiction, these serve to enliven the story. Larry Underwood has held true to the history of the expedition, giving us a realistic narrative of one very special operation during the fascinating ordeal of the American past — our own Civil War.

Dee Brown

Benjamin Grierson (Author's Collection)

Preface

To the second edition

The story of Grierson's Raid through the Mississippi in the Spring of 1863 has been told. On May 18, 1863, readers in the New York *Times* saw the story for the first time. It had been filed from Louisiana two weeks after the raid was completed. Two years later, in 1865, Richard W. Surby, a sergeant in the Seventh Illinois Cavalry, told his version of the story in a book entitled, *Grierson Raids*. Two other stories were related in the same volume, *Hatch's Sixty-Four Days March* and *Chickasaw the Scout*. The Illinois State Historical Society in its Transaction for 1907 included Stephen A. Forbes' version, "Grierson's Cavalry Raid." And in 1911, when Benjamin Henry Grierson was dying, he revised his autobiography which included the story of the raid. There were other stories too, but perhaps none from participants as Surby, Forbes, and Grierson had been.

Of the non-participants, Dee Brown's *Grierson's Raid* (University of Illinois, 1954) is an excellent work. Brown combined his unique style of writing, his knowledge of the Civil War, and the stories of the participants into an unusually interesting history of the raid.

This story is different. It takes the reader through the raid from the viewpoint of the enlisted men, the real leaders of the raid, the Butternut Guerillas. It is through their eyes and ears that the raid occurs to the reader. To insure historical accuracy, and to clarify omissions in Richard W. Surby's book published in 1865, the *Reports of the Adjutant General of the State of Illinois, 1861-66* was consulted as well as *The War of the Rebellion: Official Records of the Union and Confederate Armies*.

Biographical sketches of some of the participants of the raid from *History of Gallatin, Saline, Hamilton, Franklin and Williamson Counties, Illinois*, published by the Goodspeed Publishing Company in Chicago during 1887, were helpful as well.

Finally, there are all those others that encouraged the publication of this work. They know who they are and have received their thanks. I am especially grateful to Bruce Campbell who made this possible, to Dee Brown who gave me the seed for the book, and to my family who gave a great deal of their lives that these men, the men of the Sixth and Seventh Illinois, could again live.

Larry Underwood
Box 66A
Meppen, Illinois 62013

Preface

There is a magic about history. One can be transported in time and space by the mere opening of a book. A visit to an historic site will do the same thing. That magic may rise up out of a morning fog or a marvelous sunset. What was life like then? What did people hate? Love? Die for?

Every historian, every reader longs for that magic. This story of Grierson's Raid has created that magic for me. This 1863 Raid is as exciting — and magical — to this author as it was fourteen years ago when I first began research for *The Butternut Guerillas: A Story of Grierson's Raid.* In the thirteen years since the book appeared — and sold out, interest continues to build.

Writing a book is a lonely business. Publication of a popular book is not. Readers of the First Edition shared their thoughts, their information, their heart-felt interest in this Civil War event.

Civil War buffs from North and South, East and West continue to write, inquire about incidents, share Civil War letters and send along war records of relatives. Artifacts, especially bullets, that belonged to 6th and 7th Illinois Cavalrymen, were also shared with the author.

Between April 17 and May 2, 1863, Union Cavalrymen in the command of Col. Benjamin H. Grierson scratched out a remarkable place in United States and Civil War history. It is still one of the most exciting stories to come out of the great and terrible Civil War. The historical renderings of the events of the raid create a sort of magic, one that transports the reader back to those times, those days.

Along with the magic, the story creates its own excitement. The daring men who led the raid, "the Butternut Guerillas," continue to be dashing and risk-taking in their endeavors to traverse Mississippi with the purpose of giving Gen. Ulysses S. Grant an edge in the crucial contest at Vicksburg.

In the amazing sixteen-day foray behind enemy lines, Grierson's command struck fear into Mississippi folks in New Albany, Pontotoc, Houston, Starkville, Louisville and Philadelphia. Confederate hatred of these Illinois horse soldiers boiled at Decatur, Newton Station, Garlandville, Montrose, Pineville, and Raleigh. Fear followed the blue-coated cavalrymen to Westville, Gallatin, Union Church, Bogue Chitto, Summit — and then there was the incident at Wall's Bridge.

The story has breathed life and magic into re-enactor groups, as well. One of these, the 7th Illinois Cavalry from Springfield, Illinois, continues to make that magic. Commanded by Major Karl Luthin, a veterinarian, this group will take your breath away. Almost if by magic, they sweep away the 20th Century and propel their audience into another age.

A few years ago in Mississippi, while the 7th Illinois Cavalry prepared to re-enact the raid on Newton Station, an incident demonstrated this magic. A mother and her daughters, while driving along a country road, spied two horse soldiers dressed as Confederate scouts riding toward them. The woman stopped, backed her car off the road, and waited for the soldiers to pass. She encouraged her daughters, one just five to get out and wave to the men and horses as they passed.

To their surprise, the riders did not pass, but wheeled their horses within a few feet of the automobile, reined to a halt, and one announced sternly, "Ma'am, we are scouts on our way through the area warning all women and children to take refuge. Grierson's Raiders are close behind us, and they are burning and destroying everything in their path."

It was too much for the youngsters. Frightened, they scampered into the safety of the car. The riders, realizing what they had done, explained that they were only "pretending." But for one magical moment, those little girls knew what it was like to have been in the path of Grierson's Raiders in the spring of 1863.

A couple years ago, I drove the length of Mississippi, paralleling as closely as possible the route these Illinoisans rode, searching for some of that magic. I wondered about "Citizen Beers," who was killed at Pontotoc. My Sunday morning visit to Philadelphia may have been as quiet as it was when the scouts found the streets deserted 130 years earlier. And in Decatur, what happened to the old-fashioned country inn with pigeonhole windows? The magic was there at Newton where a new station had been built to replace the one burned in 1863. Where are those brave Mississippians armed with shotguns that defended Garlandville? Can a visitor really hear bullets tearing through the trees, wounded horses screaming and dying men crying at Wall's Bridge over the Tickfaw along Route 584? The magic is still there in the fields, forests, rivers and towns of Mississippi.

With the coming of the Second Edition of *The Butternut Guerillas: A Story of Grierson's Raid,* I can only hope that the magic will be there for the readers. The Civil War, the 6th and 7th Illinois, and the Mississippi raid in the spring of 1863 all have a special magic about them.

TUESDAY, APRIL 21, 1863: "Riding up through the nooning bivouac of the Sixth Illinois, we excited some little curiosity and sold the boys completely. They thought we were prisoners and bored us with a thousand questions. After this we went by the name of "The Butternut Guerillas.""*

Sgt. Richard Surby, Co. A, 7th Illinois Cavalry

*Butternuts was a nickname for Confederate soldiers whose uniforms were dyed butternut brown with walnut hulls or copperas solution.

Approximate route followed by the Butternut Guerillas through Mississippi in the spring of 1863.

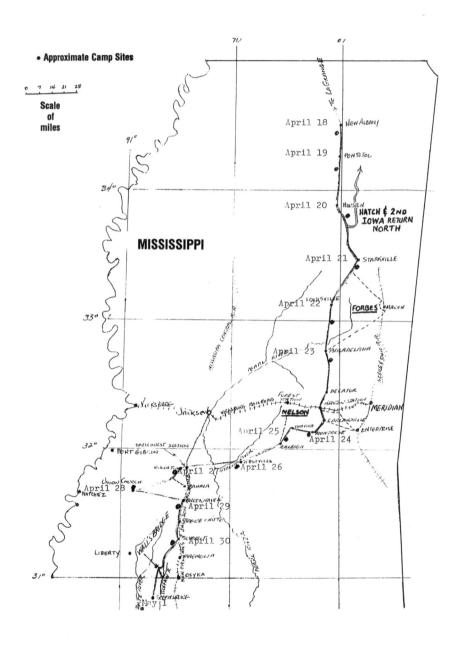

Chapter 1

Noon — April 16, 1863
Near La Grange, Tennessee

A sudden breeze ruffled the young leaves on the tall trees as the blue-uniformed soldiers strolled sporadically back to their ragged, flapping tents in the oak grove. The stew and beef they'd gorged on made some drowsy; others crawled into their tents on their knees scratching around looking for bits of stationery to write a letter home.

Nearby a tailed pennant flapped, the words "7th Ill Cav" stitched neatly onto it. Then someone felt a drop of moisture and too quickly, it rained. The pennant ceased fluttering. Soon it sagged lifeless against the staff, soaked.

In an officer's tent, a tall, barrel-chested man ran his fingers through his rumpled hair. He pulled a stub of a pencil from his breast pocket. Smoothing the paper with his strong hand, Lieutenant-Colonel Blackburn began to scrawl his last letter — ever.

Direct Via Memphis

La Grange, Tenn.
April 16"1863

My dear Old Friend Jud,

I have been a Colonel now near Two months. You will be glad to hear that I am not one of them mean officers you are hearing about. We got a good Company and our Cavalry is the Best. I got the Colonel because of the long time we were gone in December. Maybe you heard of it in the papers. We will be in the papers again when you get this letter. Watch for my name. I may be a General by then. Ha.

I sent a Revolver for Silas Morgan. I expect you will get it before you get this letter. If he cannot get the Cartiges in Paris write in your next letter and I will send you the address of the manufacturing company and you can get a lot if you would rather have a Cilinder that you can use in fixed ammunition you can get another one and the Bullet moulds with it by sending to New York. It will not cost much. I think that a splendid Pistol. I did not have a oppertunity of trying her out one of the boys which owned her before I did says he could hit a man 150 yards.

You ask of my horse. He was killed. But I have one now that is much beter. He is a huge bay Morgan. Can run like the Wind.

I hear the Beef sells so high I would be rich now. Is that right. Is it as high as They say. Maybe I will go West when I get out the War and maybe Kansas will be the place. If the R.R. goes there it will boom much more than Paris.

Richard Surby is still here with me. He has no word from his brothers that he used to talk about. He is much worried that they are Dead. But he does not talk about Them. They are in the Infantry and you get Dead there so easy. But not in the Cavalry. We don't loose many Men except to sickness. It is terrible in the Winter.

I guess I have written all I can think of at present. Don't forget to watch the Papers for me.

Your old Friend.
(Signed) William Blackburn, Lt.Colonel
Co.A, Seventh Ill. Cavalry

Not more than ten yards across the bare, grassless mud from the Sibley tent, under a brush and canvas-draped lean-to, Richard Surby scratched out a reply to a letter received a day earlier. He pulled a blanket around his shoulders, shook off the dampness and began:

direct via Memphis

La Grange (Tennessee)
16 April 63

My dear beloved Father and Mother,

I received you ever welcome letter of The 2nd Inst. and was glad to hear you were all well. I am in Tolerable good health. I had Two very severe shakes, but got Them broke. It is raining and our Tents do not afford The best shelter in The world but I hope I may escape having any more chills for They are very unpleasant. There are various conjectures as to what we are about. I can only say that we are going for another ride such as the one I wrote of in January.

As in The past, I ask That you not fret. Since leaving you years ago, I have always looked out for myself in the safest ways That I know how. I have many Friends and if anything every slips me up They will come and Talk to you. My oldest Friend, Col. Blackburn is still with me and as daring as ever. I will Tell you more of him when I visit you after this war. I have mentioned him so much already That I feel you know him. I wish you Two would visit me in the U.S. after the war.

Have you word of my Brothers? Are They all fighting in the East? I hear it is bad There, but they will survive it.

Affectionately your son
Richard Surby
Co.A, 7th Illinois Cavalry

At the same time that Richard Surby and William Blackburn wrote their letters, a private in nearby B Company tried to begin his letter home. Bill Buffington had torn up two attempts to his wife and now decided on a short message to his son. The mud-splattered shreds of paper flopped back and forth in the first drops of rain, then finally flowed away like so many little boats as the steady downpour began to cut its way to a ditch at the edge of the oak grove.

Drawing in a deep breath, forcing back a soft sob, the private scribbled out a greeting:

My dearest sonny boy.

I have not written you too much before. Now I feel I must. I am sorry you cannot get to go to school like the rest but if you pap doesnt get home by next winter you will have to wait a while longer and maybe I can let you go in the spring. I believ the war will be over before a year. The people here do not think the south can stand it much longer for they are about starving now. We had a rebel colonel prisoner here. He think there will be peace before the spring He think they were in a starving condition in the south.

I can be proud that I ain't been too scared. yet. You will see when you are older that this warring is very bad. I want to come home to you as bad as any body can but it won't do for me to quit this war and have you hear your pap deserted the rest of (your) life.

I pray ever nite to get back and see you and mommy again I'd be so thankful even if it was jist one time. May be some day it will happen either here or Up There. You take care of mommy and be a good boy until I see you.

we are riding out tomorrow but there are many of Us and we wont be gone long. May be 1 week. Tell mommy I will write her then your loving daddy

(Signed) William Buffington, Pvt.
Co.B 7Ill.Cavalry

Close by, a tent sagged under the weight of the soaking rain. Inside, two men squirmed around trying to get more comfortable. Arthur Wood was young and lithe with sparkling blue eyes. Unlike the other man, he had no beard and only shaved every third day. Wiping his runny nose with his wrist, he then touched up the point of his pencil with his wet tongue on the backsweep.

The older man in the tent gasped as he rolled onto his pot belly and ran his hand over his balding head, then down to the five-day-old stubble on his prominent jaw. He glanced toward the blond youth beside him and smiled when he saw the lead line in the letter: "Dear Dottie." It was too hard on his stomach to stay there, so he moved and sat up.

By now, his shy, uncertain tentmate was well into his letter. It read:

Direct Via Memphis Tenn.

Dear Dottie

It seem I been away many years, not just 2. Remember all we talked about?? Youre letter does not sound rite to me. Tell youre father I like know what use I got for any land. If I was married or had any notion of getting marred it would do to talk of buying land. I think if I get throgh this war I will go to Texas or Mexico or some other out of the way place. That is Some Body wont agree to do my cooking and washing etc. etc.

This is not to far fetched you know. I am older now and what this war has taught me is to depend on me. I have been riding all over Tennessee and Mississippi and I can handle my self. I am a man now you know. The rebels have try very hard to catch me and you may never see me again but I will be so brave you will here of me if I do not come home to north Illinois ever again.

I may try that cattle ranch business in Texas and become rich and famious after this war. And maybe just not have one girl.

We are leaving this place for another raid in the morn. so if you never hear form me again dont every worry none. Maybe youll be happy with some of youre men at home!

Do you know what I am saying and believe it.

> Youre Affectionate friend Arthur S. Wood
> Co.B, 7th Ill.
> Calvary Regt.

Some where in Tenn.

The older, prematurely balding man was nearly through his letter by now. He turned momentarily when he heard his young friend crumple the letter, but continued writing as he saw him straighten and smooth it again. He continued writing and soon was finished. Outside, the rain had slowed, but Isaac Robinson pulled the wet corner of a blanket inside the crowded tent and began to read his letter, correcting mistakes as he read.

————Memphis————

> La Grange, Tennessee
> April the 16

My dearest Father,

It is a queer war we fight. We run all around the country and return to our base camp her in La Grange. It is not like the war you fought 15 years ago. All December, we rode around. Some say 900 miles, we rode. Tomorrow, and that is why I write, we ride around again.

I do not expect to write again for some time. We drew rations for a few days, but these Army People are queer. You cannot tell from what they give us.

In Elkhorn Grove you are, I suppose, beginning to farm extensively by this time. I hope you may have good crops this Summer. Perhaps next Summer I can help with the crops. I hope you do not lose more horses and I hope we will have sound horses in their place for I do not believe in farmers keeping poor horses. George from you told me is not very great I did not think he would make such a sheep of a horse.

How is Creighton's store doing near the crossroads? I once thought I'd like to do that after the war, but now I am thinking more about helping you with the farm. I see wheat & corn are much better priced now. I hope the prices stay up for when I get out.

You won't know me when you see me. Most of my hair is gone now and so I'm trying to get some of it back on my face.

Listen, Paw, if anything happens to me, you just go on working and living a good life like you always have. I've lived a good, long life already. Don't you worry none. I've always been proud to be your son and I hope if anything happens to me you can be proud that I was your son.

I'm about out of anything to say so I'll close now.

Affectionately Your son

Isaac E. Robinson

Co.B., Seventh Illinois Cav.Reg.

Nearby, a long-faced, almost scrawny little private wrote pretentiously, carefully dipping a pen in a bottle of ink he'd secreted for months. Reed Munger, his friend and tentmate, prodded him and asked, "Georgie, who you writin' anyhow?"

The wiry little man, George Steadman, only grunted.

"You writin' a gal ain'tcha? Huh? Ain'tcha?" Munger laughed.

Ignoring the bigger man, the sweeping strokes continued to scratch from the pen. Finally near the bottom of the letter, Steadman said, "Hey, Mung?"

"Yeh."

"What's that doggoned thing what goes at the top of the letter?"

"You meant the mail route?"

"Yeh, that's it."

"Memphis. Di-rect via Memphis."

"Put that at the top?"

"Top left."

The skinny private grunted a thank you, wrote the words and then, head twisting from side to side, read the letter to himself. His lips moved silently as he checked everything carefully.

Dyrect via Memphis.

My Dear "Plug Ugly"

You know not what you miss not being in the army. I've never seen so many fine men. We ride all day and shoot rebels like cattle. My old pistol is smoken hot most the time. Only thing I hate most is boozen, spitten, cusses what are around me. Most none care for Army Life. They are not good patrots some of them.

Got me nother horse but still donot ride him much ifen I can find me mule. Mule got most since I think.

Not too many here. Ever body wanten secesh horse. that strange and odd. Me I like mule to ride.

How come you tell Cora I write you? You plum crazy!! She thinken we get together. You dum kid.

The feed they got there donot keep my belly good. Salt Horse and Sheet orn crackers is what we get. Sock coffee is my specalte.

Ifen you get old nouf to come in donot come calvery unless they give you mule. You tell Uncle Prod hello and believe what I say.

your Cousin
George Steadman, Privat
Co.C. 7 Ill Calvery.

In what was left of a log hut, a corporal and a private labored through messages to loved ones. The private, Charles Weedon, struggles with his handwriting; Corporal Kelly's pencil dashed across the page gracefully. His big, thick-fingered hand nearly hid the piece of pencil he'd carried for nearly six months. Almost dream-like, he stared out the open door of the hut and listened as the rain pattered on the canvas roof. Occasionally a twig would drop from the oak trees overhead. He pulled gently on a long corncob pipe, let out the smoke, and spit between the gap in his tobacco-stained teeth.

Looking down at the paper in front of him, he continued writing. Shortly, he paused and scanned what he had written. His grin turned again to a smile which followed his hand through his light-red beard and across his face.

Dear Sis,

I have just received a letter from you and I hasten to answer it. You said you did not receive very many letters from me. I have written three since January. I have been very busy. And not like you think. I am not like father and do not touch the spirits often.

I was glad to hear that you were all well. I am as well as I could wish to be. You do not hear much from William, well I would not worry. I hear his regiment is in camp near Nashville and I suspect him to be in little danger. He is a good man, he will return to you safe.

So you think I should write Emma M. I do not think so. I do not like to run the risk to haveing my letter sent back to me, or I would write.

We are haveing a good time here. And I expect we will stay in this vicinity all summer. We are leaving tomorrow for a while, but that is all.

Charlie Weedon is all right and so are the other Wabash men. I got a letter from my old fist fighting buddy Michael O'Connor a week back. He is fine and in Virginia.

Tell Aunt Sally if I do not get a letter from her soon I will have to write to her again.

I forgot to tell you we came near burning our tent up the other night. One of the boys was on guard and got up in the night and lit a candle and went out and left it burning. It fell through the bayonet and set the straw on fire. The first that I knew of it the boys tramped on me and pulled the blankets off of me. I thought the rebels were coming certain when I first waken up. But I soon found out my mistake. I jumped and went to stamping the fire. One of the boys took his blanket and whipped the blaze out. I then got my boots and put them on my hands for it was rather hot on the stocking feet to tramp and began to pound the fire.

The Baptist in my tent that I told you of nearly lost his religion. He does not like me to cuss, but the smoky air was blue when he saw the fire. He gathered his clothing and threw them out of the tent. He said finally that he had no idea of going naked the next day. I got my blanket burnt very badly.

If you could send me some cigars I would thank you. They are hard to get in camp and too expensive.

I went to a Baptist church meeting Sunday. The Baptist in my tent tricked me. He asked me if I wanted to go to see the girls. Of course, I did not want to go where there were any girls! I put on my boots and blacked them on my feet and got the black Boy to brush my coat, eat my dinner and started for town. Got about half way there and it commenced to rain. Well how many girls do you think we saw? There were three married women and four children. Served me right did you say.

Well I will try it over again some of these days and I hope I will have better success.

Give my best to the Murphy girls and all enquiring friends, especially the ladies! My love to you.

Your ever affectionate brother
Lycurgus K. Kelly
Co.E, Seventh Illinois Calvary

Next to the big, red-haired corporal, but across the table made from scrap boards sat the prematurely-grey bearded Weedon. He was looking down at the paper in front of him. He'd finished it, but fumbled in his pocket now. Pulling a twist of tobacco from the pocket, he put it to his mouth. From his boot, he pulled a long knife. Deftly, nearly missing his long thin nose, he whacked the big end away and crammed it back in his pocket. He did not take his eyes from the sheet of paper.

Shifting the tobacco, Weedon blurted, "Let me read you this, Kelly. Listen."

Kelly looked up and the private began: "My brother. This Army is still awful. I should've stayed home with you. The food is bad, the weather is bad, and I ain't sure I'll ever get used to these horses. Oh, how I long to walk through the woods with ol' Tip and Major chasin' coons. Take good care and write me soon as the bitch whelps."

The big-eyed private rolled his bottom lip and nearly smiled, "I ever tell you 'bout them dogs?"

"Aye," Kelly answered, disinterested.

"Yeh. Well, guess I did at that."

He continued to read the letter, only this time he read silently.

This war is all messed up. I joined to fight for US of A. Now its niggers, Lincoln says. I'd quit today if I could. But then just the other day I saw letters that was picked up by our calvary where the secesh camped. They all wished the War over (nothing rong with that!) and one lady was very canabilistic in her wishes. She wished her beau to bring her home three yankee skulls one for a gourd one for a slop bucket and the other I forget what purpose she wanted it for but it was something about the kitchen but I think he went back without the skulls and with a flea in his ear. I'd like to send her my compliments in the shape of a minnie bullet. Give my regards to all the friends and neibors and believe me your ever affectionate brother

Charles K. Weedon
Co.E, 7Ill.Cav.

P.S. Kelley and all the rest of the Grayville boys are well send me some postage stamps and if Jamie White does join send me two or three pair of good sock and a pair of gloves. I was sorry to hear the hogs did bad. I believe I have written all I can think about give my respects to Lizzie tell her I would like to play John Oldacre once more with her Yours truly

C.W.

While Weedon finished the letter, the big Irish corporal carefully read through his, correcting any words that did not look just right. He was a reckless writer, but a careful reader.

In the area of the dripping oak trees where Company G had set their tents, a short, hawk-nosed Uriah Fowler, sat astride a barrel. Behind him, a big-boned corporal stood running horse clippers around Fowler's head.

"You got to be the slowest excuse for hair cuttin' I seen."

"Uh-huh."

Slowly, carefully, the clippers moved around the ears, the rhythmic clicking nearly lulling the barrel-sitter into a nap. Soon, however, the clipping was done. The short man slid off the barrel, another hopped on.

Fowler ran his hand through his freshly cut hair and stepped from under the stretched canvas. Looking up at the weather, he walked back toward his company plotting in his mind what he would say in a letter to his uncle.

Dear Uncle Arthur,

Glad to hear you were building a new barn. Wish I could been there. I agree that post and beam barn is easier. Is the sawmill working now with all the spring rain? You can use my tools if you want. I'm going to buy me some new ones when I get out.

You said Henry was trying to get back in the war? I cannot understand him anyhow. He got out so slick before. He'll find he jist cannot go when he gets cream hungry.

We need men, our regiments are all short. We even spent much of winter looking for horses. I do not see how some of those boys back there can content themselves when they know they is needed in the field. I think they could afford one year to the service of their Country. Even if I never get back I will always be glad that I helped. I think it will be a hard day for some of them copper head. The boys have them all spotted and it will be dangerous for a copper head to show himself after this here war.

Just makes me so sickly to think of them no-goods there and guys like Bill Phillips, Bill Olinget, Henry Light, Jim Carnes, Matt Stotts, and Phil Aichel laying planted somewhere because they loved their Country.

Well we are getting ready to move off again next day or too. You know I'm with Grierson's Cav. now and he leads us to big things. He is tough as a ten penny nail.

That whittling knife you said you sent never got to me. Maybe it will arrive while I'm gone.

> Uriah Fowler
> Company H, 7th Ill. Cav.

Thirty minutes later, the hair-clipping corporal laid his horse clippers aside and returned to his tent. The rain slacked off and he was in a mood to write his wife. Once a week, usually, Sam Nelson managed to write telling her of his weekly routine. His letters often read like a diary and he knew it. Today the letter would be different. He felt something in the air. His thirty-four years had taught him to recognize patterns.

For two weeks, he and about ten or fifteen others from the Seventh Illinois had been ranging north, west and east into Tennessee around La Grange gathering all available horses and mules. This was not unusual, but it seemed to him that the herd was "bulging" as he called it.

Now, with a philosophical shrug of the shoulders, he settled down with paper and pen and began his weekly letter. He did not know it, but nearly three weeks would slip by before he'd have time to write again — or have a post office that'd handle Yankee mail.

Direct via Memphis

> La Grange, Tenn.
> Thursday, April 16 1863

My dear beloved Meg,

I got here your welcome letter. You ask if Im homesick. Homesick, Im telling you, I really am, and you dont know what a kind letter means. Sure wish I was there on one of our soft Beds. Im sure I would be much Happier, But you know I was always a home boy. More than any thing else Kinda loved my little wife and kids a little more than any one else.

Well, Meg there isn't a lot to write about. Tennessee is Sure a pretty country but I sure dont like it. Under Conditions, mabe in pease time a Person could enjoy it here, dont know though, dont Believe any place will ever look as good to me as Illinois. I never saw such a rainy country Im telling you Ill be glad to see that Sun come up in good Ole Illinois Again, and will sure be glad to rest my weary bones on a bed again. When I come home I dont want to do anything but sit by fire, sleep and eat some of your good meals. So Im Hopeing and praying we can get this thing over with before long and come home.

Meg, I had to leave in such a hurry when I was home I didnt get to talk to you hardly any. So now I want to tell you a few things I wanted to then and couldnt if any thing should happen to me which I Hope doesnt, I want you if Im Send home in a Box to bury me by the side of "Lucy" if I never come home Put a remembrance stone by her side and then teach my Son who is there. Please do this for me. Just in case.

Ive learn so much, things I would love to never think about. But am only afraid I shall never forget. Id give everything I own, had I not been in it at all, to see and go through what I have. Remember Ole Mr's Rodgers use to say, Hell was Only here on Earth, Honestly I Believe she had some thing here, Ive certainly seen some of it and Im not foolen.

But im not afraid and I think I will come back home So dont worry about me. I just wanted to tell you this in case. I dont want any more than the chance to live and come home again. I should not gripe I guess, But they say this is the army, and your not a Soldier Unless you gripe a little.

Well Meg keep the Home fires burning and the Bread pan hot. Always remember I love you and the kids more than I can say.

Samuel Nelson
Co.G. 7th Ill Cavalry

P.S. Always wait until the worst happens to worry. We leave on a scout in the morn.

Sam

Chapter 2

...bound for Mississippi

A straw-haired boy, about ten years old, stood half hidden behind a slat fence, staring, some frightened, as the blue-uniformed column wound its way through the streets of the little Tennessee town of La Grange on Friday morning April 17, 1863. The warm sun burned the cool, damp air form the earth. Fruit trees were in full bloom and gardens were fragrant with the perfume of spring flowers. Birds sang while the cavalrymen looked about absorbing the sights and sounds of nature.

The boy heard someone singing somewhere in the column of twos and several voices joined in with the chorus:

> With Grierson for our leader,
> We'll chase the dastard foe,
> 'Till our horses bathe their fetlocks
> In the Gulf of Mexico.

At the head of the column, a slender colonel led the three regiments. He ran his long, tanned fingers through his black beard. His thoughts ran whirling through his brain. He took inventory of his command. The Sixth Illinois Cavalry had the advance, the lead, with Lieutenant-Colonel Reuben Loomis commanding five hundred men. Close on their heels rode the Seventh Illinois Cavalry, Colonel Edward Prince commanding, with five hundred forty-two men. Then came Company K, First Illinois Artillery Battery, Captain Jason B. Smith commanding. At the end of the column, comprising the rear guard, was Colonel Edward Hatch and the Second Iowa Cavalry with between six hundred and seven hundred men.

> Then quick into the saddle,
> And shake the bridle free,
> Today with gallant Grierson
> We'll leave old Tennessee.

The entire column, the First Brigade, First Cavalry Division, Sixteenth Army Corps of Major-General Ulysses S. Grant's Department of Tennessee, marched under the command of the former music teacher and general store operator from Jacksonville, Illinois, Benjamin Henry Grierson. Grierson, only a few months away from his thirty-seventh birthday, had already made his mark as a leader of cavalry. On several occasions, he struck the Confederate forces inflicting severe losses while losing few of his own command.

> Oh! who would not be a trooper.
> And follow Grierson's eye
> To battle for their country,
> And, if needs be, to die.

Colonel Grierson's orders were to strike the heart of Mississippi, cutting communication and transportation lines from one end of the Rebel state to the other. His march should move south parallel to the Mississippi Central Railroad. He hoped to cut the Vicksburg Railroad near Newton Station, Mississippi. General Grant waited, poised at Vicksburg, ready to attack the river fortress whenever the Confederate forces could be weakened so as to permit such an assault.

Months before, the seeds for the attack on Vicksburg had been sown. The tall, lean — and worried — man that occupied the White House in Washington sat, shoulders stooped, staring at a map of his country. With President Abraham Lincoln was David Dixon Porter, an admiral in the United States Navy. The conference had spun out nearly twenty minutes now. The President ran his eyes over the map, pointed to a thin, crooked blue line and said, "Vicksburg!"

With a sweeping gesture, President Lincoln continued, "See what a lot of land these fellows hold, of which Vicksburg is the key."

His big, bony fingers pointed into Louisiana, "Here is Red River, which will supply the Confederates with cattle and corn to feed their armies."

Again the President's finger moved, this time north into Arkansas. "There are the Arkansas and White Rivers which can supply cattle and hogs by the thousands."

He paused, glanced up at Admiral Porter, then back to the map. His finger traced a railroad line from Vicksburg to Meridian, then his hand spread and swept into the southeast United States as he added, "From Vicksburg these supplies can be distributed by rail all over the Confederacy."

Exhausted, the President leaned back in his chair and stared straight into the bearded Porter's eyes, "It means hog and hominy without limit, fresh troops from all the States of the far South, and a cotton country where they can raise the staple without interference."

Leaning forward again, Lincoln jabbed a finger down on "VICKSBURG." "Let us get Vicksburg and all that country is ours. The war can never be brought to a close until that key is in our pocket."

> So trusting in our country's God,
> We draw our stout good blade,
> For those we love at home,
> And those who need our aid.

If Grierson and his command could accomplish their mission, they would rip the telegraph lines and railroads that were the life-blood of Vicksburg. With those lines shattered, Grant would have only to wait a few days until food became scarce; until the Confederate command at

Vicksburg realized that their position was hopeless without ammunition and men being transported from points east in the Confederate States of America. The Mississippi River would at last belong to the Union and one of President Lincoln's major objectives in the great Civil War would be accomplished in less than two and one-half years.

"Two years this...uh...war's gone on now," the stocky, sandy-haired corporal complained.

"Yeh, Sam. You's prob'ly like all them others that thought the North's gonna win in a couple weeks."

Sam Nelson's blue eyes twinkled. He brushed a shock of hair over his ear and under his slouch hat with one hand, then tugged the hat down with the other. "Almost didn't join up 'cause I...uh...thought the war would end quick-like," Sam reflected. "Wrong again," he laughed.

"Get out there and get it, Sammy!" he could hear his father's words. "Life's awaitin'. Don't let it get by you. Tennessee's all settled. Move on. Them hills is all used up. Sullivan County won't miss you.

"Virginia held no place for me. Your granddaddy told me that. He'd found the same thing out when he came sailin' from England. Gotta keep movin' in this big country to ever 'mount to anything."

"Boy, you ever see such a pretty day, Sam?"

Sam Nelson heard, but did not comprehend. "What...uh...what'd you say?" Sam croaked.

"Just sayin' what a pretty day this is, Sam. You hearin' me?"

"Yeh, just thinkin' 'bout somethin' my...uh...Pa told me."

"What's that?"

Sam didn't answer. Instead, he stood in his stirrups and halted his horse. The little roan's head jerked. "Whoa, Shawnee," Sam spoke softly. The little gelding stood still. Shawnee was fourteen and a half hands high, but since Grierson's men had such a tough time getting horses, they'd let Sam Nelson keep the horse he'd raised from a colt on his Illinois farm. To his left and across a field, Sam saw movement.

"What is it, Sam?"

Nelson said nothing. The man with him stopped and now stood in his stirrups. His eyes skipped across the weed field too. A thicket of oak trees stood about three hundred yards away. The man could see nothing unusual.

"What in hell you lookin' at, Sam?"

"Them trees...uh; saw somethin'," Sam said, concerned.

The man looked toward the trees again. Now he could see it. Movement. A deer? he thought. A loud "thwack" split the air. A bullet ripped over the two rider's head's and tore through the trees behind them.

Both men fell from their horses and scrambled into a low spot near a split-rail fence. Then everything was still.

"You see 'em, Sam?" the man gasped.

"Just inside the trees. Reb on a horse. Saw his horse bolt when the gun went off."

"How many of 'em?"

"Five; maybe six."

Nelson and the man could hear horses running now and Sam, breathless, stood on his knees and peered through the railing of the old fence. His right knee hurt and he brushed a walnut hull away without looking.

"They're, they're goin'," Sam stammered in a whisper.

"That was close," the man with Nelson said as he rolled onto his back, his arms spread, hat in hand.

"Yeh, but we'd better tell Trafton. And quick."

They ran low along the road to their horses, mounted, and, checking to make sure the Confederate soldiers were indeed gone, spurred their mounts north along the road to where Company G of the Seventh Illinois Cavalry was proceeding casually, not mindful of what had happened.

G Company Captain George Trafton suspected something was wrong when he spotted Nelson and his companion riding down a slope toward the company. Trafton prodded his horse to a trot and met them twenty-five yards in front of the column.

"Matter, Sammy?" Trafton called.

"Rebs. Took a shot at us, Traf."

"How many?"

"Five or six. They're runnin'."

Another rider approached astride a big, spirited Morgan. He was Bill Blackburn. His blue uniform bulged over his huge chest straining the buttons. His facial features were too large — almost humorous. Dark, firm-set eyes asked the question.

Trafton answered, "Rebs, Colonel Blackburn. Five or six of 'em."

"They run?" the colonel almost squealed.

"South and east," Nelson responded, his head cocked to one side.

"Damn. Not much we can do then." Turning to Trafton, Blackburn continued, "Figure the Sixth'll have all the fun. They missed a turn a spell back and swung off to the east. 'Spect they'll join up later. They ought to be right south and east of here."

Nodding agreement, the little group separated and rode back to their appointed positions as the remainder of the column drew near. The sun slid down in the Mississippi sky now. They'd make camp soon.

Four hours later, settled for the night, word spread to Captain George Trafton and Corporal Sam Nelson, that the Sixth had captured three Confederate soldiers. No one knew if the Rebs were the ones that had fired at Nelson.

The eighteenth of April, 1863, dawned clear and delightful. The Union soldiers huddled around campfires to ward off the early morning cold until time to move out. Many complained when bugled to their mounts, but the warm sun took the place of the campfires and soon, the Sixth and Seventh Illinois snaked contentedly along a narrow path pushing farther south into Mississippi. The Second Iowa followed in their tracks.

Toward afternoon a rider ordered Graham's First Battalion from the Seventh to force-march to a bridge ahead. That pleased Sam Nelson. It was too quiet. The advance units had all the excitement. And they'd been fired at again. And like yesterday, the Confederates got away again.

There was concern that the Rebs might burn the bridge on the Tallahatchie River, but it still stood when, a few hours later, their horses well lathered, Sam Nelson's company and the First Battalion arrived. Surprised Confederate pickets fired a few hasty greetings and fled. Sam Nelson, the river's blue-mud smell strong in his nose, dozed the rest of the afternoon waiting for the main column to catch up.

Movement on the nineteenth slowed. Gummy, clay mud clung to the horse's hooves as the skies dumped buckets of water on them. Captain George Trafton took two soggy companies to New Albany and they routed a group of militia that had gathered there during the night. Other companies plodded off to gather fresh horses. With the mud, the horses tired fast.

It was obvious that this "outing" through Mississippi was going to have its down days. But for Sam Nelson, every day was a good day. His daddy always taught him that. "Always look ahead, Sammy," Nelson's father preached. "Don't do no good to think about yesterday, when tomorrow is always just 'round the corner."

Nelson felt secure with the nine hundred or so troops that were marching through this hilly, rocky country. The Rebs that fired on them couldn't "hit a barn with a corncob," so why worry. Only five days' rations for the men; so what? There was bound to be food all the way to southern Mississippi. Horses get tired; need replacing. Don't make no nevermind; there'll be fresh horses.

All these things and more, Sam Nelson thought. Things always worked out in his mind. If they couldn't get the goods they needed to continue their march, they'd have to turn back. That would mean, simply, that they were not supposed to make the trip and cut the railroad lines in the first place. Fate determined all these things. Do what you could, the best you could; if it didn't work out; wasn't meant to.

That night, Sunday, April 19, while wriggling around under a damp blanket, Sam's mind worked with the same thoughts. Only now he applied them to a civilian that had been killed earlier in the day at Pontonoc, Mississippi. Somebody said his name was Beers. Citizen Beers and a group of locals were set on defending their town against the Yanks — that is, until a column of fours, slinging mud and lead, bore down on them. Everyone ran except the one man, Beers. He stayed, defiant and firing wildly, and was shot dead for his bravery. That was the way it was supposed to be, Sam Nelson figured. Then his wife, Meg, slipped pleasantly into his thoughts and he slept.

Cold, wet, and complaining, the Sixth and Seventh Illinois and the Second Iowa awoke on Monday, April 20th. There was no sun to warm the soldiers, no blue sky to brighten their outlook. Their horses, nevertheless, plodded south, around the town of Houston, Mississippi, through a muddy wheat field and all the time, Colonel Benjamin Grierson was thinking that there ought to be a better way.

Elsewhere in the column, mounted on a mud-splattered, dancing, bay Morgan was another man with the same idea. There was too much risk involved, the way the column was moving. An ambush could be just ahead at the next patch of woods, or next town, or at the next bridge. And if the Rebs could fire on the column and run, then it was doubtful anybody would live long enough to visit southern Mississippi in late April, 1863.

William Blackburn wiped grime off the big bay's shoulder and flung it into the brush along the road, then wiped his hand on his boot top. "Damn mud," he muttered.

"What's that, Colonel?" Richard Surby asked. Sergeant Richard Surby had known Bill Blackburn for several years now. Surby was a medium-sized man and rode a brown gelding taller than him — over sixteen hands high. His thick, short legs straddled the big horse's back giving the appearance of a small boy riding a pony.

"The mud, Richard."

"Yeh, it's bad."

"What do you think 'bout these Reb pickets tryin' to cut us up?"

"Can't say I thought too much about 'em," Surby said, realizing his old friend wanted his advice. "But I don't think they'd be jerkin' shots at us, if we's out front checkin' the country side."

"How do you mean?"

"Just get out there and find out where they are and make sure we can get by 'em before we bring up the column." Surby eased his horse out of the puddled road and onto some thick grass, then he continued. "Why shoot, we could even dress like 'em. I worked in the South' know how they talk. Wouldn't be hard to talk our way out of anything."

"What about the clothes? Where'd you get them?" Blackburn asked, his mind searching the idea for feasibility.

"Well, figure we'd get 'em same place we been tryin' to get horses; from the people that live hereabouts."

"How many men you think you'd need?" Then, after pausing and while Surby rubbed his finger along side his nose, "And where'd you get them?"

"Most of the Reb groups we been runnin' into have had five or six in 'em. Figure somethin' like that." The grassy roadside became too soft and Surby clucked his horse across the shallow, rain-filled ditch and back to the clay road.

"As to where I'd pick these men," Surby continued, "I'd say, just off the top of my head, the boys that did most of the horse-stealin' back at La Grange'd be good. They did this same sort of thing there. Most of 'em from the South. Just off hand, Sam Nelson comes to mind. He's from somewhere in Tennessee. Least ways, he's born there."

"Well, I'd say let's set on this for a while, Richard. But I like the idea; spies and all that."

"Whatever you say, Colonel."

Sergeant Richard Surby, Company A, Seventh Illinois Cavalry, watched the big man ride away. He remembered the first time he had seen

William Blackburn. Just north of the main square in Paris, Illinois there was a livestock pen where cattle growers throughout eastern Illinois brought their cattle to be shipped to the stockyards in Chicago.

Blackburn was leaning on a stockpen fence looking over fifty head of all kinds of scrub cattle. Surby sidled up to him and, like Blackburn, stared at the cattle. Before long, Surby remarked that he didn't see why some cattle had to be so poor and scrawny looking when they got all the grass in the world to eat.

Blackburn looked at him, glowering, and said, "Son, I wanta tell you something. They's people like them ornery lookin' heifers in the world and do you know why they's people in the world like them?"

Since Surby was just passing the time of day, he did not quite understand why he had rankled this big man, this stranger, so, "No, but I guess...."

Blackburn interrupted, his temper showing blotched in his face, "I'll tell you why. There's people that don't care for people. And when a world gets so full of people that don't care for other people, then you get a world full of people that don't care about the world."

Compliant now, Surby responded, "Yes, sir. See what you mean."

"Son, don't ever go around not caring for the world, or all the people in it will end up like these cattle — headed for a swift whack in the head. No one carin'...," Blackburn's voice trailed off, dejected.

From that day forward, Richard Surby felt that he understood William Blackburn. Railroad work took Richard Surby through most of the United States and now he and a friend, Cornelius B. Griffin, were visiting in Edgar County, Illinois. He was in Illinois when word came that the lanky lawyer from Springfield had been nominated and elected President of the United States. And he was in Paris, Illinois, when on a hot, summer day, William D. Blackburn became the captain of a company of men from Paris; dead set on this war ending in no less than six months — "afore spring plowin'" was the way most put it.

Richard W. Surby was appointed second duty sergeant in October, 1862, quartermaster sergeant at Camp Butler just outside Springfield, Illinois. He and Blackburn were only friends, but they would lean on each other like brothers.

After a restless and rainy night at the plantation of Dr. Benjamin Kilgore, near the hamlet of Clear Springs, Mississippi, the Sixth and Seventh Illinois rode south again. Colonel Edward Hatch and the Second Iowa Cavalry had left the column. At a meeting during the night, Colonel Benjamin Grierson ordered Hatch away from the main column as a decoy to draw off the Confederate forces. Now, with fewer horses traveling over the muddy, rain-soaked roads, the going would be some easier.

Even in the rain, the advance column continued to run into scattered opposition. Near the head of the column, two men rode along discussing the Confederate pickets that had just fired and run.

"All right, Bill. Get your boys together while the column is moving. Then at noon, have 'em get their clothes and things together. They'll start scouting after we stop for a spell."

"Colonel Grierson, you won't regret it," Bill Blackburn said, beaming. Five minutes later, the big man on the big horse found Richard Surby. "Richard," he yelled. Surby a hundred yards up the road, swung his horse around. Blackburn called out, "Grierson says, 'Get 'em together.'"

Surby rode back to Blackburn before answering, "All right! Now we can get serious about this business of marchin' through Mississippi!" Surby said, elated.

"Didn't think he'd buy it; he's afraid if you get caught you'd be shot for spies."

"Well, that's always a risk, but war's a risky business," Surby contemplated.

"Anyway, get it together."

"Grierson say how many men?"

"No, just get what you need."

"I've been thinkin' about a few. I'll do some checkin' and askin'."

"Sounds good to me. Sure wish I could work with you; just itchin' to get in a fight."

"Colonel, that'll come soon enough." Surby thought a minute, then added, "Tell you what, meet us about a half mile up the road from the next plantation house. I'll have 'em ready durin' noonin' time."

"Fine. See you then."

During the next two hours, Richard Surby collected his "spies" and outfitted them in the dress of the enemy. These men would be the eyes and ears of the regiments with Colonel Benjamin Grierson. They would be resourceful and always suspicious. They would be brave. They would scout ahead, not only for the enemy, but for the horses that Grierson and about a thousand men would need to make this trip into enemy territory. And since Confederate uniforms were usually "butternut" in color, they would be called the Butternut Guerillas.

This, then is their story.

Chapter 3

...butternut and "secesh" guns

By nooning time, the sky seemed wrung out. The rain finally stopped. Drops of rain fell carelessly from the trees when light wind gusts dumped them. On the plantation grounds, hundreds of muddy, tired, hungry Union soldiers lay about smoking and exchanging tired talk. At the head of the lane that lead from the plantation house to the hoof-marked, muddy road, several riders turned in and rode down the lane. A few of the weather-beaten soldiers noted their entrance and slowly a rising tide of murmuring spread along their path.

Soon the murmur turned to a cheer and someone yelled, "Yahoo! Look what the Colonel done gone and got hisself!"

From behind the brush and scrub oaks alongside the road, a hundred eyes stared at the Union officer on his big bay Morgan. In front of him, he herded nine men all dressed in ragtag, variegated, butternut-colored uniforms.

"Where'd you get them Rebs, Colonel?" a soldier yelled.

Another laughed and turning to a friend said, "Them ol' Rebs better watch it. We'll bust this whole state wide open."

The tall, strong colonel looked like a mountain on his big horse as he rode along the road. The slush and mud at every step was the only sound the men in front of the colonel made. As they rode down the road toward the huge plantation house that served as headquarters for the Sixth and Seventh Illinois, a Union soldier standing along their path drawled softly, "Where ya'll from?"

One of the prisoners looked up and toward the voice, his face round and sunreddened, "Miss'sippi," he blurted.

"Where'bouts?"

"Laurel."

"'S that right? Why I'm from Mobile," he drawled.

The colonel told his prisoners to move on and the conversation ended. Now the real test is coming, the colonel decided. Just ahead, he could see the boys in Company G lazing around under a grove of oak trees.

Someone yelled, "Hey, Colonel, where'd you get them Butternuts?" Others laughed.

The colonel kept riding, not looking at the voices. Then he decided differently. Sam's from G Company. We'll just see how he can do. Looking toward the red-faced prisoner, the big colonel snapped, "Tell 'em, Reb! Tell 'em where you're from."

Sam Nelson stopped his horse and turned toward a group of the Yankee cavalrymen sprawled under a big oak tree. Nelson showed uncertainty, his face puzzled, but decided this was as good a place as any to find if his disguise would work — or get him killed.

He stammered, "Why...uh...me and the boys was just down the...uh...road a ways and, and," Sam hurried his speech, "Ya'll took us!"

One of the Yankee privates slapped his thigh and guffawed, "Listen to that boy. Hot-damn, ain't he scared though?" The private's face straightened, "C'mon boy. Tell us some more. Say somethin' else."

"Uh...ain't talkin' to you no more, Yank."

Before the Union private could step toward Nelson, another of the prisoners rode his horse across Sam's path, not in control of his mount.

"That horse a little fidgety, is it, Reb?" the Union private laughed.

"No, suh." This prisoner was a wiry, little man. His face was that of a boy. Two years ago when the war started, he would have passed for sixteen. Now after battles at Corinth and Iuka and the death and destruction that he had seen, on close inspection lines of grief and sorrow streaked his forehead.

Some other Yanks were asking questions now. "What's your outfit, Reb?"

"First Tennessee Cav'ry," the wiry prisoner responded proudly.

A Union sergeant shifted onto his elbow and yelled, "Where you Rebs been last couple days?"

A tall, lean Irishman among the prisoners answered, wonderment in his voice, "Chasin' you Yanks! Of course!"

Someone else yelled above the others, "How many in yo' reg'ment?"

"'Nough to lick you Yanks," the youngest of the prisoners muttered, a smile on his face.

A burly private, his head cocked to one side, roared out of the crowd, "When you 'spect this here war's gonter be over?"

The reply burst from a bearded prisoner, "Quick's you Yanks go home and leave us be!" Then a stream of tobacco juice punctuated his answer and splattered menacingly close to the burly Yank's mud-covered boots.

More of the Union cavalrymen had crowded around and then the questions died out as the crowd made a path for an approaching rider. The rider set his horse easy. His spade-shaped beard was mud spattered, his eyes clear and sharp. He commanded authority although he did not speak or ask for riding room.

All faces turned to the rider. The prisoners, too, looked in his direction. He had a slight scar on his forehead, but no one noticed it at first glance. His long, slender fingers held the reins and rested easily over the front of his McClellan saddle.

"Well, Bill. See you got 'em rigged out."

"Yes, sir, Colonel," Lieutenant-Colonel Bill Blackburn smiled. "We've got us some genuine guerillas."

Looks of astonishment appeared on the faces of the Union soldiers standing around the prisoners. They heard Colonel Benjamin Grierson and Blackburn discuss how these men should start the afternoon scouting south toward Starkville.

Sam Nelson began to laugh. He and the others had worked it. They'd actually fooled their own friends! Someone grabbed Sam's leg. It was Georgie Rinehold from his home county in Illinois. Georgie was the Yank that asked Blackburn where the prisoners were from and his friend, Sam Nelson, answered him.

"Sam, I don't believe it! I know'd you nigh onto ten years." Rinehold janitored in a bank in Shawneetown where Nelson banked when he had need to. They'd joined G Company of the Seventh on the same day and Sam saved Georgie's life at Corinth.

Georgie, serious now, asked, "Sam, what in thunderation are you up to?"

Sergeant Richard Surby, leader of the Butternut Guerillas, answered for Nelson, "We're gonna scout ahead and make them Rebs clear out before you boys even get there."

"What you mean, Sarge?" someone from Surby's company yelled.

"Colonel Blackburn has got us dressed like this so we can spy on the Rebs. That way, we can get the word back to you boys and keep you out of trouble. We're gonna spy our way through Mississippi."

There was mumbling and laughter in the crowd of soldiers as Sergeant Surby began distributing weapons to the scouts. Earlier, Surby confiscated three Sharps carbines and four shotguns. Four sabers were passed around and each man received a .36-caliber Navy Colt revolver, except Surby kept an extra Colt for himself. One operational, but rusty, sporting rifle eventually was taken by one of the scouts. They all looked like genuine, "secesh" Rebs now, Lieutenant-Colonel Blackburn mused, shaking his big head and smiling. Then he congratulated Surby on the successful disguises.

The men that Richard Surby picked received their orders from Blackburn and soon rode off south in a group. Soon Surby began casually explaining what he expected of them.

Richard W. Surby, a former Canadian, left home during his youth. He arrived in the United States while only fifteen years old. He was an adventurous young man and to him life was travel, and travel provided the excitement he yearned for. He was more than familiar with the Southern states since he had worked all over, but in the past years had concentrated on railroad work. When the South began to fall away from the government in Washington, he signed along with most of the other men and boys in Company A of the Seventh Illinois Cavalry.

The men that Richard Surby handpicked were men he had known for over a year. Some, he had trained with; others, he'd fought beside. All had displayed unusual resourcefulness in their abilities as scouts during their duty with the Seventh. All of the Butternut Guerillas were good shots and all had knowledge of firearms that extended back to their squirrel and deer hunting days in rural Illinois.

Some of the men were the fearless type. Lycurgus K. Kelly, for example, was an Irishman who would "fight anything or anybody at anytime," as he like to boast. He was not only respected, but feared by every man in Company E. Every man, that is, but five-foot, six-inch Charlie Weedon.

Charles K. Weedon did not join the Army until February, 1862, but he had notched a place in the hearts of his comrades with his "gutsy" behavior while scouting near Cape Girardeau and later in the fighting near New Madrid, Missouri against Jeff Thompson's Confederates. Weedon was the bearded, tobacco chewer in the group. He hated the Army, but had never quit a job he'd started in his life.

The others had their share of scouting in and around La Grange, Tennessee. Will Buffington, Woody Wood and Ike Robinson kept B Company riding some of the finest horses in the Seventh. They also supplied the remainder of the Third Battalion.

Sam Nelson and Richard Surby worked in the same capacity for the First Battalion and Bud Fowler and George Steadman did likewise for the Second Battalion. They had proven themselves not only to their officers, but to the men as well. They were trusted and looked up to. Now Surby told them what he wanted. Search the country ahead for streams, creeks, and rivers. Could they be forded? Was there a bridge? Was the bridge guarded? Where did the roads go? Were there towns, villages, or plantations? Were the people sympathetic with the Union? Radically opposed? Neutral? Any signs of Confederate forces moving in the area? What was the strength of the military garrisons? Were the citizens armed? Would they fight?

And there were routine things. The Butternut Guerillas were instructed to look for places where the regiments could stop for noon and night bivouac. "We need water and forage places for the horse," Surby reminded them.

Each man in the column had started with rations of hardtack, coffee, sugar and bacon for a five-day march. That would be gone soon. "Men are gonna need food too," Surby added.

"Beyond everything," Surby told them, "be careful and report back at regular times. I'll expect you out in the mornings before the command moves."

"Ever'thing gonna be the same during nighttime, Sarge?" the wiry Steadman inquired.

"No, Steadman. Colonel Grierson always alternates the point — the advance guard — and if one of you boys come creepin' down the road at night with them butternut hats on, you might get your head blowed off. We'll use signals. Nothin' fancy. Just our own names ought to do."

Surby stopped his horse, turned, and placed his right hand on the back of the civilian saddle. He looked at the others and said, "Now, boys, we're comin' out of these woods. I'm goin' to go ahead a ways. I want you to follow at about a quarter mile. I'll be back in a while, or stop up ahead and then one of you can go to the front. You've all scouted before; this won't be much different."

Surby paused, looked around, then added, "One more thing. Just remember, you're not in Union blue. Don't run when you see Rebs. Use your heads. Remember, you're from the First Tennessee Cav'ry," he emphasized, "not the Seventh Illinois."

With that, Richard Surby clucked his horse forward. The sky was darkening again. The morning rain had stopped about noon, but now it looked like it might start again. Surby's "uniform" was ragged and he wondered how it would do if the rain started.

The tan jacket and blue-grey pants did not match, but most Confederate soldiers in the West wore just such a garb. It was convincing enough, Surby decided. The battered old gun which he had issued himself was certainly typical of an army that was slowly running short of supplies. But as he neared Starkville, he grew uneasy about his garb again. Would the civilians there see through his disguise?

Soon the rain began. As Surby entered the town, soaked and chilled, he felt good that the downpour had run the residents of the little Mississippi town indoors. He surveyed the abandoned street, saw no sign of Confederate troops, and as quickly as he could without attracting attention, slogged through the mud back to report to Blackburn that Starkville was quiet.

The other scouts pressed ahead while Surby reported and by four in the afternoon, the entire command was displaying the Union blue from one end of Starkville, Mississippi to the other. The townspeople calmly looked on not totally surprised, nor did they seem impressed at first. Tennessee was not far away. But as column after column continued to file through the little town, they became puzzled, then astounded. Where could so many Yankees be headed?

Colonel Grierson ordered his men to confiscate anything of military value, but Starkville yielded very little. Grierson wondered if the Rebs weren't picking the town clean. Soon, the command was headed south.

Meanwhile, the Butternut Guerillas continued down the road toward Louisville and captured two Confederate soldiers. There was no fight. The Confederates were only surprised to find themselves taken so easily. The scouts joked and cackled, elated at their success. Their disguises had passed another "inspection." This time, however, it was not Yanks they fooled, but real, live Rebs.

But the enemy had not caused the aggravation the weather was causing. The soaking rain continued, the sloppy road got muddier and the lowlands south of Starkville made the going so tiring on horses and men that an early camp was ordered. Plodding along belly deep in flood waters sometimes and knee deep mud at other times, the men and horses of Grierson's raiders finally halted along a swollen stream that looked too vicious to ford, heard the order to dismount and camp, and slid from their mounts onto the saturated ground to search for a place safe from the rising, noisy stream that would finally lull them to sleep.

With the stream only yards away, over nine hundred men tried to sleep and could not. They crawled closer to the trunks of trees, wondered if the stream would overflow and drown them, and dozed off thinking what a miracle it would be if the sun were shining when they awoke.

Still wide awake, George Steadman turned on his side and said, "Sam? You awake?"

"No," came a response from the pitchy darkness.

"Doggone it," he said in a while. "What day you figure we'll get to the Vicksburg Railroad?"

"What day's today?"

"Tuesday."

"Maybe Friday; maybe Saturday."

"Night, Sam."

"G'night, George."

Chapter 4

...the enemies' backyard

At dawn, April 22nd, the dull landscape came alive as the sun painted the sky. Benjamin Grierson's men awoke and sighed relief. Laughter returned to the encampment and rain dripped noisily from the trees, but if anyone was fooled by it, their fears were dashed by the rays of sunlight spraying the ground. The pesky mosquitoes continued their blood raids, but somehow the ferociousness of their attacks no longer bothered any but the few who nursed huge welts on their faces. Most important, the sun had returned. Soon, the musty stench of damp wool would depart.

Captain Henry Forbes and B Company of the Seventh prepared to leave the column early in the morning. They were on orders from Grierson to create a diversion by marching to Macon, Mississippi. Forbes accepted the challenge, but asked that his scouts join him. He wanted Buffington, Wood and Robinson. So the Butternut Guerillas began their first full day shorthanded.

While Forbes and his company, led by Will Buffington, Ike Robinson, and Woody Wood, plodded through the mud and early morning sun east toward Macon, Mississippi; the main column sized up their route for the day. The Noxubee River was certain to be flooded and Grierson suspected it would be no easy task for the column to cross. Then, too, the muddy roads would be churned into slop as horses passed over them. Toward the end of the column, the road would be little more than a quagmire.

A night raid by the First Battalion of the Seventh with Major John Graham commanding destroyed a Confederate tannery, but the ride through the mud and back country sapped men and horses. Every way the First turned, Graham said, they rode over swampy roads.

Blackburn gave Surby Grierson's orders, "Colonel says we'd better move west; try and get around as much of this flood we can. Headwaters of the Noxubee could be shallower," he continued. "Try and ford the stream west of here."

So west it was. Surby didn't question the order and soon took the lead. The land was sparsely populated in the direction they were moving, but a few civilians were encountered. They asked the obvious questions and Surby, or Nelson, or Weedon, Kelly, or Fowler — whoever was on point — drawled the obvious answers. They were "from the First Tennessee Cav'ry and lookin' to whup them Yanks all the way back to St. Looie!" It was a dull morning for the scouts.

At mid-morning, while Sam Nelson rode point, he approached a schoolhouse. The weather-worn siding needed whitewash and the new spring grass in the schoolyard had already given in to the children and disappeared until next year. The children were having recess, but mostly they huddled around the steps and along the side of the weather-beaten building where the sun had partially dried the ground.

Kids, Sam thought, a lot like mine. His tired horse was due a rest, so Sam paused and watched them watch him. A minute or so later, a brown-haired woman came out the door, through the clutter of children and toward the fence that surrounded the school grounds. She wore a plain dress and didn't seem to mind that it was recklessly close to the muddy ground.

Nelson had no intention of talking to the teacher, but wisely con-ceded that it might be better if he prepared her for what followed him. The column would be along soon and he could see no point in her being frightened unnecessarily. He was about to speak when the woman lifted her eyes from the muddy ground long enough to look up and smile at him. She had a pretty face, just lightly freckled. "Are ya'll with the Missis-sippi troops?" she beamed.

"No, mam. Uh, Tennessee," Nelson croaked.

"Oh, I was so in hopes that you was Mississippi," she exclaimed, the smile disappearing.

"Sorry, mam, but the column comin'...uh...by is First Tennessee."

"Well, makes no matter anyhow. I's just hopin'...," her voice trailed off. The sun struck her hair just right and it shone so that Nelson had to draw a breath to quell the yearning in his stomach. She looked so much like his own Meg.

He wanted to say more, but the words wouldn't come. Sam won-dered what he would even say to his wife if he could see her now, and then he knew they wouldn't speak. What could you say when you had been apart two years?

The woman's blue eyes stared up at him; Sam blushed, staring back. Then he heard himself stammering, "Well...uh, mam...the...uh men'll be here pretty soon. Best I move on."

She nodded a farewell and Sam touched the brim of his rumpled hat and reined his horse to the left and up the road just as the "First Tennes-see" came in sight.

The teacher let the students stand by the fence and see the "First Tennessee" march by. The muddy blue uniforms could have been grey, butternut, or any other color to the students. Some even spotted an occasional trooper that they thought they knew. One bright little girl ran on the road and cried out to a passing rider, "Where's John? Is he ridin' with ya'll?"

The soldier, dumbfounded for a moment, answered in his best drawl, "Naw, dahlin', he's not along."

"Is my uncle along?" she asked.

Embarrassed, he clucked and prodded his horse out of line and to the front of the company on some important business he'd just remembered.

Meanwhile, Sergeant Richard Surby decided, with Blackburn's permission, to send some of the scouts looking for fresh mounts. The mud was telling on some of the horses. They were so used up the herders turned a few loose. They were hard pressed for remounts during the noon bivouac. Besides, some of the Mississippi horses would be more convincing than the animals the Army bought in Illinois and Indiana during the past year.

By noon the scouts felt they had put in a pretty good day. They rode together now and all complained about the pace they were keeping. Their mounts slipped more in the mud — not as sure-footed. Down the road, the entrance to a plantation house came into view and Surby rode ahead to survey the grounds. Then with a hand signal, Surby called the other scouts to join him.

To George Steadman, Surby ordered, "Get off the road and watch us. If we're fired on, get to the column and tell 'em to come double-quick and bail us out."

Surby nodded and the scouts moved with him toward the entrance road to the house. The tree-lined path was shorter than most. By all appearances, the war missed this place. The lane was well kept. Matching flowerbeds, rock-bordered, lay on either side of the three steps onto the covered porch.

Before the scouts were halfway to the house, Surby noticed movement in an upstairs window. "Watch it, boys. Upstairs! Saw somethin'!"

Fear seized Surby. The front door burst open and as he thumbed the hammer back on the Colt, his eyes fell on three beautiful young women — "Secesh gals," the scouts called them. And they were all dressed in white, frilly dresses.

Their oval faces beamed with smiles and the middle one, the oldest and prettiest, Surby figured, called sweetly, "Would ya'll like to come on in?"

At the front stoop, Surby giggled nervously, then swung down off his horse and sweeping his hat off at the same time, "Why sure 'nough, mam."

Bud Fowler, with a toothy grin, drawled, "Mighty nice of you folks to invite us."

Quickly, Surby moved to the door and held it open for the ladies. Weedon shifted his chew from one jaw to the other, losing some juice into his beard in the process, and followed the ladies, glancing down the hall into two side rooms while the ladies chattered to Surby about news of the war. Nelson and Fowler, inside the hall now, stood slack-jawed, looking at the three women. Kelly stayed outside, pretending to adjust his saddle. The big Irishman waited until everyone was inside, then led the horses to the rear of the house looking for a well and scanning the trees for any sign of Confederate soldiers.

Inside the two-story house, the ladies were relating how their father and brothers were off helping General (John C.) Pemberton hold that "madman" Grant out of Vicksburg. Surby asked if they had seen any other

Confederate forces. The older sister replied, turning to her sisters, "Why, Lawd, it's been two months, hasn't it, sisters?" They nodded and the conversation turned to what the "brave soldiers" were doing "here'bouts."

Surby, still giggling, answered that he and the others were advance scouts for the First Tennessee Cavalry on their way to General Pemberton at Vicksburg. He added, "The regiment'll be 'long shortly."

Kelly stepped through the front door, took the cob pipe from his teeth, and raised his long nose, looking toward the door that led out to the kitchen, "My, my, that smells of me mother's cookin'!"

This caused the younger of the sisters to exclaim, "Why ya'll have to pardon us. We're just gettin' ready to sit down. C'mon out to the kitchen; we've got plenty."

Surby hesitated, then apologized, "No, mam. Now we wouldn't want to do that." But he did not speak fast enough; Sam Nelson was already breaking for the door at the end of the long vestibule. The others followed, but Surby insisted, "Now, boys! C'mon. Ya'll know we got to get back and report."

"We'd be proud to have ya'll," one of the ladies offered, almost begging.

Surby apologized again as Sam Nelson filed out followed by Weedon, Kelly and Fowler. One of the blond, blue-eyed girls turned and went out a back door, but before Sergeant Surby could be concerned, she returned with two black servants. They were loaded with a meal of biscuits, sweet cakes, and fried sausage. And there was a golden ham and a juicy peach pie. They were astounded by their good luck.

Outside, as soon as the scouts were mounted, the servants handed the food up to them. They all nodded their appreciation and Surby said, "Sure do thank you, ladies." The others mumbled their thanks as they wheeled their horses to ride out to the road.

The oldest of the girls touched her hand to her full bosom and thanked Surby and then bade the others farewell with much success in their "holy cause." The sisters were still standing on the pillared veranda waving when the scouts looked back from the main gate.

On their way to the road, Surby and the others laughed and debated whether to share their food. Finally, George Steadman, who had stood guard on the road for them, was voted a share.

After eating, and while Weedon, Fowler, Kelly and Nelson wiped and licked their fingers, Surby reported to Major Matt Starr at the head of the column that they had found a plantation. He asked Starr to have the word passed that the ladies were friendly and thought the column was the First Tennessee; no need to do anything to make them think differently.

The noon bivouac in a shady, pleasant piece of woods was a welcome rest for the men of the Sixth and Seventh Cavalries. It had been a grinding march even though the column wasn't making the required three miles an hour. Every one knew Grierson would be anxious to drive a little harder during the afternoon. As it turned out, there wasn't even time to smoke a bowl of tobacco after eating. From up the road, a bugler blared the familiar "Boots and Saddle" and shortly the column moved.

Richard Surby and the other Butternut Guerillas heard the bugle call, but no one moved from the fallen log they sprawled around. They were all miserable from the meal they'd eaten less than an hour before.

Charlie Weedon, his slouch hat pulled down over his eyes, leaned against a tree trunk while sitting on the only dry spot he could find, a patch of moss. He shot a mouthful of tobacco juice between his teeth and mumbled to himself when he heard the bugle call and George Steadman answered him, "Chaz, when you gonna quit the doggoned complainin'?"

"When I get home," Weedon growled.

"Yeh, well you probably never get home 'cause you'll be grumblin' when they plant you," Steadman replied, a scowl on his face.

Weedon was tired of such talk and said so, just as Surby got to his feet and stretched, screwing up his face and staring through the trees at the sky. "C'mon, you boys. Let's move. The Sixth is in the advance and Starr'll have 'em breathin' down our necks 'fore you know it."

Amidst grumbling, Kelly, Steadman, Weedon, and Nelson strolled lazily to their horses, collected the reins and climbed sluggishly into their saddles. Fifteen minutes later, they all felt better, except maybe Weedon, and were back into their normal routine. They were exchanging places on the point, finding roads with fordable streams, breaking off to gather horses and mules, and reporting back to the advance guard, the Sixth Cavalry.

The flooding was still bad along every road and the horses waded water belly deep in places. About mid-afternoon, Sam Nelson spied a plantation house. He was hungry again and thought he might have some of the same luck they had earlier. Sam called for Sergeant Surby to come forward. In a few minutes, they were following the same plan as before. Except, this time only Weedon went along.

On the veranda, two Confederate soldiers stood watching as the three sauntered down the lane. Surby and the others cautiously slipped their hands near their Colt pistols, ready. Within seventy yards of the house, the two soldiers smiled and waved. "Where you ol' boys headin'?" one called out.

"We're First Tennessee lookin' for Yanks here'bouts," Surby responded. "Spotted 'em a ways back. They're comin' 'bout two thousand strong. What you boys doin' home?" asked Surby, halting his horse a few yards from the front of the house and leaning on his saddle horn. His eyes danced from side to side, deftly sizing up his position. A broken rocker leaned against the porch railing, the seat protected from the rain. An old lantern hung on a spike near the house entrance.

"We're on furlough. Our ol' Daddy's died," one, the curly-headed one, replied. The other, obviously the oldest, turned and walked quickly to the west of the vine-draped veranda; Nelson's horse pranced that way following him. Sam cocked his revolver, then eased the hammer down

when the soldier yelled, "George," to a slave resting beside a stable.
"Saddle horses for us and round up all the horses and mules!"

George, the black man, knelt near a barn entrance, a bridle strap in
one hand, an awl in the other. He rose easy and waved at his master. He
turned through the stable door in no apparent hurry.

"Ya'll wait now, hear? We'll ride with you. Meantime step down and
rest a spell," the younger soldier invited Surby. As he spoke he turned and
strode into the house. Surby looked at the others, shrugged his shoulders
and stepped down and onto the porch.

In less than a minute, the young Reb returned, his fingers woven
around the stems of five glasses; a decanter hung from his wrist. He placed
the glasses and long-necked bottle on a small cane table and said, looking
up, "Help yourselves to some old rye."

Shortly, George, their slave, led the saddled horses around and one
of the brothers went inside the house. He returned carrying two shotguns,
both double-barrelled. Weedon watched while George and seven other
slaves herded fourteen mules and six beautiful horses out of a corral west
of the house.

Weedon squirted a stream of tobacco juice through his teeth and
snapped at one of the slaves, "Hey, boy!"

The young black man turned his head toward Weedon sharply, then
Weedon asked, "Where'd you get them horses?"

"They's Massa's."

"I know that, boy; where'd he get 'em?" Weedon asked, disgruntled.
Dumb nigger, he thought.

"Why reckon they's all reared here."

"What you tryin' to say, boy? Reared here? Mean he raise them fine
animals?"

Before the slave could answer, Sam Nelson called, "Hey, Charlie,
c'mon over here."

The young slave dropped his head and turned away from Weedon as
Weedon jerked the reins on his horse toward Nelson. Weedon was looking
off into the trees when he approached Nelson; he knew Nelson had
overheard him.

"Charlie, uh...wish you'd lay off them poor folks," Nelson said softly
when Weedon was within hearing.

"I know, Sam. I know. But they's just niggers and the way the
Lincoln's talkin' in the White House, I'm s'posed to be down here freein'
'em," Weedon said through his clinched teeth, while leaning out of his
saddle toward Nelson, his face flushed.

"Charlie, me and you been through that. If Ol' Abe Lincoln wants to
say his Army's fightin' to free them people, he can. But what I'm sayin' is
that they just ain't no call for you to be treatin' 'em like you owned 'em!"
Nelson's temper flared, then calmly, he added, "Now...uh...come on.
You're fixin' to get us shot, that's what."

"Shot?" Weedon asked, jerking his head around to see who could
have been listening.

"Don't you see? Them two Rebs is starin' this way wonderin' what the hell we're up to."

Weedon saw that Nelson was right. The Confederate brothers were looking. Surby was glaring too. Weedon thought he could see trouble and when Surby jerked his head toward the road, Weedon knew he'd better move out. He muttered to himself and prodded his horse up the lane toward the gate, following the mules and horses the slaves herded from the grounds.

Weedon couldn't say why he didn't like black men, but he was certain he didn't like them. His family had never lived around them at any time, but his father told stories, about "chicken-stealin'" and the like. This occurred while his father was a young man in Virginia. And there were always jokes about "lazy niggers" doing this and doing that. So Charles K. Weedon had grown up with that sort of feeling about black men and now that he was around them for the first time, he was sure that all he'd heard was true. "Damn this army life," he cursed aloud.

Back at the house, the brothers mounted now and Surby yelled to Weedon, "Have 'em hold up at the gate, Charlie."

Weedon threw his hand up in the air as answer and the slaves in front of him, hearing Surby's command, slowed the mules and horses. They waited for the others to catch up.

At the gate, Surby said, "This way, boys." And the Butternut Guerillas and the two Confederate soldiers turned toward the column which, Surby calculated, was through a woods, a mile and half away.

Surby and the older of the brothers rode side by side, the others followed. The slaves were busy darting around, keeping the mules and horses in the road. On occasion, a horse or mule broke off into the woods and soon Nelson helped the black men round them up. Weedon, tobacco juice running from the corner of his mouth, ignored the commotion.

Finally, Surby turned to his Confederate companion, "Sure a fine lookin' shotgun you got there."

"My ol' Daddy bought it for me. Week after we beat them Yanks at Sumter."

"Is that right?"

"Yeh, throws a real good pattern, 'specially with double-ought buck."

"Mind if I hold it?" Surby extended his hand.

"Nope, have a look."

Charlie Weedon watched Surby take the gun. "Ya'll's gun new too?" Weedon asked the younger brother.

"Same as my brother's; bought same time."

"Can I look?"

"Why sure," the younger soldier said. He handed Weedon the gun.

Richard Surby smiled and said, "We sure taken ya'll's guns easy now, didn't we?"

Beside Weedon, the young brother laughed uncomfortably. His brother told Surby, "Why, hell, you ol' boys are on same side as us. We'd never give our guns over that easy to a enemy."

Surby examined the shotgun, pulled the hammers back, released them, broke the barrels down, re-locked the gun, and pulled it to his shoulder; then dropped it and said, "Sure a fine piece."

Up the road, Lieutenant-Colonel Blackburn came in a lope, the Morgan's beautiful mane flying. The Confederates with Weedon wanted to speak to his brother, but the older glanced at him. Silence.

"Road clear ahead?" Blackburn asked.

Surby told Blackburn what they'd done. The brothers listened and paled.

"Well now." Blackburn smiled. "What do you know?" The older brother spit in a high arch. Blackburn laughed and rode toward the column. The Sixth Illinois was in sight now.

After the prisoners were turned over to Colonel Grierson, the slaves rode to the rear with the new additions to the horse herd. Surby rejoined the scouts just in time to reconnoiter the next town on Grierson's map, Whitefield. A deserted general store and a handful of houses, all seemingly abandoned, nestled along their path in a grove of trees. Assured that there was no opposition, Surby told George Steadman, "Tell Matt Starr to keep 'em movin'."

"Want pickets set while they march through?"

"No need for that, George."

Soon, the entire column trot-marched through Whitefield.

The road to Louisville was mud and water. The rainstorm flooded the swamps and in one stretch of six miles, the skittish horses waded in belly-deep water. Fortunately, there was no current, just black, stinking, swamp water and trees overhead. The road would dry out in two weeks — maybe.

Near Louisville, Kelly and Fowler rushed back to Blackburn with news that Nelson and Surby captured a "Reb courier." They "took him easy" a few miles from Louisville. He carried dispatches and a registered package stuffed with "secesh" money. Blackburn's comment: "Yahoo!"

Surby and the other scouts walked their horses slowly into Louisville. It was a ghost town! Not a soul on the streets! Every window curtained or boarded! A dog barked somewhere, then whined and was quiet.

"What's matter here, Sarge?" Steadman whispered.

"Don't know," Surby murmured, his eyes darting form building to building.

"Too dead for me."

A soft wind suddenly gusted, slapping shut a fence gate. Down the street smoke slipped out of a chimney and disappeared with the wind. Not a townsman in sight. No horses. No children. Nothing.

"Hold it," Surby said, his voice soft and threatening.

The scouts, all of them, felt surrounded. Even the dark sky threatened them. Each fully expected gunfire.

"Let's turn and walk out of here just like we come in."

"Sounds doggoned good to me, Sarge," Steadman agreed.

"All right, let's do it."

Sam Nelson was behind the others, so he turned his mount cautiously and led them north.

For what seemed like ten minutes, but was only three, the scouts grimaced like men walking a tight rope. It wasn't a platform they were straining for though. It was the edge of town and out of sight of the hot eyes they felt peeping from the boarded-up windows.

Minutes later, Surby asked Blackburn, "What do you think? Do we go around or what?"

"Awful muddy."

"Yeh, but mud's better than bullets."

"You think they'll shoot?" Blackburn asked.

"You think they won't?" Surby sighed, shaking his head.

"We'll find out! Starr," Blackburn ordered, "move 'em!"

Louisville knew that "Yankees" were in the area. For a half hour, its residents watched through cracks in the boards that hid their faces. They saw Major Matt Starr and the First Battalion of the Sixth gallop in and set guards. Then they watched in horror as nearly a thousand of the invaders followed and rode slowly south out of town.

At the head of the column, as the sun set, Sam Nelson shivered.

"Okay, Sam?"

"Uh...yeh, Charlie."

Then, "Charlie...uh, what'd you think back there?"

"Where?"

"At Louisville."

"I don't know," Weedon said.

"Boy, they scared me," Nelson shook again.

"Me too."

"Wasn't that way at the school."

"I know," Weedon said.

"S'pose them folks treat us the same if they...uh...knew we's Yanks?" asked Nelson.

"Hard tellin'," Weedon answered.

"Know one thing."

"What's that?"

"We're in big trouble," Nelson said, his voice tired.

"Yeh?"

"In the enemy's backyard," he said gravely.

"Yeh, guess you can say that."

Colonel Benjamin Grierson worried too. He needed a plan. "What do you do when surrounded by the enemy?" he asked himself aloud. Already, Louisville lay behind. He ordered a guard from the Seventh Illinois to make sure there was no rush from town to report his raiders' whereabouts. He sent two soldiers, Captain John Lynch and Corporal Jonathan Bullard of E Company, Sixth Illinois, to cut telegraph wires leading into Macon along the Mobile and Ohio Railroad. In addition, he cautioned Blackburn, "The scouts'd best lead us as far away from this place as they could."

Surby did not agree. The Butternut Guerillas were already scouting into more swamp. "It'll be all night before we find a dry place to camp," he warned Blackburn.

"Grierson don't want to stop."

"But it's too dangerous!"

"You think being close to Louisville's better?"

"All right; all right," Surby agreed, disgusted.

Three and four feet of water covered the road and the swamp at each side of the road did not allow his scouts to see what was out there, although they all agreed, "Nothin' but snakes, frogs, mosquitoes, and more damned swamp!"

The night was terror filled. But it was not rebels they feared. It was nature's wrath, the thing not a man among them could escape, shoot, or ignore. Twenty horses drowned. If a man fell asleep in the saddle, he could slip from his horse and be drowned under the hooves of slipping, plodding horses and never be missed in the blackness.

Deep water forced Captain Jason Smith's Company K, First Illinois Artillery to haul most of their equipment on horseback. Caissons were emptied. Ammunition was carried by hand through the murky waters. One gun carriage broke down, but Smith's men saved the gun. The carriage was rebuilt later with spare wagon wheels.

Finally, on high ground near Estes Plantation, the Butternut Guerillas proudly informed Blackburn that they had a place to sleep. They were ten miles from Louisville. It was two o'clock in the morning when the Sixth Illinois arrived. The Seventh rode in an hour later. The troopers slid from their weary mounts, most praising God that they'd made it through the night. Some dropped their rubber blankets before they collapsed to sleep, others didn't bother. They were still fifty miles from their objective — Newton Station.

George Steadman tossed and squirmed for several minutes, trying to sleep. Then, frustrated, he called softly, "Sam?"

No answer.

"Sam, you asleep?"

Still no reply.

"Doggone it, Sam?" Steadman spoke, his voice louder.

"What's matter with you, Steadman?" Charles Weedon said, irritated.

"That you, Charlie?"

"Yeh, George."

"Wonder if that doggone Forbes and B Company made it?"

"How'm I s'posed to know that?"

"'T's just wonderin'."

"Yeh."

"Yeh, what, Charlie?"

"Prob'bly made it. Settin' in Macon at a hotel now."

"How you know that?"

"Go to sleep, Steadman."

George Steadman grumbled, then flopped over again. At that precise moment, the Butternut Guerillas with Forbes — Buffington, Wood and Robinson — were having trouble sleeping too. Their sleep was interrupted by the coughing of steam locomotives hauling Confederate reinforcements to Macon from Meridian.

Chapter 5

...the ambush?

Fifty-mile rides strained nerves. A rider's back and legs stiffened as his head fought to endure the pain. No one slept well. Three hours after Sergeant Richard Surby spread himself on the ground — mud and all, he heard Lieutenant-Colonel William Blackburn calling.

"Surby. Hey, Richard. Wake up," Blackburn whispered.

"Yes, sir, Colonel. I'm awake." Surby's response was hoarse.

"Surby, Colonel Grierson wants you and your men to get on to Philadelphia. Look at that bridge on the Pearl River. Find out if it's still there. Grierson's afraid word spread that we're closin' in."

"Yes, sir. Understand," Surby replied. He rolled his rubber blanket around his bedding now. Couldn't sleep anyhow, he thought.

"If the bridge is still there, might be guarded. We can't take a chance on takin' a bridge; slow us down too much. We've got to get to the Vicksburg Railroad, cut it and get out of here."

Surby listened carefully.

"You and your men see if you can find a place to ford the river. We're hopin' it ain't rained so much south of here."

"Yes sir. I understand."

Nelson sat up. He scratched. Steadman was awake and complaining about the mosquitoes. He probed the ashes of a fire. "Gonna smoke 'em out," he told Nelson.

"Colonel," Surby asked, "What do we do if it's not guarded?"

"Guard it! Column'll be there by noon," he grunted, while groping for a stirrup.

As Blackburn mounted, the big Morgan backed up, bringing a yelp from a sleepy trooper. And then the horse walked quietly out of the glow of the campfire. They all scurried about now: Weedon, Kelly, Fowler, Steadman, Nelson, Surby. They would eat on the move to the Pearl.

Their horses were ready, their gear packed, and their weapons checked. Nearby someone yelled, "Hey, you guys have a good time now, hear? Take it easy on them secesh gals today."

"Oh, ...uh shut up!" Nelson grumbled.

"At least," Steadman muttered, "we got fresh horses." Maybe today he would get in on some of those eats. He was a hungry little man. He claimed he could eat more than anyone. He was in an eating contest one time with two troopers in C Company. One of them weighed nearly two hundred pounds, but Steadman won. Every time the hotel owner brought another plate of pork sausage and potatoes, Steadman beat the other two men to a clean plate. Then he would get up, go outside into an alley along side the building and run his finger down his throat. Up it all came and back to the table Steadman went. Seven servings later, they gave up, paid the bill, and each gave him a dollar.

Kelly and Fowler were half asleep when they mounted their horses, but the blistering pace that Surby set jogged them awake. Now they wished they'd been able to sleep longer. Weedon felt the same and his horse seemed half asleep as well. He had trouble keeping up with the rest. He even forgot to load his jaw with tobacco.

At last, the night contained a hint of morning. Soon the sun was lighting their way more and more. It was a beautiful Thursday, April 23rd. "There's a high sky and horse-tail clouds; sign of more good weather to come," Sam Nelson said quietly to himself. His mount kept him side by side with Sergeant Surby.

Surby's mind was elsewhere. If there's a picket on the bridge, do I try "Butternut" tactics with them? Good chance every Mississippian for miles around knows we're here by now — Butternut garb or not.

Up ahead, Surby spotted a tree line — the edge of the Pearl River valley? As the horses ran down a gently sloping road, Surby pulled back on his reins and held up his right hand. Nelson and the others bounced their mounts to a halt. They continued slowly, the horses panting and chafing a bit, their heads bouncing from side to side impatiently.

*Action by the Butternut Guerillas saved this bridge over the Pearl River north of Philadelphia. (From **Harper's Pictorial History of the Civil War**, Author's Collection)*

Surby spoke. His voice was just loud enough for all to hear. "I'll take the point."

It was only a couple miles to the bridge — if these were the Pearl bottoms. Surby felt like he was creeping along. He clucked his horse forward; the horse responded too much and he reined him a little. Occasionally, he turned in the saddle to check the rest of the Butternut Guerillas. They rode silently in twos with Nelson leading down the narrow, tree-covered road.

From time to time, Surby lost sight of them, but for only a few seconds — never more than a minute. Then he was riding around a long bend with thick underbrush on both sides of the road. Suddenly a man riding a mule appeared just ahead; he rode toward Surby.

Surby and the man saw each other at the same time. Too old to be a soldier, Surby reasoned. Surby restrained his hand from jumping under his coat after the Navy Colt revolver. The rider had to be a civilian.

His eyes watery, the old man stared at Surby and Surby stared back as they approached each other in the narrow road. The old Southerner dropped the rope reins and with both hands tried to close the collar on his light coat against the morning breeze that chilled him. The collar flopped open again as both men whoa-ed their mounts and sat face to face. The old man spoke, his voice strong, "Mornin' son."

"G'mornin'." Then Surby added, hesitantly, "Nice day today."

"Yes, 'tis, considerin' all the rain we been havin'. Where you headed?"

"Down to the Pearl. Thinkin' of crossin' the bridge. Still there?" Surby inquired, craning his neck down the road.

"Just come from there. Should be." The old man paused, then added, "But prob'bly not for long."

"Why's that?"

"Yanks — hear them raiders is comin' this way." The old man turned in the saddle and pointed saying, "Why, we got a picket down there now. My boy's one of 'em," he smiled proudly.

"Think you can hold 'em? If they do come, I mean?"

"Don't rightly know, but we got a picket to blow it up just in case. Got some planks ripped up too." There was a pause. Then the old man cocked his head and asked, "Say, what's your regiment anyhow?"

"I'm with the First Tennessee Cav'ry. We're down here lookin' for them Yanks," Surby lied.

While they talked, the remaining Butternut Guerillas approached within twenty-five yards and halted. They spread themselves across the road, blocking it.

Surby asked, "What's your name and where you from?"

The old man looked puzzled. He glanced from Surby to the blocked road. Fear spread over his face. Surby fumbled around inside his coat, unbuttoned his shirt, and took out a piece of paper and a stub of a pencil. The old man glared at Surby. Then staring wide-eyed at the Butternut Guerillas, he exclaimed, "Gentlemen, gentlemen!" Shaking his head, he blurted, "You are not what you seem to be!"

Surby grabbed the mule's reins; the old man scolded him, "You're certainly Yankees! We got news in Philadelphia last night that ya'll were comin' this way."

Wet weather harrassed Grierson's men, especially north of Philadelphia. Today, some of the swampy areas in that vicinity still exist. (Author's Collection)

Sam Nelson came up and held the mule now. Richard Surby jerked his Colt from his belt. He waved it at the old man and spoke menacingly, "It lies in your power to save your buildings from the torch; you can save your own life; probably that of your son, by saving the bridge. You hear me?"

The old man trembled some as he nodded his head. "I can save the bridge, but I don't think I can get my friends and son to surrender." His voice faltered.

"The bridge is the important point. Now you go down there now and tell your son and friends to surrender. We'll parole 'em; they won't be harmed."

"Yes, suh. I'll do what I can, but I can't promise nothing."

"Old man," Surby said. He waved the big pistol again, "If another plank is harmed on that bridge — just one plank, remember we'll make damn sure your house and barns are burned!"

"You want me to go now?"

Surby nodded. The old man turned the mule and coaxed him back toward the river. The scouts and Surby followed to within three hundred yards of the bridge.

"You go on now, old man. And 'member what I told you."

The Butternut Guerillas dismounted and led their mounts off the road into a thick growth of underbrush. The bridge was in sight from where Surby lay on the ground. It was a high bridge, otherwise it would have been submerged in the flood water that covered the bottomland. Logs and brush gathered rapidly on the huge posts that formed the trestlework. Surby thought, there will be no fording this stream. In both directions, current-creased water swirled chasing logs and debris along the swollen river.

The old man and the mule kept the same slow pace to within a few yards of the bridge ramp. Then they halted. The old fellow began telling the men and boys on the other side what was expected of them, but before he was half done, they were gathering their horses and tightening their cinch straps. Before he'd finished, they disappeared over a small rise, headed toward Philadelphia.

Surby and his men mounted. As soon as the bridge guards were gone, they galloped to where the old man sat, head in hands, astride his mule. Surby and Nelson rushed without word, jumped their horses onto the bridge, and thundered across to the other side. Weedon, on his slow mount, pulled up beside the old man and Steadman, Kelly, and Fowler dismounted and searched under the ramp for the missing planks.

Across the bridge, Surby noticed two shotguns that the excited picket had forgotten. He continued to the top of the rise. The picket was gone. Back at the bridge, Surby yelled at Weedon to stay with the old man. Nelson pulled the explosives from the middle of the bridge and Surby prodded him, "Hurry up, Sam. Steadman and Kelly, you and Fowler ride with me toward Philadelphia."

"Right, Sarge," Kelly responded.

"When them pickets get help, they'll be back' I want to know what we're up against."

It was under five miles to Philadelphia and along the way, the Butternut Guerillas saw sign that the bridge picket alarmed the countryside. The scouts occasionally flung a shot at a mounted civilian. Fortunately, the civilians stayed away from the main road, out of pistol range.

The Mississippi sun beat hotter on Surby and his men now. The sand road dried quickly. Surby slowed the pace. They were excited and tense. Off in the distance, now and then, a farmer jogged across a field, a gun in his hand, always headed in the general direction of Philadelphia. The scouts thought this just as well; they wanted the main column to catch up before the shooting started. Walking their mounts cautiously, they strained to see any tell-tale signs of an ambush on the piney, rolling landscape.

Sam Nelson slipped his hand nervously inside his saddle bag. Surby noticed, but before he spoke, Nelson said, "Thought I'd have a little nip."

"Think you ought to?" Surby asked, concerned.

"Why not?" Nelson said. He turned the spare canteen of whiskey up and sipped from it, checked its contents, replaced the lid, and prodded his little gelding on.

After a minute or two, Surby asked, "Feel better?"

"Don't upset me none, uh...them folks fixin' to shoot us dead. Bother you?"

"Sure is hot," Uriah Fowler mumbled, grinning.

"You betcha," Nelson agreed. "Want a snort, Kelly? 'Fore I put it back?" Nelson asked.

"Aye," the big Irishman smiled, wiping sweat and dust from his lips. Nelson handed him the container.

The hot, baked, dusty road was a change from the mud. Sam Nelson wondered what would happen next, "Think they'll shoot...uh...at us?"

"Not before we get to town," Surby figured.

"That's good. Always like gettin' shot at in town better."

Surby grunted, "Uh-huh."

About three hundred yards from town, just ahead on the dusty road, groups of armed civilians raced about preparing to defend their community, Philadelphia.

Surby slowed the Butternut Guerillas even more. He watched carefully as a defiant line of farmers and townsmen formed across the entry to Philadelphia. Finally Surby halted his horse, turned in his saddle and said, "Fowler, get back to the advance guard. Tell 'em to send me ten men. Double-quick!"

Fowler wheeled his mount and raced a cloud of dust toward the bridge.

A few minutes later, Surby and the others heard the advance and saw the dust rise along the road they'd just traveled. When the horses were in sight, Surby turned to Steadman, Nelson, and Kelly and said, "Well, boys. Let's show 'em our hand!"

With that, Surby yelled. His horse and the others bolted toward the line thrown up at the edge of town. They tore down on the civilian soldiers, shouting and screaming, and commenced firing their revolvers wildly. That was all it took; the line broke and the Philadelphians broke for cover. They only fired a few shots. None hit their mark.

Five minutes later, the main column arrived and took over the entire town. Six prisoners were brought to Colonel Benjamin Grierson and through them, he found that the townspeople heard this morning that the Yankees were on their way toward Philadelphia. The townspeople resolved to destroy the bridge and were preparing to do so at the time the bridge was captured.

"What did you hope to gain by throwin' up this line of resistance?" Grierson asked the prisoners.

One of the prisoners, the Neshoba County judge, replied, "We set the ambush, 'cause we feared for our lives and property. Simple as that."

"That's right," another prisoner spoke. The others nodded.

"Ambush?" Grierson muttered. "What for?" Before any of them could answer, he turned his horse toward the few civilians in the street. Most others hid behind closed doors.

Firmly, Grierson began. "Now listen," he shouted. "Understand, we are not here to interfere with private citizens or to destroy their property or to insult or molest their families. We are here after the soldiers and property of the rebel government."

Finished, Grierson stared from face to face. Then he called to a cavalryman, "Get Colonel Prince and bring him to the hotel. That'll be headquarters for a while."

Sergeant Richard Surby watched this scene, then noted the people following Grierson's speech. Philadelphians talked softly to each other. There were no smiles, no nodding heads. Some turned and walked to their homes; others moved off the street to a favorite resting place, a store front or a shade tree.

"Well, nothin' more we can do here," Surby said to the others. "Let's find Colonel Blackburn."

A short time later, the Butternut Guerillas found their colonel and Blackburn told them to find a shady spot. "Get some rest. Grierson'll be wantin' to move pretty soon."

"What you want us to do now, Sarge?" Sam Nelson asked Richard Surby.

"Wait around a while like Blackburn says. I figure he may want us to scout ahead before long."

"All right if I...uh...find my company?"

"Don't see why not. Know Grierson's goin' to stay a spell. Don't know how long."

George Steadman, Uriah Fowler, and Lycurgus Kelly trudged off on foot leading their horses following Sam Nelson.

"Seen G Company, Seventh?" Nelson asked a passing soldier.

"Not unless they're on picket. Some of the Seventh's on northeast road."

"Much obliged," Nelson said. He walked north up the main street.

It took nearly ten minutes, but he found George Rinehold. Fowler, Kelly and Steadman stretched out beside a white fence while Nelson and Rinehold talked a short distance away.

They asked each other about home — southern Illinois — and the conversation became a general one.

Finally, Rinehold asked, "How's Meg?"

"Fine, fine. Had a letter three days 'fore we left La Grange."

"Kids doin' good?"

"Sure. How 'bout yours?"

"We lost our youngest; you knew that?"

"Yeh."

"Had a note from the wife. My boy...my boy's dead."

Sam Nelson stared straight ahead. He thought a lot about his own son. Now he wondered to himself, how do you ask a man about losing his only son?

"Pox got 'im, wife said," Rinehold added. His voice trailed off almost to a whisper.

"Sorry...uh...real sorry to hear that, Georgie."

Rinehold smiled, then squinted at the sky, "Almost makes a fellow want to die; know that, Sammy?"

"'Spect it...uh...would, George. But you and your wife can have another."

For nearly a minute the two men avoided each others eyes. Then Rinehold spoke quietly, "He's so special though, Sammy. You wouldn't believe how special that boy was."

Nelson searched for words, found none, then listened as Rinehold continued, "Don't reckon I'll ever have me a son no more."

"You'll see, Georgie. Wars don't last forever."

"No, guess they don't. Some end sooner'n we 'spect."

"Say, well you just cheer the wife up now when you write again," Sam said, his voice nervous and strained.

"I already wrote her; got the letter here," Rinehold said, patting his chest.

"Well, no post office where we're goin'; maybe you can mail it from Vicksburg," Sam said, a nervous smile crossed his lips. Rinehold did not smile. He shifted around, then stared miserably into the sky.

"Yeh, maybe," he said finally.

Sam Nelson knew there was nothing more to say. He apologized for having to leave, looked around for the others and called to Kelly, Fowler, and Steadman.

In a few minutes, they were back in town. Surby was gone, but Blackburn gave them directions. It was two in the afternoon.

The last the scouts saw of Philadelphia, the town they had taken nearly single-handed, the Philadelphians lined the sides of the street, arms extended perpendicularly, and Colonel Edward Prince stood facing them. Prince, commander of the Seventh Illinois, was swearing the civilians not to give out any information for a certain length of time.

In fifteen minutes, all the Butternut Guerillas were together again. Weedon rode on point. He had switched mounts at Philadelphia. The herders took one look at his morning mount, laughed, and one remarked, "You Butternuts gonna get shot up ridin' that kinda stock!"

Weedon did not share their humor and punctuated his feeling with a string of tobacco juice. He did not like horses, never had. But in February, 1862, when he signed on as a recruit, he was not concerned about what he signed for. "Just wanted to get in on the fight," he complained. "Not ride horses from one end of the country to the other. And the Army was worse than expected. Poor food, poor gear, and butchers for doctors."

Surby joined him. "Weedon, be lookin' for a place to rest. Colonel Blackburn just sent word. Grierson says there's a plantation ahead. We'll rest there a spell."

"How's Grierson always know about where these plantations are?" Weedon asked, shaking his head.

"He's got maps."

"Whoever heard of a map with plantations marked on it?"

"Well, he's got 'em," Surby said. "You just find it now."

And so, near five in the afternoon, the welcome word spread through the Sixth Illinois Cavalry — the advance guard — that the scouts had found a resting place. They had advanced nearly ten miles beyond Philadelphia.

"I's just thinkin'," George Steadman said to Kelly. "We sure scared them folks back there."

"Aye, but don't be so sure of yourself, Georgie."

"What you mean?"

"I mean, they're a bit embarrassed now," Kelly answered.

"Embarrassed?"

"Aye."

Steadman asked, "Doggone it, what's that supposed to mean?"

"I had me a fight with a little man one time. Beat him bad. Had no reason to."

"So what? Don't mean you can lick any little man," Steadman snarled.

"No, no, George. Wait. You are missin' what I am meanin' to tell you," Kelly replied.

"Yeh, well...."

"Hold on, George," Kelly interrupted. "The man was so embarrassed that he was determined to skin me hide — and he did. He was alert to a chance to get even. No more chances for him. He cracked me below the ear with a hardwood club. Cracked me skull."

Steadman laughed.

"'T wasn't funny. But I'm sayin' to you that the citizens of Philadelphia will not be so easy to take next time."

"Yeh, think I see what you mean."

"They might even be so angry that they'd follow us," Kelly added.

"You think so?" Steadman asked. He turned in his saddle and looked back down the road to their rear.

The afternoon sun lit the front of the big plantation house painting it in a reddish, fiery glow. It had been a long day, but with their target, the Vicksburg Railroad, within twenty-five miles, no cavalryman in the column was simple enough to take this for a night bivouac. None cared to stay either. They were nearly one hundred fifty miles into Confederate territory. One mistake, one error by their leader, one wrong turn could kill or put all of them in Libby Prison or some other Southern hell-hole. They feared that.

Two hours after settling themselves, the Butternut Guerillas received good news — and bad news. Blackburn walked out of the plantation house to the steps of the high, vine-covered veranda. He surveyed the lounging soldiers. Surby raised his hand, Blackburn saw him and nodded, then began walking toward Sergeant Surby.

"Lynch and Bullard got back from Macon!" Blackburn announced before he reached the straw beds the Butternut Guerillas rested on.

"Good. Find out anything?" Surby asked.

"Sure did. Forbes and B Company must have struck gold. Macon was crawlin' with Rebs. Maybe we can run down to Newton Station without too much trouble."

"Newton Station?"

Blackburn nodded, "Leave at ten sharp. We're takin' two hundred men from First Battalion of the Seventh to ride straight through."

It was cooler now. The sun slid behind the pine woods to the west. Nelson shivered, but not because of the night air. He feared a night ride this deep in enemy territory. Anything could happen.

Companies A, G, D, and K of the First Battalion moved quick and quiet. A few sharp commands and then only the sound of crickets, night birds, and the squeak of saddle leather followed them into the night.

At the front of the column, a mile ahead, Lieutenant-Colonel William Blackburn rode silently with Sergeant Surby and two scouts. Riding out of the pine forest, the stars lit their way down the dusty road through the cool night. The butternut jackets felt good against the cold.

Blackburn stared into the blackness and worried about an ambush. He said, "If we ain't damn careful, we'll walk right head-on into somethin'. But then our luck's held so far," he sighed.

"You're right," Surby agreed. "Those Rebs in the last town are bound to have got the word spread that we're headin' south."

"These Rebs know their own country, too."

It was nearly a minute later when Blackburn added, "Well, Richard, I'm goin' back to the advance guard. Want to make sure those movin' pickets are keepin' proper pace."

"Right, Colonel. Be up later?"

"Sure. Say I'd keep Nelson on point when you're not there. Talks like a Southerner. Might save us, case we walk into some Reb outfit."

"Right, Colonel. We'll keep switchin'."

"You know what to do if you get ambushed now, don't you?" Blackburn inquired.

Puzzled, Surby tried to read the Colonel's face for the answer, but the night was too dark. He said, "Well...what's that?"

"Run like hell!" The big bay and his rider wheeled and pranced back toward the advance guard; Surby didn't hear Blackburn laugh. And the night wrapped itself more closely around Surby and the others.

Near midnight Surby sent Nelson to the front. Nelson's horse loped along about one hundred yards, then slowed to a walk. Nelson and the others were about six miles from where they had rested earlier. Nineteen more miles, Nelson figured, and then we'll be at the railroad. Then out of Reb country? Hate to be Grierson. Wonder if we'll go to Alabama and swing into Tennessee or join ol' Grant at Vicksburg?

Sam Nelson's gelding shied and stopped. "What's matter, boy?" Nelson asked. His voice was almost a whisper.

Nelson's eyes were wide open. He stared into the blackness — a fork in the road! Sam sighed relief. The little gelding had been walking with loose reins. Now Sam clucked him forward and down the left fork, headed due south.

Shawnee, the gelding, walked on one hundred fifty to two hundred feet. His path led through the tree-covered lane and around a gentle turn until Nelson said, "Whoa boy! This the right road, I wonder?" He leaned forward, patted the horse's neck, and said softly, "We'd better just hold it a couple minutes, fellow."

At the fork in the road, minutes later, Sergeant Surby, like Nelson' horse, hesitated. There was no sign of Nelson. Turning his head, he whispered, "Steadman?" Steadman rode out of the darkness. "Steadman, there's a little shack back a hundred yards or so. Go back and find out which fork is the Decatur road."

Steadman said nothing. Rider and horse moved off silently.

Surby sat for two or three minutes, then coaxed his horse down the right fork toward the southwest. The lane was also tree covered. A hundred yards from the fork, the road opened into a clearing.

At the edge of the dim shadow formed by the trees, Surby stopped and turned his horse crossways in the road. He looked back through the tunnel of trees and saw movement, a rider.

"Is this the right road?" Surby called, breaking the spell of the cool, clear night. In the trees, a startled bird fluttered from its roost.

Steadman nearly jumped from his saddle. If that's Surby, he thought, must be crazy to yell like that! Steadman eased his horse down the right fork toward the voice. "Ever' damn Reb in the country heard that," he mumbled to himself. He made a slow approach.

Steadman stared into the blackness. He could see a rider standing in the middle of the road. Is that Surby? He rode on. He wanted to call out, but he could not bring himself to do it. Don't look like Surby. Within a few feet of the figure, Steadman leaned forward in his saddle and stared eagerly, trying to see the face of this man whose horse blocked his path. Could be a doggoned Reb! he thought, startled.

Panic!! Steadman spun his horse. In an instant, he fled back to the fork in the road. At the fork, he dismounted and ran, stumbling in the dark behind some trees!

Somewhere, a pistol boomed once, then twice more. In seconds, the black night was alive with screaming bullets and blazing muzzles. There were carbines firing. Hot lead filled the triangular woods between the two roads that met at the fork. Shouted commands bounded through the trees.

On the right fork, Surby shuddered. When Steadman exploded away from him, he jerked around, staring into the starlit road that lay ahead of him. Nothing! What in blazes was he running from? he asked himself. Then Surby heard the pistol shots. When the carbines or rifles boomed — he couldn't tell which — he saw a spark fly from a rock near the roadside. A series of bullets whizzed over his head. He needed no more explanation.

Surby yelled and dug his spurs into his horse. Horse and rider plunged straight into scrub oaks and a brier patch. The briers tore at Surby's face and legs; his hat came off. A small limb lashed his forehead before he could stop the frenzied horse. He jumped to the ground, one hand clutching his revolver, the other clung to a rein. More shots tore into the timber. He ran, dragging the horse, stumbling over roots, briers tearing at him. He crouched lower, then stopped.

Silence!

Surby's ears rang. He strained for a sound. Anything! Blackburn warned him. Ambush! Rebs let me go by, then fired into the advance. But why'd the shooting stop? His brain whirled. Sweat tickled his face. Blown and hot, he sat to cool and nurse his bruises and scratches.

After a few minutes of listening to himself breathe, Surby made up his mind, I'll move back to the command before I'm caught.

He led his horse cautiously through the triangular woods until he was out of the undergrowth at the edge of the other, the left lane. He mounted and rode slowly, pistol cocked and ready, forward.

Suddenly, he was on the road and face to face with Sam Nelson. Neither man made a quick move, but slowly lowered the hammers on their revolvers and held their weapons to their sides.

Surby motioned Nelson off the other side of the road through a narrow line of trees and into an open, starlit field.

A quarter of a mile from the road, still silent, Surby turned his horse north and galloped along, the cool night air drying the nervous sweat from his face. Nelson followed. After a half mile, Surby held up his hand and both men reined to a halt. Nelson blurted, "Happened, Sarge?"

"Don't know," Surby gasped. He paused, then continued, "Steadman went back to a house to ask about the road to Decatur."

"House by the fork?"

"Yeh, he got back and rode up to me," Surby puffed. "Looked up the road, say somethin', ran like a scared rabbit. Then the firin' commenced."

Again Surby paused. "You see anything?" he asked Nelson.

"No. Uh...just heard, heard the shootin'."

They turned their horses west now, walking them toward the road. Ahead, they saw a long, low shadow. "Must be the main column," Surby observed, relieved. "Watch for pickets, Sam. Should be about a hundred yards this side the road."

Sergeant Surby and Corporal Nelson rode without interruption or objection into the side of the column. Surby called out to the trooper closest to him, "Hey, we're comin' in!"

"Well c'mon." The trooper hesitated, then added, "Hey, Sarge. That you?"

"Ditto?" Surby thought he recognized the corporal from A Company.

"Yeh, Sarge. We thought you's dead. Or at least shot up."

"No, I'm in one piece, but what happened?"

"Don't know," Corporal John Ditto answered. "Colonel Blackburn just passed by here an' I ask' him what the shootin's about. He said you's lost."

"Which way Colonel go?" Surby asked his friend.

"Headin' to the front."

"Thanks John," Surby said. He and Nelson prodded their mounts into a trot toward the head of the column. Nearly an hour had passed since Sergeant Surby had drawn the fire. Steadman, in a panic, had jerked three pistol shots in his direction. The advance guard rushed forward, thinking the Butternut Guerillas were in trouble. They fired into the wooded triangle formed by the forks in the road. In measured words, George Steadman tried to apologize. Of course, Surby wanted to shoot Steadman, but for now that was an unreasonable feeling. He told Steadman, he'd await a better occasion. Steadman wasn't sure if Surby meant it.

Blackburn was much relieved to see his scouts back. But the solemn night was not over. The silent First Battalion of the Seventh Illinois Cavalry closed in on its target. They were face to face with war. Before a nine o'clock freight train made its stop at Newton Station on the morning of April 24th, Grierson's raiders would complete their mission to cut the vital supply route from Vicksburg to all points east in the Confederacy. Tomorrow was the day.

Chapter 6

...a great day for Grierson

Decatur, Mississippi lay silent and ghostlike under shimmering star-shine on Friday, April 24th, as Sergeant Richard Surby rode slowly into the outskirts off the main north-south road. It was nearly three a.m.

Lieutenant-Colonel William Blackburn ordered Surby to go ahead, enter a house, and ask the occupants if there were any Confederate soldiers at Newton Station.

As Surby surveyed the street, he saw an inn and stepped from his horse near the front of the old building. It was an old-fashioned country inn with the pigeonhole windows standing halfway up the slanting roof. A sign board hung on a slanting pole; HOTEL. He handed the reins to George Steadman, looked up and down the street, saw no one, stepped onto the porch and rapped on one of the twin doors. HE waited a cautious few seconds, stepped a stride to the right and rapped hard on the other door.

"Who's there?" a gruff voice called from the inn.

"A Confederate soldier. On important business. Need information."

A metal latch slammed open, the door squeaked, and then the voice rasped, "Come in."

"'Scuse my untimely visit, suh," Surby drawled. "It certainly is a late hour to be callin'."

"'S all right, 's all right," the proprietor said as he carried a metal poker to the fireplace. He knelt on rheumy knees and scraped a few coals to the front of the fireplace. The bright coals cast a dim glow through the combination sitting room and bed chamber.

The old man raised himself slowly from his kneeling position, moved to a table at the center of the room, pulled a chair back, and nodded for Sergeant Surby to sit down. Then he sprang back into bed!

The action startled Surby. He had watched the old man cautiously while he had the poker in his hand — not knowing what to expect, but the move into bed was handled with the agility of a cat. Surby looked at the bed in the lurid light and saw what inspired the old gentleman's agility. Beneath the covers, by the wall, a pair of sparkling, roguish black eyes, tresses black as a raven's wing, and a mischievous mouth, belonging to a young and charming woman could be seen. She was beautiful and at that ripe age when beauty in a woman seems more solid than in the budding period of girlhood. Can it be possible that she is married to this old man? he considered.

Surby nodded to the woman resting on her elbow beside the old man; she smiled back. To find such a woman in this out of the way....The old man broke the spell, "Watcha doin' here, soldier?"

"Why, suh," Surby said, smiling now at the young lady, "I'm scoutin' for General (Earl) Van Dorn of Columbus."

"Van Dorn, heh?"

"Yanks is raidin' toward Decatur and I'm carryin' the word to the railroad. Ya'll know where I can find them forces?"

"Ten miles south at Newton Station would be the nearest force, but they's only a hundred sick and wounded soldiers there." The old man paused, then added, "Might be some infantry though."

This was great news! Surby frowned and went on evenly, "Ya'll sure that's all that's there?"

"Well, now that's all I heard 'bout. Some cav'ry passed east of here a couple days back. All I know." The lady nodded in agreement — and smiled.

"I sure do thank ya'll for your kind help. Right sorry, mam, to interrupt your rest like this. Hope ya'll forgive me."

The old man grumbled and tossed around in the bed, straightening the quilt. Surby walked to the door, opened it, and started to step outside when he heard a sweet, whispery voice say, "Ya'll call if you come this way again, you hear?"

Surby stuck his head back in the room, blushed and promised, "Yes, mam. I sure will. G'night now." He closed the door, chuckled to himself, walked to his horse, and mounted.

Surby lashed his horse toward the advance of the column just north of Decatur. His information ran through his head and he laughed aloud. Later when he thought about the old man and young woman, he would chuckle. Finally, when George Steadman asked him what was so "dog-goned funny," he told him, but could never convince Steadman that he had not made up the story. Surby did wonder later if his imagination wasn't helping his memory.

After his report, and before dawn with Nelson on the point, the men filed quietly, and without incident, through Decatur. Between five and six miles from Newton Station, the sun began to streak the sky and climb steadily to crown the day. From the point, Nelson reported a small stream, "Be a good...uh...place to water the...uh...horses," he muttered to Richard Surby.

Lieutenant-Colonel Blackburn took the advice, had the men remove the bits, and let the horses drink. Surby and the Butternut Guerillas stood on the south side of the stream waiting for Blackburn to come to the front.

Blackburn, his bay mount splashing through the water, forded the stream and ordered Surby to take two scouts and proceed quickly to Newton Station. "Reconnoiter and report what force is stationed there. Find out what time the train arrives and anything else that'll help us get that railroad busted up."

Surby nodded to Nelson and Steadman and they each whirled their mounts as Blackburn yelled after him, "Be quick!"

Surby, Nelson, and Steadman arrived less than an hour later atop a rise overlooking Newton Station, Mississippi. There was a large, drab-looking building near the railroad track which ran east and west through a town of scattered buildings. The town was not old enough, seen at a glance, to be dilapidated, but if it gained anything by being a depot on the Vicksburg Railroad, it did not show it.

The three Butternut Guerillas dismounted and Steadman led the horses below the rise while Sergeant Surby and Corporal Nelson lay prone studying the movement at the train crossing. Only a few men walked about; none appeared to be armed. There was no telltale sign of tents in any direction. Surby and Nelson agreed on the huge building being the hospital. The wounded the old man in Decatur informed Surby about would be there.

Surby scanned every inch of the little town, then did it again just to make sure everything was in order. He looked at Nelson, jerked his head, motioning that they should join Steadman.

They scrambled to their feet and brushed the red dust off their Rebel uniforms. Steadman was anxious, "How's it look?"

"Good," Nelson replied.

Then Surby added, "But we'd better go in and have a closer look."

Steadman grimaced. Surby's crazy, he thought. Then he asked, "But, Sarge, won't it be better to wait a spell for the First Battalion to get a little closer? They must be only an hour's ride away."

"C'mon Steadman. Now you know them Rebs'll think we're of 'em," Surby jabbed, then laughed. "Besides," he continued, "they may've set a trap. It's a long ride off this rise into town. I'd rather have 'em shootin' at us than the entire battalion, wouldn't you?"

Nelson and Steadman did not respond, but Surby knew they weren't happy with him. Still, he felt it had to be done.

The three riders cantered their mounts down the long, sloping road toward Newton Station. The sun had burned the cool morning air away and that, and the excitement of what might lay ahead, had them in a sweat.

At the edge of town, a man drew water from a well by the side of his house. The three stopped and Surby asked, "Suh, can we have a drink of that cool water?"

"Sure 'nough," the man smiled, reaching for a gourd dipper hanging on a post beside the well.

Surby swung down off his horse, walked to the man, took the heavy wooden bucket and returned to where Nelson and Steadman sat their horses. They drank in turn.

Surby walked back to the well, "Know when the next train'll get in?"

The man pulled a watch from his pocket, held it down and away and said, "'Bout three quarters an hour."

Surby volunteered, "We're from Van Dorn at Columbus, scoutin' this way. Any forces to 'mount to anything here at Newton Station?"

"Was some. All gone now; chasin' them Yankee raiders."

"We heard they's comin' this way. You hear anything?"

"Not nary a word, other than they's suppose' to be up at Macon. Least so's a conductor off the Meridian train says last night."

That would be Forbes, thought Surby. "Well, we sure...." In a distance a long mournful whistle stopped Surby in mid-sentence. "What train's that?" Surby blurted, surprised.

"Why that's the west-bound freight. Due at nine," the man answered.

Surby turned to see Nelson walking toward the well with he bucket. He thanked the man and walked toward the horses. As he passed Nelson, he whispered, "Hurry up, man!"

At the horses, Steadman had heard the whistle and was ready to ride. "Tell Blackburn — two trains, freight and passenger — double-quick!" Surby ordered.

Steadman disappeared up the grade north of town. As Nelson and Surby mounted, the man at the well yelled something. They paid no attention and lashed their horses toward the rail depot. Surby and Nelson hastened to get to the telegraph office before anyone saw the force of cavalrymen that would be screaming down the slope into town in a very few minutes.

At the depot, the two scouts dismounted and ran onto the station platform. They looked quickly into a series of windows. A sign overhead announced: TELEGRAPH OFFICE. There was nothing! The office was deserted. Not even a telegrapher's key! "C'mon!" Surby barked.

The two men darted around the corner toward their horses. With their Navy Colts drawn, they reached the back of the depot. Down the street, the door of the hospital swung open. Several wounded soldiers limped out. They were not armed and nearly a hundred yards away. Surby aimed the big revolver at them and screamed, "Stay inside! Don't come out or you're dead!"

Nelson noticed the cloud of dust rising from the slope north of town, "Troops comin'!" he yelled to Surby. "Blackburn comin'!"

The frightened Confederate convalescents looked north, saw the dust, and walked pitifully, but wisely, back into the hospital. The wild yelling of the battalion startled the peaceful little town. The residents did what others had done when Union soldiers appeared; they retreated to the safety of their homes and expected the worst.

Blackburn's Morgan bounded to a halt before Nelson and Surby, "You cut the wires?"

"No need now. No operator in the depot," Surby explained. "No equipment neither," blurted Nelson.

"All right, we'll take care of the wires later on. What's the situation?" Blackburn asked.

"There's a train due," Surby pointed east down the track toward a patch of pine. The smoke from the locomotive puffed above the trees.

"Must be a mile or so away. It's a freight. Passenger train'll be along from Vicksburg."

Blackburn said nothing, but wheeled his horse and began shouting commands. In a few minutes, pickets closed the roads into town. The company commanders, Charles Hunting, George W. Trafton, William H. Reynolds, and Joseph R. Herring, dismounted and hid their men from view of the approaching train. Two men ran along the tracks to make sure the switch brought the freight on the siding.

The big bay carried Blackburn through the street for a final check and then to the station where the colonel dismounted, wrapped the reins around a hitching rail, and joined Surby and two other scouts on the station platform.

The four men hid in the shade; two of them sat on a ledge smoking. The other two stood face to face as if talking. Blackburn's dust-covered uniform concealed his identity and then Surby said calmly, "Here she comes."

Down the track, the squat engine puffed and blowed dragging the weight of twenty-five cars. Slowly it approached the switch box. Would the engineer stop or run? Would he suspect something? The men hidden and waiting to rush the train would know in seconds.

The engineer eased the throttle back, slowed the locomotive, and gave the men under Blackburn the first sensation that their trap had worked. In seconds, the old, rattling train was on the siding, screeching to a halt in front of the depot. An instant later, swarms of soldiers captured the locomotive and twenty-five cars. There was not time to begin destroying the railroad ties, bridge timbers and planks that the old locomotive labored so valiantly to haul. Another train was due in minutes from the west.

Blackburn's men hid the crew of the freight and returned to their hiding places just as the whistle wailed from the passenger train west of town. Slowly, much like the freight, the big cowcatcher grew larger and larger as the passenger train clanked and swayed toward the station. As before, Blackburn, Surby, and two scouts stood calmly on the station platform.

The engineer slowed the train near the platform. Escaping steam shrouded the scouts and Blackburn. Then Sergeant Surby took four quick steps, grabbed a railing with one hand, his Colt with another, and presented himself to the engineer. Over the noise of the clanking, hissing engine, Surby announced, "Don't reverse engine or I'll put a ball through you!"

The engineer stared at the uniform and the man that wore it. The .36-caliber muzzle stared back at him. He obeyed Surby's next instructions, "Shut 'er down!" The old locomotive screeched to a halt and Surby and his prisoners, the engineer and fireman, stepped out onto the platform.

Blackburn's men poured from their hiding places amid shouts of "The train's ours; the train's ours!" They swarmed among the frightened passengers, who sat in disbelief, amazed that so many Yankees could be 175 miles inside Confederate territory raiding trains.

It took Blackburn several minutes to restore order, but soon an inventory of the train was made. Among the passengers were several citizens of Vicksburg fleeing with their household goods for a safer residence east into the Confederacy. Blackburn's men began throwing trunks and furniture onto a pile near the station platform.

Surby took the engineer aboard and ordered him to move the train onto the siding with the freight. Four cars of ammunition and weapons and six loaded with commissary and quartermaster supplies were moved out of town away from the buildings so they could be burned. All of the freight cars and those of the passenger train were afire within minutes.

By eleven o'clock, both trains were blazing and the fire had reached the cars loaded with ammunition. Surby thought, this sounds like an artillery duel. He turned to Blackburn who watched the blaze and spurting bursts. Blackburn laughed, "Grierson and the others'll think we're all goin' to hell in a pile! They should be here double-quick!"

In a matter of minutes, Grierson and the remainder of the two regiments charged over the rise to the north of Newton Station, bugles blaring and guns blazing. By the time they reached town, they could see the blaze of the freight cars and had settled their horses to an orderly trot.

*Grierson's raiders destroyed rail lines and depots from one end of Mississippi to the other.
(Author's Collection)*

Grierson found Blackburn smiling, proud of what he had accomplished. Surby watched the two men slapping each other in congratulation. This was a great day for Grierson. His mission was accomplished. The Vicksburg line was cut!

Still there was work to do. Blackburn ordered Surby to send Nelson and Kelly with Major Mathew Starr and two battalions. Nelson and Kelly were to scout east along the railroad track while Starr and his men burned bridges and trestlework for six miles in that direction. Blackburn added, "Send Steadman and Fowler with Captain Herring and have them do the same to the west."

Surby gave them their orders and in half an hour, black smoke rose in both directions along the tracks east and west of Newton Station. In town, the railroad depot was fired along with a building that contained a quantity of U.S. rifles and clothing.

At the hospital, sugar, coffee, and clothing were given to the patients, while Regimental Adjutant George A. Root filled out parole forms for the seventy-five wounded Confederate soldiers. With these forms, the wounded prisoners would be able to go home for the remainder of the war. About one-thirty, Colonel Benjamin Grierson walked to where the wounded prisoners were being paroled out of the Confederate Army. He asked Root how many more forms he had to fill out and then told him to hurry up. One of the paroled soldiers asked Grierson, "Which way you Yanks goin' to try now?"

Grierson looked at the soldier and said, "Why, Reb, we're figuring on joining Union forces to the east and raiding our way through Alabama to Tennessee."

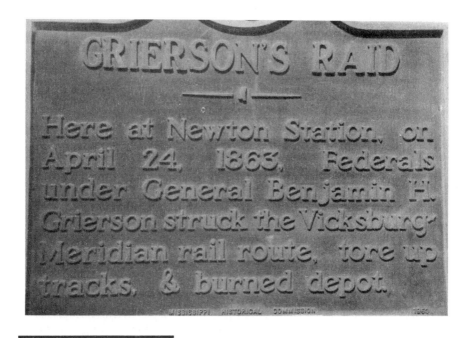

Photo of plaque placed by the Mississippi Historical Commission at the site of Newton Station in present-day Newton, Mississippi. (Author's Collection)

The Confederate soldier smiled. Grierson said then to Root, "If you're not finished by rally call, keep a few men with you and catch up on the east road. When we leave town, we'll go a couple miles and then double back. No point in your riding that extra distance. Just follow the track east of town. We'll join you near Meridian," he said loud enough that all could hear. Then Grierson added, smiling, "Those Rebs'll not know what hit them."

Grierson strode away. Behind him, the Confederate soldiers smiled, elated with their new information. They'd inform on these raiders and this boasting, wiry bearded man that was becoming a bigger-than-life leader of a thousand, two thousand, and in some reports, three thousand men and this daring raid into their homeland. Elsewhere, Sergeant Surby listened to all kinds of tales from the citizens of Newton Station. Some asked Surby "how many they'd murdered" at Philadelphia, or Starkville, or Decatur. Others said they would all be "damned to hell" for the atrocities they had committed on their way through the South.

Back from their missions along the railroad, Nelson and Kelly found Fowler and Steadman lying in the shade by a ramshackle dry goods store at the edge of Newton Station. Fowler slept; Steadman needed to.

"Hey, George?"

Steadman grunted a reply. The lines around his mouth were deeper, his eyes bloodshot.

"What's up, George?" Kelly asked.

"Rest, man. Got to rest."

"Aw, come on. You can rest anytime. We've cut the road. Mission's over."

"Yeh? Well how do we get home, doggone it? Fly?" Steadman said, irritated.

"Forty miles to Alabama."

"That ain't exactly God's country, you know. 'Sides, Alabama-Mississipp' border is crawlin' with Rebs."

"How are you knowin' that, George?" Kelly inquired.

"Man said so. Conductor off Meridian train told him."

Bud Fowler pushed his hat off his face with one finger and entered the conversation, "That ain't the half of it."

"What are you sayin', Fowler?" Kelly asked.

"Troops east like George said; Jackson, the capital, is west. Bound to be more troops'n you can stir with a manure fork there."

"What about north?" Kelly asked, concerned now.

"What about it?" Steadman began. "You want to face all them irate folks again? You ready for that?"

"Let me ask you a question, boys," Nelson interrupted. "Where you think the Rebs figure we're headin'?"

"That's a good question. Where do you think, Sam?" George Steadman asked.

"I'll tell you exactly what I think, boys. I think the only way we're...uh...goin' to get home is when we're exchanged for some Reb prisoners. We'll be blamed lucky if we…uh…don't visit Libby Prison on the way back." To add emphasis, Nelson added, "And I mean it."

A young soldier came up to them, "Corporal Nelson?"

"Yeh?"

"Sergeant Surby wants you and the scouts."

"Uh…right. Thanks."

At two p.m., the buglers sounded the rally call and soon both regiments were lined up ready to march. As the advance marched off to the south, several of the troopers remarked at the wisdom of their commander. None were ready to go against the forces at Meridian. Others paid little attention, their faces were black with smoke and the whiskey on their breaths and in their canteens would make their afternoon march less painful, but more miserable.

Fortunately, Surby thought, none of the Butternut Guerillas were drunk. Their job this hot afternoon would be pure hell. Even though they closed off Newton Station someone surely slipped off south, east and west to alarm the countryside.

Sergeant Surby, Lieutenant-Colonel Blackburn, and the Butternut Guerillas couldn't gamble now. They had to be sure of the right roads. They could afford no delays. Because they would be moving faster now, horses had to be found and the advance would need more and quicker protection from the frightened citizens in the towns along the way.

Five miles from Newton Station, on the south road, the advance guard came on a number of fleeing refugees. They carried food. The soldiers grabbed what they could. At Bogue Falema, Grierson ordered the column to halt and eat. After a three-hour rest, the column took up the march. Just as the last light of day faded and the air commenced cooling, gunfire exploded at the front of the column.

Garlandville was a sleepy little town lying along the Newton Station-Montrose road. Word had spread that the "Yankee raiders" might be coming in that direction and the townspeople, mostly old men, decided that they did not want the "atrocities" visited on them — not without a fight, at least. They formed a line and held it — for a while. But their shotguns were no match for the charging cavalrymen. Finally, the old men threw down their guns and surrendered peacably, but not before they'd wounded one soldier and shot a horse from under another.

Surby and others looked on the old men with pity. One of the Butternut Guerillas remarked, "If not for those wild stories spreading wherever they went, this sort of thing could be avoided."

Grierson and Blackburn spoke to the gathered townspeople assuring them that no harm would come to them or any other civilians in Mississippi. While the officers calmed the citizens of Garlandville, Richard Surby and the scouts moved ahead to make sure no more such events took place.

A short distance out of Garlandville, Mississippi, the weary, strung-out column stopped for a short rest before moving southward. Surby ate and then lay on the ground with the other Butternut Guerillas. No one spoke;

they were too tired. Nelson and Kelly dozed, but Surby and the others just stared through the pine needles at the sky. For two hours, they weighed the hopeless situation they were in. They were too scared to sleep.

Too soon word was passed and two regiments of weary men checked their cinch straps, tied on their gear, and mounted their horses for another night in the saddle. Nearly two days had passed since the horses had been unsaddled. There just had not been time to bring up horses from the rear, them out in the advance like they were. For many, it had been nearly three days since they had slept, but deep in enemy territory as they were, there was little complaining. Movement was the one thing that could keep them alive.

A Mississippian from Garlandville joined the column as a guide and now led them quietly out of the pine forests and into bottomland blotched with water oak and sweetgum. Surby accompanied the guide for a time, but someone noticed Surby asleep in the saddle and Lieutenant-Colonel Blackburn ordered him to the rear.

Surby turned back and a half mile down the road, found the advance guard. He identified himself and fell in alongside some members of A Company — his old outfit. His eyes soon felt like two rocks; the foul, salty taste in his mouth became almost unbearable. He was faint and dizzy. The saddle he clung to squeaked with every gentle sway of his mount. Finally, amid thoughts of white, soft sheets, feather mattresses, and..., he nodded into a deep sleep.

How long he slept, Surby did not know. But suddenly, he was awake and about to tumble forward over the head of his grazing horse. His body tensed with fear. His heart pounded him wide awake. There was neither sign nor sound of the column in the blackness. He was alone!

Instinctively, he scrambled from his horse and crawled about on the damp ground. His hands found the hoof-marked road; his fingers sought answers his eyes could not see. The hoof prints were distinct. Gently, his fingers traced the prints; he found the heel calks, then the toe.

Surby groped wildly in the dark, found his horse, mounted and with a hard kick to the flanks, cantered in the direction that the tracks demanded. Within two miles, he caught the rear of the column. Sighing relief, Surby slowed his horse to a trot.

The column drowsed along for almost an hour, then a passing rider announced; "Camp mile ahead." Some soldiers in the tired column murmured, "Thank God," but most cursed Grierson for pushing them so.

Surby wondered if he could sleep now. Suddenly his mind registered a neat, whitewashed fence bordering the road. In the dark, a horse whinnied. Surby turned into the lane and walked his horse a short way, then dismounted. He tied his spent horse to the fence and climbed into the barnyard with a beautiful, cream-colored horse. Light from the stars blinked off and on with the rush of low clouds. The horse Surby sought was elusive and still pranced about, neighing at the passing cavalry.

"Whoa, boy," Surby cooed softly. The animal eluded him. He coaxed and cursed, but could not get close enough to grab the horse's mane.

"Only a mile to camp," Surby said after fifteen minutes. "I'll get you in the morning, big fellow."

Most of the column had slipped past the plantation by now and Surby walked across the fenced enclosure toward his mount. A noise from somewhere startled him and he stopped, holding his breath and straining, his head half turned, listening for the sound again. Nothing.

Nearly a minute later, Surby continued, now alert. Then, the dim outline of a rider appeared, standing in the lane. The horse and rider moved and Surby eased the Navy Colt from under his tattered jacket and cocked it, trying to muffle the click. Cautiously, in a half crouch, he moved toward the fence. His footsteps were muffled in the soft earth and quickly, he was beside the fence. Head bent low, he crept breathlessly toward the Confederate soldier in the lane.

Rider and horse stood by Surby's mount. He leaned out of his saddle and inspected the shotgun hanging across the civilian saddle. As Surby drew near, his horse detected his scent and neighed, his feet shuffling. Surby lunged swiftly onto the fence, the revolver aimed directly at the chest of the rider.

"Surrender!" Surby screamed.

"Surrender, or I'll put a ball through you," he called again.

"BOOM!!"

Surby spun and slammed into the fence. His hand, torn from the fence, groped for his side. The gun hand fell toward the ground to ward off the fall he knew was coming. And then he lay on the ground. He screamed, "I'm hit! Oh, God! I'm hit!" Surby's hand had finally found the warm ooze of blood about three inches above his hipbone.

"Don't shoot," he begged. "Don't shoot again, please!" The ringing boom had still not left his head. "I'm from the Seventh!" he shouted instinctively. Surby scooted along the ground a few feet, digging his heels into the soft earth.

"Don't shoot; please don't shoot. What are you firing at me for?" Surby whined. Then the night was silent, deathly silent.

"Sarge? Sarge, is that you?" Surby heard a voice call. Surby knew the voice. Then above him, the man knelt, pistol still smoking and dangling from a hand draped over his knee. It was Bill Pollard!

Pollard said, his voice scared, "Why, Sergeant, that's Captain Skinner of the Sixth."

"Skinner? Who's Skinner?" Surby asked, surprised.

"My God, you're hit!" Commissary Sergeant Pollard yelled.

"Is he hit?" the rider in the lane called to Pollard.

Richard Surby fumbled with his revolver, trying to replace it in his belt as Lucias B. Skinner dismounted and scrambled over the fence to try to aid Surby.

Surby, still gripping his side, replied through clenched teeth, "Yes, I'm hit."

"My God," Pollard continued, "I thought you's a Reb and fixin' to shoot Captain Skinner."

"I...I don't think it's serious," Surby interrupted.

Pollard said, "I saw him ride down the lane."

Skinner blurted, "You all right, Sergeant? God, I thought I was done."

Pollard added quickly, "I's prowlin' around here lookin' for food for the men."

Surby sat up now. He laughed, "Guess I'm the fool."

Skinner asked, "You all right then, Sarge?"

"Guess so," his side only burned some now.

Skinner and Pollard chuckled nervously. Surby added, "Thank God, you're such a lousy shot, Pollard."

"I sure thought you's a Reb in that get-up you're wearin'."

"Good they didn't teach you Massac boys to shoot any better'n that," Surby responded.

Pollard sighed and apologized, "Guess we're all a little jumpy."

Lucias Skinner helped Surby to his feet and said, "C'mon Sarge. We'd better get you to camp."

"I'll make it all right," Surby protested.

"No, now don't take any chances; we'll help you."

Surby, Skinner and Pollard arrived in camp several minutes later. Already campfires blazed, illuminating the pine boughs in front of C.M. Bender's plantation house, just two miles west of Montrose, Mississippi. Grierson's command had made better than fifteen miles since leaving Newton Station.

Less than sixty miles west, Confederate General John C. Pemberton sat fuming over the success of the Yankee raiders. They were making an ass of him and he knew that he must dispatch forces to annihilate them.

Late the next morning, Pemberton would dispatch a unit from Brandon, Mississippi to pursue and harass Grierson's forces — especially if Grierson was foolish enough to try and swing west in an attempt to join Grant on the Mississippi River south of Vicksburg.

Previously, Pemberton had taken other precautions. General William W. Loring at Meridian, Mississippi, less than thirty miles east of Newton Station, was ordered to send troops. In case Grierson tried to move into Alabama, General Simon Buckner at Mobile and General Joseph E. Johnston in Tennessee were warned and told to send troops for the pursuit of Grierson's command.

"That'll learn you horse thieves!" a soldier from a neighboring campfire teased.

"Pollard, 'tween you an' the Reb civilians, we'll most likely not make it to ol' Grant," another trooper added, laughing.

Surby's side burned where the bullet had grazed him and he felt nauseous; he wasn't interested in what everyone thought of his narrow miss with fate. He escaped under his blanket and soon the remaining tired cavalrymen did the same. It was eleven o'clock.

Lost sleep was an elusive commodity, especially with the excitement of the past several days flashing in their brains. Slowly, creeping in their direction, however, were Pemberton's forces. They would press them to the point that the fun of the game they played would disappear in favor of the deep, dark fear for life.

The tables were slowly turning. The South was humiliated. The only retribution would be revenge and only revenge could erase the atrocities that Southerners everywhere read of in their newspapers.

From this night, April 24th, things would be different.

Newton Station Depot was reconstructed after Grierson's raiders burned the original in late April 1863. (Author's Collection)

Chapter 7

...huntin' any good?

With mixed emotions, the cavalrymen of the Sixth and Seventh Illinois yawned and stretched on Saturday, April 25th. Gray clouds with rain pillowed the low sky.

Charlie Weedon complained, "It rains again today and I'm quittin' this Mississippi mess."

Uriah Fowler, his nose in the air, sniffed and said, "Don't smell like rain." He sniffed again, "No, don't reckon it'll rain today."

"Bet it will," Weedon said.

Fowler smiled, "Hope it does."

"Well, I'm not rollin' my ground cloth. Say Fowler, how come you hope it rains?"

"My nose."

Weedon ignored him; Fowler busied himself checking his gear. Then Weedon asked, "What you mean, your nose?"

"You stink," Fowler said, matter-of-factly.

"So do you."

"I know it," Fowler replied. "But not like you."

"You know where you can go!"

"Where's that?"

"Straight to...."

Richard Surby walked up to the two men, favoring his side. "Don't roll your ground cloths," he interrupted.

"What's that, Sarge?" Weedon asked.

"Don't roll your rubber blankets; looks like rain."

"Right, Sarge."

Surby sniffed, "Weedon, you all right?"

"Sure, Sarge," Weedon answered, puzzled.

"Man, you ought to wash. You stink."

Bud Fowler laughed as Surby strode away. Weedon stood. Legs spread, blood rushing to his face. Fowler knew not to irritate him more.

At eight a.m., the column marched onto the road headed west. Sergeant Richard Surby and the Butternut Guerillas followed Lieutenant-Colonel William Blackburn's orders and moved in the advance.

Surby and Nelson rode the point together for a while, speaking rarely and then only to comment on the bad roads and how they would get worse if the rain came again. Already, they had forded several swollen streams. Finally, Surby told Nelson to drop back. "You can take the point later."

"Will you be…uh…all right? The wound I mean?"

"Sure, Sam. It's just a scratch; put some salve on it earlier. Feels pretty good now," Surby replied.

"Don't want it to…uh…get poisoned," Corporal Sam Nelson added. He waited for a response but got none. And so he turned his horse and trotted off toward the rear.

The sun was two and a half hours high, Sergeant Surby figured, looking at the overcast sky with its low, lazy mat of clouds. A soft breeze rustled the weeds at the side of the road and chilled him.

Ahead, Surby eyed a plantation entrance, but could see no fancy house. However, a lane overgrown with weeds led to a double log cabin in a state of decay. The yard was grassless with rubbish thrown liberally around. A bench near the door held a tin washbasin and a pail of water. Two gaunt hounds raised their weary heads to stare at Surby, but if they had the strength to bark, they didn't. There were only a few sheds, and the log barn had no size. There was a stoop in front made of board planks.

As Surby neared the house, five women, all shabbily dressed, appeared and took their places on the porch and bench. They seemed nervous, their eyes darting about to see if Surby was alone. Now Surby looked around, too; he felt uneasy this morning.

"You ladies got any menfolk here?" he finally called.

They replied in unison, "No, suh. Our husbands're all in the Army at Vicksburg. Ever' last one of 'em."

"And so, ladies, you're all married?"

"Yes, suh. Anythin' strange 'bout that?"

"Oh, no," Surby replied and laughed. He was calming now. "Only it's strange to see so many married ladies at one house."

"We's just livin' here so's we can be with each other while our menfolk's off fightin' the ol' war," the youngest of the group responded.

"Well, say, could I bother ya'll for a drink of milk?" Surby asked. He squirmed in his saddle; his side pained him.

"Got water you're welcome to; no milk," one of the ladies, dressed in dirty homespun, responded. Another stood and walked toward a well in the yard. She was tall and thin. Her hair was straight and pulled loosely behind her ears. Her dress was more suited for a bigger woman.

There was a moment of uncomfortable silence, then the eldest woman spoke low and earnest, "When you 'spect this horrible war gonna end?"

"What's that, mam?"

She raised her voice and repeated the question.

"Well, can't says I know, mam. When do you figure?"

"I got my notions."

"What's that?"

"Things're goin' to have to change some."

"How you mean?"

"Well, change; that's what I'm meanin'."

"You mean change, like just as soon as the old Stars and Stripes floats triumphantly over all the South." Surby jumped right in. May as well find where their sympathies lay, he reckoned. Something told him they were, at least, not pro-Confederacy.

The old woman looked down and then directly at Surby. He watched her eyes carefully. She said softly, "I always did like that old flag, and I think this here War for Separation all wrong."

"Me too, mam," Surby said. He nodded.

"If it hadn't been for those big larned folks, we'd be livin' in peace," she went on. "Why, take my husband, he'd no lawin' not lawsuits in court, but minded his own business. He ain't had nothin' to do makin' this here war." She shook her head and clasped her frail hands tightly in front of her.

Taking a deep breath, she continued, "But they had to...to come and conscript him and take him off to Vicksburg. I don't 'spect to see him again." She paused, then continued, "Lawdy, Lawdy, after bein' together for thirty-six years to be parted this way."

She shook her head again, her voice broke, and tears began to form in her eyes. She looked toward the well where the tall, slim girl was tugging, trying to raise the bucket of water. In a high pitched voice, she complained, "I s'pose you're conscriptin'."

Surby started to explain his business, but the old woman interrupted and exclaimed indignantly, "Well, you'll find no men 'round here. You'd just better conscript all the women too; we ain't no one left to care for us; we don't own nary blacks."

Richard Surby was neither a slow, nor a stupid man. He knew Northern sympathy when he saw it. Still he practiced caution and said, "Well, mam, what do you think of the Yanks?"

"Well," she answered, wiping her eyes with the sleeve of her soiled dress, "we've hearn a heap about 'em that wasn't good, and I've hearn tell a heap about 'em that was right smart in their favor."

"Yes, mam. Let me ask; have you ever seen a Yankee?"

"I ain't never seen but one, that's Mr. Pierson, what lives four miles from here."

The old woman craned her scrawny neck to look down the road past Sergeant Surby. Sam Nelson rode toward the log house. She waited until Nelson halted his horse beside Surby, then she asked, "And who might this be?"

Surby responded to the woman's question, "Now, mam, what would you think if I should tell you that we're Yankees?"

Almost before Surby could finish, the old woman threw up her hands, "Now young man, just stop that there kind of talk. I ain't goin' to be fooled in that there way."

"But, mam...."

"Now you just hush now. You ain't no Yankees, and you can't make me believe it, and I ain't goin' to tell you nary a word 'bout where the menfolk are."

Sam Nelson bumped Surby's horse and nodded toward the road. The advance of the column appeared less than a quarter of a mile away. Surby stood down from his mount and walked over to the old lady. Taking her arm gently, he led her to the edge of the yard. He pointed as the advance column marched nearer. "Those are all Yankees too."

Surby watched, smiling, as the old lady's eyes widened. She turned to him and raised her hands, praying, "Good Lawd, deliver us! What will we'uns do?" Quickly, she called toward the house, "Gals, come out here right now! See these here Yankees!"

In an instant, the cabin emptied and the other women stood by her side looking at the column. One, the youngest, began moaning and crying, "Oh, Lord; oh, Lord!" The others were startled, but calm.

Nelson dismounted and tried to comfort the young one, "Now, now, shush now. They're not gonna hurt nobody."

"Now, ladies. No harm's goin' to come to you," Surby assured them.

The women stared first at Surby, then at the passing column. Finally as the column continued to file by, they retreated toward the porch and seated themselves. When one of the passing soldiers called out to them, the young girl waved and was scolded quietly by the others. Their discomfort returned when George Steadman and Uriah Fowler rode back along the column and turned into the lane.

Surby called to them to keep scouting as they entered the yard, but Steadman continued up to Surby and said, "You gonna eat, Sarge?"

"Steadman, get out of here and to the head of the column. Don't bother these ladies, you hear?"

"All right, Sarge," Steadman said, shrugging his shoulders, "just askin'."

"All right, all right," Surby said impatiently, "but get out of here."

Surby shook his head as Steadman turned toward the road. Surby watched him move slowly out the gate and then heard him shout, "Sarge, if you and Nelson don't let me eat with you one of these days, I'm gonna dry up and blow away."

Surby laughed and turned back to the house. The ladies insisted that he and Nelson come in "and set a spell."

Upon entering the tired cabin, the old woman pulled a cloth off the table in the center of the room and began setting out food. There was pie, bread, butter, and even milk. "He'p yo'selves," the old woman offered.

Nelson hitched up a chair and stuffed his mouth with fresh bread. Surby gulped down two cups of milk before bothering with a piece of cherry pie that had been placed in front of him.

While they ate, the old woman pulled a battered chest from under a bed. Surby watched carefully, but did not ignore the food. Nelson kept eating uninterrupted.

The old woman struggled with the lid until one of the women helped her. Very carefully, she placed odds and ends of memorabilia on the bed.

Sixty-some years of her life lay there, Surby guessed. He paid polite attention and finally the old woman unfurled the prized possession she had labored to expose. It was an old and tattered American Flag. Tears welled in Surby's eyes as the old woman held it proudly in front of her.

Nelson stopped chewing and looked back and forth from the old woman to Sergeant Surby. The other women stood in a semicircle staring at the flag. The silence was broken when one of the women looked at Nelson and Surby and said, "Oh, I wish that John and William only knew what you were, how soon they'd come out of the woods."

Nelson and Surby stared while the old woman placed the flag neatly and carefully back in its hiding place. There was little to say and they refrained from saying it.

Soon, Surby and Nelson finished eating, thanked the old woman, and excused themselves. At the front of the cabin, as Surby mounted, the old woman squeezed his hand and looked into his eyes. She pleaded, "I wish that God, in his mercy, will spare my husband and that peace'll soon be back again to our great country."

"It won't be long, mam," Surby said.

"Then I won't be needin' to keep the banner of liberty hid away in that old chest much longer."

Surby nodded; his voice sincere, he said, "God bless you, mam."

Again, the two men thanked the ladies, wished them well, and clucked their horses past a flower garden and then galloped by the column. War inspired few men to righteousness, but people often did. They felt that righteousness now and wanted more than ever to rid their country of this plague — this terrible war.

It wasn't long until these thoughts left them. Ahead, the pine-tree lined road soon wound into a village. Sam Nelson wondered aloud, "Sure is strange. Saturday mornin'; not a soul to be seen."

"Wouldn't worry me none, Sam. Them folks back there are no doubt sufferin' the same misery as all the folks in this part of Mississippi. They're more worried about gettin' taken by a conscriptin' Reb than a Yank."

"Well, maybe so, but I don't like the looks of this."

Nelson and Surby were on the outskirts of the town now. Still there were no people. The two scouts rode on, their eyes straight ahead, through the entire village. At the west edge, Sam Nelson removed his hat, wiped his brow, and sighed, "Guess you's right, Sarge."

Surby and Nelson waited until the advance entered the town. Then they trotted ahead, side by side, looking for a nooning place.

A short distance from Pineville, the Butternut Guerillas found the first large plantation since leaving C.M. Bender's.

"There's food and forage enough for the two regiments," Surby reported to Lieutenant-Colonel Blackburn.

Nelson and Kelly, along with Weedon, Steadman, and Fowler, remained at the plantation house and snooped around. There was no sign of anyone nearby. Finally, Steadman wandered into the backyard, found a smokehouse, entered and soon returned with a small ham which he had sliced and was eating despite its being too salty. Kelly teased him about "finally gettin' a wee bit to eat," and then a small boy appeared from around the corner of the whitewashed house.

The boy was black and looked to be about eight years old. He wore neither shoes, nor clothes. Fowler dismounted and walked to the boy. He appeared scared of Fowler, but not frightened enough to run. Fowler asked, "Hey, feller. What you doin'?"

Weedon sneered.

The little naked boy only stared. He was thin, his knees rickety. "Where's your mammy?" Fowler continued.

To this question, Fowler got a response. The boy pointed toward a clump of trees a half mile away from the house. Steadman approached the boy, brandishing his big hunting knife. The boy backed away, fear raced across his black face. With a deft stroke, Steadman sliced off a slab of ham and offered it to the boy. They boy's wide eyes darted first at Steadman, then at the ham. He snatched fiercely at the ham, grabbed it from Steadman's hand, and ran, all in one motion.

Steadman stood, still staring after the fleeing youngster as Blackburn's voice rang out, "Find out anything?"

"Nigger boy says his mammy's in the field over by the clump of woods," Weedon told Blackburn and Surby.

Blackburn turned to Surby, "Fetch the owner up to the house — if he's down there."

Near the patch of trees, Surby heard voices. He stopped his horse and listened for several moments then continued around the north edge and into a field fresh with sprouting corn. In the middle of the field, a large shade tree and a stump stood side by side. On the stump, a fat, tall man sat holding a leather whip. The whip was three or four feet long with a foot-long buckskin cracker attached to the end of the plaited leather. It was obviously not a cutting whip since those barebacked slaves in the field had no cut marks on them. Almost lazily, the dozen or so slaves — men and women — chopped weeds from between corn rows.

As Surby neared the stump, the man saw him and spoke, "Howdy. How are you?"

Surby nodded and readjusted the shotgun cradled in his arms. "Gonna rain?" Surby asked. He looked first at the sky, then at the slaves.

"Most likely. Huntin' any good?" The man paused, looked puzzled, and continued, "Say, you from Pembe'ton at Vicksburg? How's he gettin' along?"

Surby answered curtly, "I 'spect Vicksburg is safe against the whole Northern army. As for huntin', I ain't on that kind of business."

"What is your business then?" The fat man wiped his forehead with his arm.

"There's a right smart force up at the house. I's sent to ask you to come up and join us," Surby smiled.

The big man did not respond, but called to an old slave working with the others, "Mose. Mose, come 'ere."

Mose walked slowly to the stump, took the whip, and as the fat man slid off, mounted the stump. The man pointed and said to Mose, "Watch them Negras now."

To Surby, he ordered, "Well, boy, let's go."

The two men headed for the house, Surby on horseback, his prisoner, Elias Nichols, on foot.

Near the edge of the cornfield, Nichols asked, "Whose command you with?"

"We're with Williams from Tennessee."

"What ya'll doin' here?"

"We're out of Jackson and searchin' the countryside for commissary stores. Gen'ral Pemberton's got us lookin' for deserters and pickin' up conscripts too."

"Humpfh," the man grunted.

Halfway between the woods and house, the big man spoke with feeling, "My Lord, I've never seen so many troops in these parts. And they're takin' my grain! They didn't even ask for it," he added, astonished.

Surby rode on, Nichols at his side. He grumbled, "The pay vouchers of the Confederacy are good, you understand." He looked up at Surby; Surby ignored him. "I always helped out before; fed several squads," he mumbled. Surby rode on silently. "Why there's near on to a company through here a week ago; I fed 'em." He was sweating profusely and pulled a large bandana from his pocket and soaked the sweat away. He and Surby passed through the various companies and Nichols' eyes flicked about, looking at the cavalrymen who lounged about the yard.

"You boys sure are well dressed," Nichols said to Surby.

"Yep," Surby answered.

"Looks like a crack outfit. Never seen such a remarkably healthy lookin' bunch."

"Uh-huh."

"Good lookin' weapons too. Those Yanks better not give you boys any trouble."

Surby agreed, "Best equipped cavalry in Confederate service. Been in several battles. Ain't no Yankee outfit can stand with us."

At the steps leading to the pillared veranda, Surby dismounted and tied his horse beside Grierson's. He accompanied the plantation owner into the house. The man's wife stood just inside the door wringing her hands, then wiping them on her apron. Her lips were pressed tight.

Before Nichols could speak to her, Surby interrupted, "'Scuse us, mam, but the Colonel'll want to see your husband."

A guard stood by the double doors at the left of the entrance and Surby held out his hand and motioned with his head, guiding Nichols over the threshold.

Nichols stepped into the room and Surby brushed past him, saluted and introduced his Colonel to the plantation owner, "Colonel Williams, from Jackson, Mississippi, former from Tennessee."

Surby turned to Colonel Grierson, winked and reported, "Colonel, this gentleman is the owner of this fine plantation and has graciously consented to givin' us information of deserters, conscripts, and provisions."

Grierson understood, thanked Surby and excused him. Surby exited the house found the Butternut Guerillas, and joined them in the shade just off the veranda.

Thirty minutes later, Colonel Grierson and several officers stepped onto the porch. A young soldier waited for them, "Sir, would you please come with me?"

"What is it, Private?" Grierson asked.

"This way, sir," the private insisted. The group looked at each other, then trailed off after the young soldier. Surby and the Butternut Guerillas watched as they disappeared toward the rear of the plantation house.

Surby, too relaxed to move, asked the others, "What's goin' on?"

Kelly answered, disgusted, "They found a slave chained to the floor of a hut. Colonel Blackburn had us cut the manacles from him. The flesh was near gone from 'is bones. 'T was a sad sight."

"He gonna be all right?" Surby inquired.

"I could not tell." Kelly answered. "One of the lads said he wished to go with us; Blackburn said he would be takin' 'im."

"Why's he chained?" Fowler asked.

"Aye, but he ran away."

Surby shook his head. He noticed the group of officers returning toward the front of the house. They were helping the black man. Surby sighed, "Boys, I've been in New Orleans and seen them slave auctions, but I tell you I never dreamed that sort of thing went on when they's sold. My God...."

Charlie Weedon sat taking all this in, a look of disgust on his face also. He muttered, "Serves the lazy nigger right." He shot a stream of juice onto the ground.

Surby and the others heard him, but ignored the slur.

Finally, Weedon asked, "Gonna add him to the horse herders?"

"What they're sayin'," Fowler answered.

"Hell, we got more niggers'n horses."

"Yeh, an' it's a good thing," Fowler said.

"Bah," Weedon growled. "How you reckon?"

"They ain't only takin' care of the horses and mules, but they know ever' inch of the country. And that ain't the half of it," Fowler added. "They're gatherin' food and sharin' it with the others at the end of the column."

"Yeh," Nelson interjected. "You fellows remember Lambert, the quartermaster sergeant in L Company, the Sixth. Ol' Aaron's from down near Shawneetown and he's tellin' me...uh...they knew ever' grain crib in southern Mississip'."

"Aye," Kelly broke in. "They seem to be knowin' a great deal about the Southland that our own scouts are not findin'."

"What are we goin' to do with 'em?" Fowler asked. "When we get to where we're goin'.'"

"Free 'em, of course," Surby answered.

Weedon, disgusted with this kind of talk, let it be known with his looks as he stood quickly and stalked off toward his mount.

About two o'clock, the command mounted and Surby and the Butternut Guerillas were dispatched south to scout toward the Leaf River Valley. Two detachments left through the main gate at the same time Surby and the scouts rode out. Nelson yelled at one of the men, "Where you headin'?"

"North. Goin' raidin' to the north. Tryin' to throw them Rebs off."

Weedon yelled after them, "Ya'll take care now, hear?"

The Butternut Guerillas worked hard finding a passable road through the rough, gully-laced terrain. The afternoon heated up even though clouds shielded the sun. It was muggy and men and horses were well lathered before the day slowly died. Then with nightfall, fog crept in and enveloped the column. The flanking pickets rode closer to the column, not so far out. From time to time, the thick night was pierced with a yell as these pickets plodded back into the side of the column. Somehow, no one was shot.

Later, as the Butternut Guerillas neared the Leaf River, Lieutenant-Colonel Blackburn came forward and told Surby, "Colonel Grierson says we're nearin' the Mackadore Plantation. Wants to camp there for the night."

"Fine with me. 'Fraid we can't find our way much longer in this soup."

"Colonel says this Mackadore is a doctor. We got a couple men need tendin'. Charlie Hall, the hospital stewards, says he'd done all he can for 'em."

"Reckon I'll ride ahead then and check the plantation," Surby said.

"Good, shouldn't be too far."

At the plantation, Surby found slaves near a fire at the back of the grounds. No one was home at the main house. "Other soldiers've camped there before, so it's all right. Doctor's not home, but should be later on," Surby reported to Blackburn within the half hour.

The column filed into the plantation grounds and the men set up camp by nine o'clock. Nearly every night, rumors spread though the camp, usually just as the men began to bed down. Somehow, though, tonight was different. Everyone seemed to have already heard the rumor: "Reb force out of Mobile's hot on our trail." Then the typical answer, "Yeh, what I hear tell."

For now, however, most just shrugged the shoulders as if to say, "So what?" They had made it through another day. That was all that mattered now.

Surby and the Butternut Guerillas built a cool fire. Throughout the grounds, the campfires glowed against the fog. It was an eerie scene. The horses were skittish and stamped nervously. Occasionally, a dog howled.

Soon Lieutenant-Colonel Blackburn led his horse into the light of the scouts' fire. He called, "Surby, that you?"

Surby answered, "Over here, Colonel."

"There you are. This fog is thick enough to slice. Sam Nelson with you?" Blackburn shielded his eyes and looked into the shadows.

"Yeh. Sam?" Surby called into the dark. "Sam, come here."

"Sure, Sarge." Nelson came out of the dark, rubbing his eyes. "Uh...what's up?"

Blackburn said, "Sam, Colonel Grierson wants to see you."

Nelson looked at Surby and then at Blackburn. "Sure," he said, puzzled.

"Better get your horse." Blackburn continued, "Or better," Blackburn looked around, "Fowler, go to the herders and cut out a fresh horse. Bring it to the house."

Through the fog, a lantern appeared just before Nelson and Blackburn stepped onto the veranda. Inside, Nelson followed Blackburn into a large room. A candle sat on a map in the middle of a table and Grierson and several others stood looking down into the dim light. Sam Nelson recognized Colonel Edward Prince of the Seventh. Prince hailed from around Quincy; Payson, somebody said once. The adjutant, Sam Woodward was there and so was Tom Herod. They'd both signed on in Gallatin County at Shawneetown. Nelson had known Herod for several years. Finally, Grierson turned to Nelson and said, "Sam, come on over here. Somethin' I want you to look at."

Nelson walked briskly to the table and Grierson commenced, "About twenty miles west of Newton Station there's a town on the railroad called Forest Station. It's about thirty miles due north of here," Grierson pointed to the map.

"Uh...yes, sir." Nelson understood now.

"Well, Sam, we want you to ride to that railroad and cut the telegraph wire between Jackson and Meridian. If you make it, bring us a piece of wire as proof that you carried out the order. Understand?"

"Uh...yes, sir."

"Ought to be a bridge there too. If you can fire it before daylight, do it. If not, get back as quick as possible. Any questions?"

"No, sir. I think I can...uh...do it all right."

Nelson turned to leave the room, but Grierson stopped him. "Just a minute." Turning to Major Thomas Herod, Grierson ordered, "Tom, give 'im some of that Reb money; he may need it."

Major Herod pulled a wad of bills from a bag he carried on his shoulder, held the money down by the candle, and peeled off a few hundred dollars.

"Here, Sam," Herod said. "Let's make ol' Gallatin County proud of it's boys tonight."

"Yes, sir, major," Nelson smiled.

"How's your family, Sam?" Herod said.

"Meg an' the...uh...kids are just dandy."

"Good, Sam. Good."

"Godspeed Sam," Grierson said, as he shook the young, red-faced man's hand.

Nelson nodded, somewhat embarrassed at getting all this attention, and was quickly on the veranda steps where Uriah Fowler waited. Sam's mount was ready. Sam looked him over, but couldn't tell much about the horse they had brought in place of his Shawnee. His equipment, including the old, long hunting rifle and powder horn, hung on the saddle. Fowler asked, "What's goin' on, Sam?"

"Uh...headin' north."

"North? Where to?"

"Forest Station," Sam blurted.

"Lord, Sam. That place is probably crawlin' with Rebs since we hit the railroad at Newton Station. Goin' by yo'self?"

"Sure. Uh...better that way," Sam said, adjusting his saddle. He grabbed a handful of mane, pulled himself into the saddle, and said, "See you, Fowler. Oh, another thing. Take care of my...uh...horse, case I...uh...I don't get back."

"Yeh, Sam. Shawnee'll be all right with me."

"Uh...thanks," Nelson and his mount wound their way through the campfires and were soon on the road headed northeast. A half mile from camp, Sam coaxed the horse through a ditch and into an open field. An hour later, he rode along a road leading, as close as he could tell, due north. This would be the Forest Station road on Grierson's map, he decided.

Hoping the horse would have the good sense to stay on the road, Sam gave him his head and together they galloped into the black, fog-shrouded night. For two hours, Sam alternately galloped and walked his horse. Then it happened!

Ahead in the road, Sam heard something. He reined his horse to a halt and sat for a full minute straining his eyes into the blackness. It was a column!

Sam jerked at the reins and the horse stepped toward the roadside. The horse balked, then Nelson kicked him hard and cursed and the animal plunged across a small ditch. Nelson stopped suddenly on the other side.

Click!

Metal on metal? Sam wasn't sure. His heart pounded. After a long minute, Sam clucked the horse forward.

"Halt! Who goes there?"

Sam's feet jerked in the stirrups. His brain went into a spin. For a few frightening seconds, Sam Nelson had a choice: RUN! Or as the voice demanded, Halt!

"Uh...don't shoot!" Nelson heard himself say.

Two riders moved in front of him from the brush along the road. One spoke, "What you doin' here?"

"Runnin' from the...uh...Yanks," Sam replied, almost disinterested now.

The men whispered to each other, then one of them said, "Sure you ain't a Yank you'self?"

Before Sam could stammer a reply, a match flared. "Here, let's have a look at you."

The match moved toward Sam and was directly before his face, blinding him. Then his eyes adjusted to the light. He could see who he was talking to now — two Confederates, a sergeant and a private.

Chapter 8

...whiskey and flowers

Sam Nelson was born in Sullivan County, Tennessee and moved to Illinois while a young man. In the Little Wabash River bottoms in northern Gallatin County, Illinois, he was surrounded by the Southern way of life. Others from Tennessee and Kentucky migrated to southeast Illinois; some remained, others moved on. Sam's ways were those of a Southerner. Consequently, he drawled like a Southerner.

An officer in the service of the Confederate States of America, Captain R.C. Love, stood before him now. Love inquired, "What you doin' on this road, soldier?"

Groping for words, Sam stuttered, "Suh...uh...I's pressed in by the Yanks two days ago."

Sam Nelson searched the young officer's eyes for some sign. Love said nothing and Sam continued, "Made me...uh...guide 'em. Then yest'day, they paroled me; on my way to...uh...Forest Station. Uh...got an ol' friend livin' there."

Love glanced at the sergeant that had brought Nelson in. Looking back at Nelson, he asked, "You's with them Yankee raiders?"

"Uh...yes, suh."

"Where they headin'? How many of 'em?" Love demanded, traces of excitement beginning to show in his face.

"Uh...before noon at Garland...Garlandville. Left 'em there. They musta had 'bout, 'bout...uh...eighteen hundred men."

The Confederate captain drew his head back, a look of disbelief in his face, "'S that all?"

"Yes, suh. Uh...but they's well armed," Sam said, nodding. "'Spect they'd give you...uh...all you wanted, suh," Sam volunteered.

"Huh! We'll see 'bout that. Tell me, boy, which way they headed from Ga'landville?"

"Why...uh...why, they headed...uh...out toward the Mobile railroad. Southeast. Left 'fore I did, suh."

"Fine, soldier. Now somethin' else and reckon you can be on yo' way to yo' friend. What's the best route to Ga'landville?"

"Why...uh...suh, the only way I...uh...know is the way I come. 'Bout...uh...three miles south, there's a fork. Go east there. It'll lead ya'll straight to Garlandville."

The Confederate captain, apparently satisfied with everything Sam Nelson told him, wished Sam a good journey. Sam thanked him and told him he hoped he ran them Yanks all the way to Alabama. The captain laughed and allowed, "We'll do just that."

Sam Nelson rode on north toward Forest Station, the Confederate column passing south in the road. He tried to estimate their numbers. The captain seemed awfully sure of himself when Sam told him that the Yanks had eighteen hundred men. That must mean, Sam thought, that the captain's force was nearly that number too. But as Sam rode along in the dark trying to count the riders, he could not be certain.

After an hour of slow riding to let the column pass, Sam stopped his horse. He had a raving headache. He turned in the saddle and listened. No sound. He pressed his thumbs into his eye sockets. A soft breeze was clearing the fog now and Sam turned his head in order to hear better. He rubbed the back of his neck. Still, no sound.

The Confederate column would be turning east toward Garlandville about now, so Sam rode south along the road he had just been over. An hour later, he found a road going west. Confused, Sam looked around for a sign. He rode down the road a few yards. A flickering light from a small cabin attracted his eye and he rode slowly and quietly to the fence bordering the road, let his horse through the gate, and rode through the bare yard.

In front of the house, Sam dismounted. Rather than knock on the door, he peeked in the window. The light danced from a flickering fire in the fireplace. The oilcloth covering the window was torn and Sam slit it even more with his hunting knife.

Inside, in a corner, a man slept on a straw mattress. The cabin floor was dirt and a chair sat at the center of the one room. A window at the back was boarded over. There was no loft, just the underside of the split logs and a split-shingle roof.

Sam felt along the wall until he found the door. By lifting carefully and pushing, he gained entrance without a sound. He crept to where the man slept. The fire lit his way. Beside the mattress, he knelt and placed the cold muzzle of the Navy Colt to the right temple of the sleeping figure.

The man awoke. Carefully, the head turned. He was a black man. Relieved, Sam whispered, "Uh...can you help me?"

"If you'll get that pistol out my ear," the black man spoke aloud.

Sam pulled the Colt back, released the hammer, hesitated, then stuck the big revolver in his belt. Standing, he walked to the middle of the room to the chair, pulled it under him, and plopped down.

The black man sat up on the straw mattress, "That's better. Now what's the matter?"

"I got to...uh...get to the Mack..., Mackadore Plantation."

"That's about twenty mile from here. You're on the road to Raleigh. That's the right way."

"Uh...I know that, but I...uh...don't want to go by the road."

"Oh, I see," the black man smiled.

Sam Nelson wondered if he did see. There was no reason he say more however, because the man stood and said, "Let's get goin'."

In seconds, the black man was running across fields and trough woods, headed south and then east, with Sam Nelson following on horseback. By the time the black man stopped, Sam's horse was nearly jaded. Sam kept asking, "How in the Lord can you keep on runnin' like that?" The big man only smiled.

When the sun lit Mississippi, Sam saw smoke from the campfires at Mackadore Plantation. He called for the black man to stop. Sam slid off his horse and the two men sat on the dew-covered ground. Sam asked, "You want to come with us?"

"Can't."

"How come? We got a horse herd and...."

"You a Lincoln soldier?"

"No,...uh...I...."

"Yeh, you are," the black man interrupted, grinning.

"How can you tell?"

"Just could tell, But I can't go with you. I got fam'ly back there. 'Sides you Lincoln soldiers gonna win the war, ain't you?"

"Sure 'nough," Sam smiled.

The black man rose from the grass and, looking at the sky, said, "Gonna rain, 'fore noon."

"Sure you won't come?" Sam pleaded.

The black man shook his head and trotted away. Sam Nelson watched until he disappeared into a pine woods nearly a quarter of a mile away. Sam sighed, mounted and rode toward the plantation, shaking his head.

"Halt!" a picket barked as Nelson neared the road. Sam gave the password. Shortly, he slid down from his lathered horse and presented himself to the guard at the door of the plantation house.

Benjamin Grierson was awake and dressed as Nelson entered. "Sit down, Sam. How'd it go?" he smiled anxiously.

Nelson related his experience and Grierson listened carefully. Sam said, "I reckon I figured it was...uh...was better to send 'em east than south, Colonel."

"I think you did right, Sam. Time they march to Garlandville, we'll be gone to the south. Then they'll have to play catch-up."

Grierson questioned Nelson and finally, he called, "Guard!"

The door opened and Grierson ordered, "Wake Prince, Trafton, and Blackburn. We're movin'."

Grierson turned to Nelson and said, "Sam. Did a good job. I'll include this in my report. You tell Sergeant Surby to get ready. We'll go to Raleigh, tell him."

Surby and the scouts, happy and surprised, listened while Nelson spun out the events of the ride for them. Sam felt his energy return as he talked of the brush with capture, then finding his way back with the help of the black man.

Less than an hour later, all thoughts of sleep forgotten, Nelson rode on point with Surby and Lycurgus Kelly. They crossed the Leaf River soon after leaving Mackadore Plantation and now entered Raleigh, Mississippi.

Raleigh, a town of some size, consisted of scattered houses and buildings straddling a ridge fenced in by pine forest. There was little chance anyone spotted the scouts as they entered town. It was Sunday morning. At eight o'clock, even the church bell had not made its demand.

With Surby leading, the three scouts used a narrow alley to enter the main thoroughfare. Surby's horse stepped into view first.

Movement! To Surby's left!

Seventy-five yards away, a man leaped on a horse and darted east of town.

"Halt!" Surby yelled. The rider lashed the horse. "Get 'im!" Surby commanded.

Kelly and Nelson were well-mounted and caught the man at pistol point not over a hundred yards from the edge of the sleepy town. Two shots fired over the fleeing man's head influenced his decision to stop and alerted Colonel Grierson and Blackburn, who were waiting with Surby as the scouts returned their captive to town.

Grierson immediately questioned the blundering fellow and found he was the county sheriff and was attempting to escape with the county funds — five thousand dollars in Confederate greenbacks — and records.

"Any Reb forces in the area?" Grierson asked.

"Hain't been none 'round here for nigh onto a month."

Blackburn called Surby aside. "Take your scouts and move ahead; Colonel'll finish up here while the column passes. Oh, and Richard, be watching for plantation with grain — and food for the men. We ain't all eatin' as good as you and your boys," he laughed.

Surby smiled and said, "Shame we can't eat pine cones; plenty of them here'bouts." Surby motioned to the scouts and soon they were riding a full mile ahead of the advance column.

Westville, Mississippi was the next objective on Grierson's maps. The scouts traveled by back roads throughout the day. The noon bivouac was early and short. No sooner had the men dismounted in a pine woods than the trees began dripping rain. It was the kind of rain that Sam Nelson's father liked. "It makes the corn grow, Sammy," he would say. A slow, gentle, soaking rain followed the scouts and the column through the remainder of the day. At times the rainfall was intense, pelting the raiders, but as dusk settled on the pine forests of the southern Mississippi, the rain eased to an occasional, mist-like drizzle.

Near dark, Surby, Kelly and Steadman turned their mounts down a long, neat lane toward a plantation house. On a latticed veranda, a man sat puffing gently on a pipe. In the dim light, the man made no move as Sergeant Surby eased his horse forward, his right thumb hooked in his belt near his revolvers.

"Get down, get down," the big, gray-haired man called to the scouts when they were within shouting distance.

The three scouts obliged the gentleman. He laid his pipe aside and before they could sit, began a long speech about how he had captured some deserters just two weeks ago, told how he had ridden the "damn cowards" down and how his county was no place for the "yeller bellies" to hide out. He pulled a five-pointed star from his breast pocket and brandishing it exclaimed — indeed almost shouted, "Why I'm dep'ty sheriff o' this county."

Kelly and Steadman remained silent, occasionally looking at each other and winking. Surby could not get a word in, no matter how hard he tried. Finally, Surby settled back and listened, deciding the man would tell him everything he knew before he finished talking anyhow.

"Got some lip-smackin' whiskey here, boys. Made it m'self. Best in the entire state — maybe the entire Confederate States," he reared his head back and let go a rumbling laugh. "Rome?" he called. "Rome, bring these gentlemen some o' that jug."

A middle-aged slave came through the front door carrying a crock jug. He walked to his master and handed it to him.

"Thank you, Rome. You're a good Negra."

Rome re-entered the house and the deputy sheriff pulled a wooden plug from the jug, wiped the nozzle with his sleeve, and grasping the handle with his right hand, threw the jug back atop his arm, and applied his lips to the nozzle. He glugged three times.

"My Lawd, that's good," he said, handing the jug to Kelly.

Kelly imitated the man, as did Steadman. Surby hesitated, then put the jug to his lips and pretended to drink. The jug passed between the four men three times before Surby decided it was time to move on. He let the big man get the jug to his mouth and then slipped the Navy Colt into his lap, and cocked the hammer.

"Rome," Surby called, "Rome, come out here!"

The black servant appeared in the door and looked at his master. Surby said, "Rome, get the deputy's horse." Rome looked at Surby, saw the revolver, glanced quickly at his master and stepped from the veranda and around the corner. "Be quick," Surby called after him.

Before Rome cleared the corner of the house, the deputy sheriff demanded, "What in tarnation is goin' on?"

Surby did not answer.

"Well," the man grunted and stood up. Surby raised the big pistol; the sheriff made no move. Then he said, "I'm not dressed to ride. Let me get some clothes."

Surby nodded but told him not to change. "Kelly, you and Steadman go with 'im. Try's anything, shoot 'im."

When the deputy and his escort exited the house, his horse stood saddled with the reins hanging to the ground. "Damned strange I'm told what to do in my own house this way," he grumbled. The scouts did not respond.

As he stuffed the extra clothes in the saddle bags, he complained, "You can't conscript me! I'll be damned if somebody don't pay for this."

Just then, the column turned in the lane and the Colonels Grierson and Blackburn trotted forward. "Now see here," the deputy began, but was interrupted by Sergeant Surby, "General Loring, suh, this is the deputy sheriff o' this county."

The man muttered something, then began relating for the "Gen'ral" what he had earlier related to the Butternut Guerillas. Surby and other scouts excused themselves and rode out the lane and turned on the road to Westville and the bridge over the Strong River.

Surby took Sam Nelson and rode ahead of the other scouts toward the Strong River crossing. They slipped by a plantation house and continued toward the river. The bridge, they found intact and unguarded! Fate had still not turned her back on the raiders.

"Uh...sure are lucky," Sam Nelson said, when the two men got to the other side of the bridge.

Surby sighed relief, then agreed with Nelson, adding, "We needed this bridge; don't think we've made more'n thirty miles today."

Nelson scouted the road a quarter of a mile, then returned. Surby ordered him to stay at the bridge and do what he could to guard it until the column arrived. So Nelson settled himself under nearby pine boughs and Surby rode to report to Blackburn.

The remaining scouts rode along quietly for a while after Surby passed them headed toward the rear. Weariness and cold rain began to gnaw at their nerves. First, Charlie Weedon complained about the weather, then George Steadman became skittish. Fowler cursed and blurted, "George, this country's crawlin' with Rebs; want to get us all shot dead?"

This grumbling and complaining continued until Surby returned. Steadman — and his mount — shied at the same time and Surby ordered him to drop back to the advance guard, saying, "An you stay back there 'til we camp." Surby added to himself, "Nervous numbskull."

A short time later, as the scouts plodded along the muddy road, Fowler called excitedly, but softly, for the others to halt.

"What is it, Bud?" Weedon said.

"Rider comin'."

"He's right," Surby said. "Get off the road. We must of slipped by a Reb; he's spotted the column!"

Carefully, the scouts moved into weeds at each side of the narrow road. Surby slipped the rawhide loop that held the shotgun off the saddle horn. Quickly, he unlocked the old double-barrel and with his fingers felt the shells, and then relocked it, cocking the hammers at the same time. Then it was time to move, the rider was almost on them.

Surby kicked his horse into the road and yelled, "Halt!"

The rider's mount spooked and reared.

"Don't shoot! Don't shoot! It's me!"

There was a moment of silence, then Surby spoke, disgusted, "Steadman, you're gonna get killed one of these days; what in God's name are you doin'?"

Steadman tried to calm his mule and talk to Surby at the same time, "Whoa, now whoa! Blackburn sent... Whoa, now! He sent me...."

"Somethin' gone wrong?" Surby asked impatiently.

"Wrong? No nothin's wrong. Now, whoa!" Steadman added to the skittish mule.

Weedon interrupted, "Let me talk to 'im, Sarge."

"You do that, Private. Before I kill 'im!"

Weedon began, "Georgie, why'd Blackburn send you?"

"Forbes is back."

"What?" Surby asked.

"Forbes is back, I said."

"Yahoo!" Fowler yelled. "They made it!"

"They all make it?" Surby asked, calm now.

"Don't know. Just some scouts; Wood and some others, I think," Steadman answered.

"That's all that made it?" Fowler inquired.

"Didn't say that," Steadman added. "Captain Forbes and the others are tryin' to catch up. We been burnin' bridges and slowin' 'em down, but they got to Macon and are gonna join up 'fore long; prob'bly tonight."

"Well, good," said Surby.,

"Wish we hadn't burned that Leaf River bridge," Fowler said.

"They'll make it all right; least ways we know not to burn anymore 'til they catch up," said Surby.

Another rider approached the group now. Surby started to halt him, but instead heard the password, "Blackburn," and permitted the big colonel to advance.

"Hear about Forbes?" Blackburn asked. He looked around for Steadman, saw him, and added, "Didn't know whether that mule'd get him here or not." He smiled.

"Yes, sir," Surby said. "Glad to hear it."

"Then you men scout ahead. Colonel Grierson wants the Seventh to cross the bridge at Strong River and camp on the Smith Plantation. Surby, you know what to do."

"Right, Colonel. Kelly and.... Kelly, you take Steadman and go on to Smith's plantation. Tell Nelson to hold his position at the bridge until the Seventh crosses."

"What then, Sarge?" Kelly asked.

Blackburn answered for Surby, "Send Nelson back to Williams Plantation this side of the river. He'll find Surby wherever Grierson's got his headquarters."

Steadman pulled his hat down and led Kelly in a plodding gallop for the bridge crossing and the Smith Plantation. Blackburn gazed sternly, almost trance-like, at the disappearing riders. Then he shook himself and said to Surby, "Richard, let's you and me look this Williams Plantation over."

The two loped along the road for a mile, then Blackburn slowed his horse to a walk. Surby was not sure whether to ask or not, bur he felt something was bothering his friend. Finally, he asked, "Colonel, somethin' the matter?"

"Huh?"

"Anythin' the matter?" Surby repeated.

"No. Just thinkin'."

Surby and Blackburn continued down the road. Surby occasionally glancing toward the Lieutenant-Colonel. Somewhere a night bird trilled a mournful whistle. Suddenly Surby felt sad.

"Prince and the Seventh are movin' later tonight," Blackburn told Surby.

"Where to?"

"Pearl River. Know that county sheriff we caught runnin' in that one-horse town this mornin'?"

"Yeh."

"Well, he told the Colonel there's a ferry crossin' on the Pearl and...."

"And we can't ford after the rain, 's that it?" Surby interrupted.

"That's it. Su'prise me if it's not already gone. Too late to cross."

"Me too."

The cool, damp air sneaked next to the skin of the raiders with Grierson now. They were tired; they were hungry; they were scared. When it rained toward the first of the past week, they had sort of enjoyed it. Of course, they were in command then. They held all the trump cards. They were dominant wherever they went. But now, they were deep in enemy territory. Nelson's encounter had changed rumors to truth! They were being hunted. Most felt there was little chance they wouldn't be caught.

"Sunday nights are always worse," Surby told himself. "They're supposed to be spent around a warm campfire. Sunday nights are tired, lazy nights."

This night was different. Grierson's men were two hundred fifty miles into Confederate territory with every soldier and civilian in the country waiting to snuff their lives with a ball from a rusty hunting gun. That deed would make an instant hero of the assassin.

Surby's back hurt, his rear was sore, and his side burned, reminding him to put salve on it before bedding down. Then he pondered, in a whisper, "If I get to bed down."

A white fence appeared to the right of the road and Blackburn asked, "This it?"

"Yeh. We didn't go in earlier. Wanted to check the bridge and report back first."

"Would Steadman and Kelly come by here on their way to Smith Plantation?"

"Sure would've. The bottoms along the Strong River run for miles in both directions and it's been too muddy to cross. Besides, the Strong is runnin' wild."

The yard bordering the lane was neatly trimmed, but Blackburn would not enter the gate. "Let's wait for the column."

"If you say so, sir."

"No sense takin' chances. This Williams may have seen the other scouts and know we're on our way. If he plans on trin' anything foolish, he's less likely if he sees the column move up the lane."

Those words flustered Surby; a shade of uneasiness crossed his face. Blackburn always thrived on the air of indefinite expectation. He was not a cautious man. Surby began to ask himself if Blackburn wasn't losing his nerve, the strain of the march and all. He looked toward Blackburn and was about to ask if he was all right, but he hesitated, then decided to forget it — for now.

Not a sound from the house. A lantern sat on a post or so it appeared. Could be someone sitting on the porch, Surby reasoned.

Blackburn and Surby didn't wait long. They heard the hooves of horses and clank of a metal pan as the column approached. Blackburn halted the advance guard and told them to move with the rest of the Seventh Illinois to the bridge and then on to Smith Plantation.

Later, after the Seventh passed, Colonel Grierson and the Sixth arrived. Blackburn explained to Grierson about the advance. Grierson, speaking nasally as if he had a cold, said, "Good, Bill. Now let's see what this Williams place has to offer for lodging. I'm dead on my feet."

Grierson prodded his horse down the lane to the front steps of the house. In doing so, he walked his horse directly through a beautiful oval flower garden. His staff followed. By the time Surby, who had fallen behind, arrived at the flower bed, it was nearly obliterated under the hoof prints of the several horses that had passed over it.

Almost immediately, as Grierson halted in front of the house, the plantation owner slammed out the front door and stood, his feet widespread, at the edge of the veranda. He looked around at the men and horses, raised the lantern and saw his garden. "Who's commandin' here?" he screamed.

Colonel Benjamin Grierson and other officers and men paid no attention to him. As if he did not stand there screaming, they dismounted and walked their horses to nearby trees.

Major Williams, immaculate in Confederate grays with highly polished boots, stepped down off the veranda and strode in circles. He tried to find someone, anyone, in command. He continued shouting and cursing, "This is an insult on my dignity, I'll have you know! I'll be damned if I won't report the commander of this mob to Gen'ral Pembe'ton! Won't tolerate such abuse! This is my private property, you hear! Who's commandin' here? Look at my garden! Damn you, damn you all!"

On and on, the Confederate officer ranted, completely frustrated. The men with Grierson were tired. There was no time for patience, nor did anyone feel a need for it. This deep in Confederate territory, with reports coming in constantly that forces were sweeping the country, the rules of decency noticeably relaxed to the point of abandonment in favor of self-preservation.

When the Confederate major saw he was accomplishing little with his demands, he retreated into his house. A short time later he found he had been storming about in the middle of the Sixth Illinois Cavalry shouting insults that he figured should have cost him his life, but did not. He could not understand that, and said so to Grierson.

Meanwhile, the Butternut Guerillas fed their horses and tried to find something for themselves. Some ate, others only tasted their food and collapsed into a sound sleep.

Throughout the camp, it was the same. Sleep was more important now than food. The gnawing hunger had left hours earlier. Some sergeants and corporals insisted that their men cook what little food they could find and eat before they so much as sat on the ground. They were the lucky ones. Colonel Benjamin Grierson would be up and pushing his men toward the Pearl River as dawn crept over Williams Plantation.

Chapter 9

...Prince and the Pearl

While most of the scouts slept fitfully on split rails taken from a nearby fence at Williams Plantation, Colonel Edward Prince, a lawyer in civilian life from Adams County, Illinois, led the Second Battalion of the Seventh Illinois Cavalry in a forced march on the ferry at the Pearl River. Scouting for him were three of the Butternut Guerillas: Corporal Lycurgus Kelly, Private George Steadman, and Private Charles Weedon.

By everyone's best calculations — and hopes — the Second Battalion would be able to take the Pearl crossing before daybreak. But if Nelson had not convinced the Confederate captain to move to Garlandville; or if the Confederate Captain found from a civilian that he had been duped; or if word got to Jackson, less than thirty miles up the Pearl, the raiders were heading west; then the Pearl would run red with Union blood — probably near dawn.

About two o'clock on the morning of Monday, April 27th, Captains John M. Graham (Company E), William Ashmead (Company I), and Squire A. Epperson (Company L), along with Second Lieutenant Stephen H. Richardson (Company C), shouted the marching commands which headed their companies on the thirteen-mile trip to the Pearl River. At the head of the column, the three scouts moved in the fashion to which they had become accustomed — Kelly on point, Steadman a short distance behind, then Weedon.

For two hours, these three Butternut Guerillas took turns on point. They agreed to exchange places on the half-hour, "or thereabouts"; Kelly commanded since he was the only corporal on the detail.

Kelly and Weedon picked their way along the narrow road, their horses slipping from time to time in the clay mud. Weedon had just returned from his thirty-minute tour and told Kelly he was going to try and sleep. He handed Kelly his reins, spit out his tobacco wad, and soon slumped in the saddle.

Ten minutes later, Weedon felt Kelly jerk his horse's head. Weedon nearly tumbled from the saddle, yelling, "What the h...!"

"Shut up! Rider comin'!"

Weedon leaned forward, gathered his reins, and followed Kelly off the road into a thicket. The rider came closer, galloping his mount at breakneck speed on the slick mud. Then he burst by. It was Steadman!

Kelly yelled, "George!"

George Steadman recognized the brogue, pulled back on the mule's reins, and finally stopped the contrary animal fifty yards down the road.

He turned the mule and trotted back to Kelly and Weedon, who waited for him in the road.

"What in thunderation's the matter with ye?" Kelly asked as Steadman came in whispering distance.

Steadman answered, "The doggoned river."

"What do you mean, the doggoned river?" Weedon said, irritated.

Steadman, trying to get his breath, gasped, "It's just ahead!"

"That can't be, George," Weedon responded. "I's just up there and that river ought to be three or four miles yet."

"Did you see it, Georgie?" Kelly interrupted.

"No, didn't see it, but I sure smelt it."

"You smelled it? What do you mean now, smelled it?"

"The mud and water, river bottom mud; I smelled it!" Steadman was very angry.

"C'mon now, George. You smelled the bottoms. This valley is wide. Bottoms probably run a ways back from the river."

Steadman said nothing. Weedon snickered and Kelly started to encourage Steadman back to the point. Before Kelly could speak, Steadman kicked the mule, cursed, and was headed at a trot through the mud toward the river.

When the sound of the plodding mule faded, Weedon said, shaking his head, "That George. Wouldn't think he'd be so dumb."

"Now, Charlie. George was not raised in the Wabash Bottoms like you. Besides, he ain't no jumpier'n you and me."

Weedon was wide awake now, he wondered aloud, "Actually, if we can ford that river, we'll be better off. Them Rebs split us up with a hundred of us on one side and the other hundred waitin' to cross, we'll all be dead."

About five o'clock, the river appeared. Kelly was riding point. He didn't scout the far side, but satisfied himself that no Confederate forces were on the east side, his side. In minutes, he passed Weedon and Steadman, told them to stop at the next turn in the road and blurted, "River ahead."

As the first light of day surrounded the Second Battalion, they had their first look at the ferry crossing on the Pearl River. Kelly's report to Colonel Prince warned, "The ferry's on the other side."

From a distance, the Pearl was motionless. On closer inspection, it was a brawling, swift and dangerous barrier.

Colonel Edward Prince stood staring, grim faced, for several minutes. Still eyeing the river, he spoke, "Get me someone to swim it."

It was obvious that a man alone could never cross, but a man and a horse together might make it. On the other side, the rider could commandeer the ferry and return to the east bank.

Word passed that Captain Ashmead should get a volunteer from his company. "Make sure he's got a damn strong horse," someone added.

In less than a minute, Private William Henry Douer came slowly forward. Douer, like most in his company, had signed on at Decatur,

Illinois. He was a small, but strong man and rode a big, buckskin stallion that had probably been recently confiscated. The animal looked more like Mississippi stock than the Army horses recruited in Illinois and Indiana during the previous year.

Douer needed no instructions. He headed the buckskin down the bank, being careful not to mire in the knee-deep mud. The buckskin took the water without hesitation. George Steadman watched in awe, Weedon muttered an oath, and Kelly blessed himself, making the sign of the cross.

For a few seconds, Douer and the buckskin made steady progress. The water swirled by them and they headed straight toward the opposite bank bathed in the early morning light. Then, suddenly, they were out of the eddy and into the swift current. The buckskin swam downstream with the current and Douer's attempt had failed. Using his good sense, Douer slipped from the horse's back and held to the saddle, trying to turn the big horse back to the east bank. Still, the horse could not turn.

Downstream, a sand neck protruded into the river just far enough for the rider and buckskin to swing close enough to bank to get footing, and, subsequently, out of the torrent so ineptly named the Pearl.

That settled the question of someone capturing the ferry, but Prince's next move was made for him. From across the river, a man strolled toward the ferry. "Ya'll wanna cross?" the man drawled, yelling.

Prince, without hesitation, responded, "Sure 'nough. Damned if it ain't harder to wake yo' Negra boatman than 'tis to catch them damned conscripts!"

"Sorry 'bout that. He'll fetch ya'll; be a minute."

Prince turned to Captain Ashmead of I Company and said, "Get 'em ready to load, Will. When you get to the other side, send out some pickets an' tell the owner we'll help this man."

It took about ten minutes for the ferry to cross. When it arrived, it was a disappointment. Only twenty-four horses could cross at a time. A light drizzle made the wait even more miserable.

Back at Williams Plantation, the dawn did not accompany as much excitement, but Richard Surby was as alert as if he had been at the river crossing. It was the first, and the longest, period of sleep that he had suffered through in several days. Sometime in the night, he slipped off his bed-fence rails. Now, to go along with his burning gunshot wound, he dug at his worst case of chigger bites since joining the Army. The other time, and the itch was bad enough then, was when he slept with a hound under a lean-to in a rainstorm. Then, the itch was tolerable; now, terrible.

Sam Nelson watched Surby scratch while he ate crackers, he watched him scratch while he saddled his horse, and now Sam watched him scratch as the Butternut Guerillas rode to the front of the advance guard of the Sixth Illinois Cavalry. Surby rarely cursed; his oaths blistered the air now. All the time, Nelson laughed.

When the scouts reached the Strong River bridge, the itching had eased. By the time they joined the remaining two battalions of the Seventh at Smith Plantation, Surby was better. Occasionally Nelson, sometimes

Fowler, reminded Surby of "his predicament," they called it, but that too ceased, along with the itching, by the time they neared the Pearl River.

The casual joking and conversation had worn itself out and the scouts simply plodded along, already weary. Nelson, after a mile or so, said, "Guess...uh...they musta made it at the Pearl all right, huh, Sarge?"

"'Spect so, else we'd heard somethin'."

Fowler rode ahead now, complaining that if his horse was as stiff as he was, he'd not be worth much in a fight. Several minutes later, Fowler and his horse galloped back to join Nelson and Surby. He wore a broad smile.

"They make it?" Surby called.

"Sure 'nough! The Second's practically across."

"Any trouble?" Surby said.

"Got a Reb prisoner. He's tryin' to warn the ferryman; thought they's Yanks 'round here," Fowler laughed.

"That right," said Surby, smiling.

"Got one problem though," Fowler continued. "There's a Reb transport up river. Prince wants Colonel to send Smith with a gun 'bout two or three miles up there just in case she tries an' move. Want me to tell Grierson?"

"You go ahead," Surby said. "We'll go on ahead."

"All right. See you on the Pearl."

"Right," Surby said, raising his hand and waving as Fowler kicked his horse along the road toward the column.

Surby and Nelson rode to the Pearl and waited while the struggling ferry worked its way through the swift current toward them. Only a few troopers were left to cross; they were the rear guard.

When the ferry docked, Surby rode forward and told a sergeant in charge to wait, "Grierson'll be here shortly. He'll want to cross."

In a few minutes, Grierson and the column rode up at a trot. "Get her movin'," Grierson ordered. He quickly dismounted, led his horse aboard, and motioned for Surby and the scouts to come along.

On the other side, Surby quickly sought the Butternut Guerillas who had accompanied Prince. Minutes later, he found them napping under an oversized sweetgum tree.

"Hey! Wake up!" Surby yelled.

Kelly and Weedon were sound asleep, but Steadman rolled over, "Hey, Sarge. Doggone it, you sure missed a fine meal."

"Wake those other guys, George."

"Aw, let 'em sleep."

"I'm awake; I'm awake," Weedon said sitting up and twisting the sleep from his eyes with his knuckles. Kelly did the same.

For the next ten minutes, Kelly, Weedon, and Steadman ranted about what a fine meal the owner of the ferry had served the "First Regiment of the First Alabama Cavalry — from Mobile."

"Why, 'twas a scrumptious meal for 'Bama's finest," Steadman said several times, always patting his stomach.

While the scouts talked, Colonel Grierson conferred with Colonel Prince. The two men stood side by side on their horses, with Lieutenant-Colonel Blackburn looking on. Sergeant Surby, resting in the shade, knew something was up when Blackburn nodded his head and rode toward where the Butternut Guerillas lay resting.

"Surby, take your scouts and ride toward Hazlehurst Station. Colonel wants Prince to hit the New Orleans and Southern Railroad quick as possible."

"Get any word on Rebs ahead?" Surby asked, lazily.

"No, but it's twelve mile to the station. Watch yourself. That deputy sheriff got away last night. No tellin' which way he went."

"He got away?" Weedon asked, his disbelief obvious.

"Yeh," Fowler answered laughing. "Took one of the Colonel's horses."

"Wasn't Grierson's. Belonged to his orderly," said Surby.

"That's bad enough," Steadman shook his head. Then, he sighed, "Oh, well, must not of crossed here anyways."

"C'mon, Richard. Get your men movin'," Blackburn interrupted.

Surby and the others mounted and when Steadman had himself adjusted on the mule, Surby led out along the westbound road. Prince's men answered the bugler's "Boots and Saddles" before the scouts were beyond hearing distance of the call.

The scouts advanced three miles without incident, but during mile four things began to happen. Something had alarmed the civilians in the area. They were arming to resist the "Yankee invaders."

The Butternut Guerillas had few words for the first few "secesh" they saw because they either had no weapons at all, or were poorly armed. But, then, at a turn in the road, Surby suddenly met a little, shriveled man with sandy whiskers. Surby carefully and quickly surveyed him from head to foot. The little man carried an old United States issue, flintlock musket on his shoulder, one wrist draped lazily across the stock. He had a large leather pouch and a powder horn slung over his shoulder. An old belt around his waist held two large, old dragoon pistols. They were flintlock and showed some rust.

The foxy-eyed old man cocked his head and stared as Surby rode near. Surby resisted the temptation to laugh; he decided that the old man looked as savage as a meat axe, and nearly said so.

The musket slid off the old man's shoulder and was brought to "carry-arms" as he stopped in front of Surby. In a high pitched voice, he exclaimed, "They is comin', Cap'n, and I am ready! I jist bid the old woman good-bye and told her that she didn't need to expect me back until I had done killed me four Yankees and they were exterminated from out our Southern soil. Hee, hee," his nose wrinkled, his mouth void of teeth, "I'm good for three of 'em anyhow, don't you reckon? Why, I been through the Mex-i-can War and know how to use them here weapons, don't ya know."

The other scouts arrived during this display of patriotism and Surby winked at them, smiling.

The old man continued, "Why, fellers, I'm so dad-burned mean and ornery it don't even rain on me. Hee, hee. Why that Yankee Grant ain't nothin'; fit with him in Mexico. Hee, hee."

Surby smiled, said nothing, but held his hand out in a gesture which meant, let me see that remarkable musket. The old man obliged and Kelly and Fowler eased their horses forward, remarked about the quality of his dragoon pistols; and soon held them in their hands.

"What ya think that musket, Cap'n?"

"I think you're my prisoner," Surby answered, smiling wryly. "Take 'im to the Gen'ral, Lieutenant," Surby ordered Steadman. The old man's toothless jaw fell slack and then he was on his way toward the river. Steadman and the mule nudging him gently to keep him from turning back.

Two miles later, the scouts still talked and joked about the old man. Directly ahead, however, Surby spotted a group of about a dozen men. "Boys, cut the laughin'! Up ahead," he nodded.

Several riders stood in a group. Other men sat on fallen logs, while some stood nearby. "Want me to go for the colonel, Sarge?" Weedon asked, excited.

"No, now we come this far on our wits," Surby answered calmly. When they were within speaking distance, the scouts saw a small building hidden among some trees. It had a sign hanging at a slant above the main, and only, entrance. The sign had a rough drawing of a musket on it. It was a gunsmith shop.

"Them Yanks comin'?" a deep voice growled.

Surby drawled, "They's other side the Pearl and headed this way."

The men sitting on the logs jumped to their feet. There was incessant chatter and movement in the nervous group. None noticed Surby nod to Nelson and Weedon. The two scouts coaxed their horses to the side of the group.

A man in the crowd yelled, "Ya'll get quiet now!" Then turning to Sergeant Surby, he began to ask, "What ya'll want us to...."

Surby sat astride his horse, a Navy Colt in each hand. He said, "We just want you to lay down them guns, that's all."

The men started to move forward and the hammers on the Colts snapped back with a menacing click. The man paused and glanced at the others. Some were laying their guns aside. The others saw Weedon and Nelson and did the same.

"Weedon, you and Sam hold 'em here. Kelly and Fowler, come with me." Surby stepped down from his horse and the three scouts entered the gunsmith shop. The smithy had watched everything and was already out of the shop before they entered.

Surby eased the hammers down on his revolvers and slipped them inside his belt. He motioned Fowler and Kelly to start destroying the weapons in the shop. They broke the stocks, but Surby, looking around on the floor, said, "Wait a minute. Let's fix these guns proper. Fix 'em where they won't be fit for nothin' but shootin' around corners. You know what I mean."

With that, the three men bent the barrels by placing them under the wooden counter and workbench and jerking up violently. They had nearly finished when the advance guard rode up outside.

Surby exited the shop and a sergeant from I Company called, "What you up to, Surby?"

"Doin' a little gunsmithin', that's all."

"What you want done with these Rebs?"

"Turn 'em over to Colonel Prince. We got to be ridin'."

Sergeant Matt Ruby commented, "That sure was a dandy you boys got earlier." Ruby slapped his leg and laughed.

"You mean the old man? Sure was; what'd they do with him?" Surby asked.

"Put him with the other prisoners; probably cut him loose after the next town. Hell, he's harmless."

"Wouldn't be so sure about that." Surby said as he mounted.

In a few minutes, Surby and the scouts were back on point well ahead of the column. They still spotted scattered civilians. Hazlehurst Station lay only six miles away and they slowed their pace, not anxious to get too far from the security of the advance guard.

Nearly an hour later, Colonel Prince ordered Surby to return and meet him. Surby found Prince riding in from checking his flankers.

"Sergeant, I got a message for two of your men to take ahead to Hazlehurst. See the telegraph operator gets it."

"Yes, sir," Surby took the message after Prince pulled it from his coat.

"Have 'em get out of there soon as they see the message's sent. I want this to go straight through without any giveaway."

"Who's it goin' to, sir?"

Prince smiled through his heavy, dark beard, "Why, General Pemberton, of course. You may read it, Sergeant."

With that, Surby rode for the head of the column. When he caught Steadman and Kelly, he told them, "Boys, I've got a message for you to carry to Hazlehurst. Give it to the telegraph operator there."

"Who would we be sendin' a message to now, Sergeant?" Kelly inquired.

Mimicking Colonel Prince, Surby said, "Why, General Pemberton, of course."

"Pemberton?"

"Yes, Pemberton at Jackson. Here's what it says."

Surby read the message silently, laughed, and then aloud:

> The Yankees have advanced to Pearl River, but finding the
> ferry destroyed they could not cross, and have left, taking
> a northeasterly direction.

"Doggone, that'll get ol' John Clifford stirred up," Steadman said, referring to Pemberton.

"All right, boys. Get goin'."

Surby handed the message to Kelly and added, "Colonel Prince says get out of there quick as you can."

"Aye, Sergeant, that you need not worry about."

Steadman and Kelly entered the little town of Hazlehurst Station under the threat of a downpour. The early morning drizzle that ruined the mirror-like surface of the swift-flowing Pearl River had quit. The two men simultaneously spied the rail depot and aimed their mounts through the mud toward a hitching rail at the back of the building.

As they dismounted, Kelly suggested that they be ready to run in case they were suspected. Their plan was to run in opposite directions around the building to their mounts if anything went awry.

On entering the depot waiting room, eight Confederate officers and enlisted men sitting and standing around the benches along the wall looked up and toward them almost as one.

Kelly took a deep breath and without hesitation carried the note to the telegraph operator. Steadman followed. The door to the telegraph office stood open and Kelly walked through announcing, "I've a message for General Pemberton at Jackson."

"Pembe'ton?"

"Aye."

"Let me hold it," the operator exclaimed, looking over spectacles and reaching for the message. He scanned it silently, then aloud so that everyone in the place could hear him. He announced, "Them Yankee raiders are aheadin' to Jackson." To Kelly and Steadman, he said, "Who you with?"

"Fust Regiment, Fust Alabama Cav'ry," Steadman answered.

"You see the Yanks?" one of the Confederate officers said, walking toward them.

"'Bout two hours ago. Fired on 'em from the ferry crossin'."

The officer turned to the telegraph operator, "Better go ahead and send that — and quick!"

Steadman and Kelly waited while the message chattered onto the wires. As the operator finished and awaited his acknowledgement, Steadman said, "Ain't ate in a spell. Any place her'bouts what offers somethin' this time o' day?"

One of the officers, still interested in the message and now reading it, glanced up long enough to answer, "Try the hotel."

"Much obliged," Steadman drawled as the two scouts exited the building, smiling and waving to the others.

At the hitching rail, Kelly said, "We should be reportin', George."

Mounting his mule, Steadman said, "Lycurgus, I am hungry. My belly says eat. I wasn't jokin'. Column won't be here for a spell. C'mon. Let's top that fine breakfast with a little somethin'."

The mule stepped through the mud up the long street. Scattered buildings on the right and the railroad track on the left guided the two men.

"Sure is doggone peaceful here," Steadman said, looking about.

Near the hotel, a rider burst around the corner of the big building. He headed straight for them. Suddenly they realized they were going to collide with this frenzied animal and its rider.

Steadman and the mule turned crossways in the street, trying to get out of the way. The rider grimaced and reared his horse, grabbing for an old saber all in the same motion. Everything happened very fast.

When the horse planted all four feet again, the rider dropped the reins and pulled a horse pistol from his belt. "Help!" he screamed. "Stop them damn Yankees!"

Again and again, the two scouts heard the deputy sheriff whom they'd drunk "polite" whiskey with only the day before yell, "Yankees! Stop 'em!"

The mule turned slowly now in the opposite direction. Kelly was already gone. Near the depot, as Steadman's mule slung mud trying to catch Kelly's horse, someone rushed into the street and grabbed at the mule's reins. The man ended up flat on his back in a mudhole for his trouble.

"C'mon, mule!" Steadman screamed. He was as low as the saddle horn permitted and trying to become one with the animal, waiting for the deputy to jerk a shot from the big horse pistol. But the shot never came; instead, a pistol — shot sounded like a Colt. Steadman thought — whistled by his head.

It was in that precise instant that mule and rider put their minds to what they were trying to do and left the little, startled town of Hazlehurst Station well out of gunshot range.

Only a mile from Hazlehurst Station, Richard Surby saw a man on a mule trying to overtake a rider on horseback. Eventually he recognized Kelly and Steadman — Steadman and the mule now taking the lead.

As the two riders approached, Steadman commenced reining in the mule, but was past Surby by thirty or forty yard before he could accomplish the task. Kelly halted his horse and told Surby and the other scouts with him, Weedon and Fowler, what had happened.

"You send the message?" Surby asked when Kelly had finished.

"Aye, but they might of sent another after the shootin', I just don't know."

"We'd better get down there!" Turning to Steadman, who was trying to turn his mule and return to where the group stood talking, he ordered, "George, you report this to the Colonel and tell the advance we're goin' to Hazlehurst and get up here double-quick!"

Again, man and mule were on their way for another frightening ride to the rear. Kelly led off with the other scouts following toward Hazlehurst Station.

As they entered Hazlehurst, the black clouds opened up and sheets of rain descended turning the street into a quagmire. Thunder rumbled and the wind whipped the brims of the scouts' hats letting the rain soak their faces and beards.

At the depot, their first stop, Kelly and Surby entered, revolvers drawn. Fowler and Weedon guarded each end of the station platform.

Kelly barked, "Man," to one of the two old gentlemen that watched them in silence, "where'd the telegraph operator go?"

The old man did not answer. Kelly turned to the other and waved the big Navy Colt menacingly. The old man recrossed his legs, spit a spray of tobacco juice on the floor, and spoke quietly and calmly, "He done left."

"I know that, but when?" Kelly continued.

"Right after them two Yanks got chased out o' town."

"Could be he did not transmit a warnin', Sergeant," Kelly said, turning to Surby who walked from the stripped operator's office.

"Looks like he tore out all the equipment when he went," Surby responded.

Surby spoke again to the old man, "When's the next train due?"

"Anytime." He spit again, wiped his chin with the back of his hand, and added, "Don't run on schedule since the war started."

"Where's it from?" Surby asked.

"Southbound."

The scouts stepped quickly from the building and ran to their horses just as the advance guard rode breakneck and splattering mud through the downpour. Colonel Prince led and immediately, through a series of hand signals, had the guard deployed.

Minutes later, the town was quiet and the advance guard of Prince's Second Battalion waited for the southbound train. The wait was long and restless. A quarter of an hour dragged by, then the remainder of the Second Battalion arrived, saw what was happening, and took necessary precautions. Thirty minutes later, some of the men, now tired and waiting, began moving around. They were hungry and looked for food. Others were simply tired of sitting in one spot.

Toward the north end of the scattered, barren-looking, little town, a group of men walked from their hiding place toward the freight cars lining a siding. They had little more than stepped into the street, when the unmistakable clanking of a train perked the ears of those in waiting. The train rounded a curve and came in full view of the restless soldiers.

Recognizing something amiss, the engineer slammed the controls on the old locomotive into reverse and backed up the track at a faster rate of speed than he had been advancing. The luck of Newton Station was fading. And then the train disappeared just as the excitement left the faces of the men.

Colonel Prince and some of the officers were upset at their loss, but few of the men cared. Their weariness would have to await its remedy at a later time, however. There were, as at Newton Station, chores to be done. The freight cars on the siding were set ablaze. Four carloads of ammunition were moved out of town for burning. Details went north and south on the track to destroy bridges and trestlework.

About an hour after the sun would have been straight up in the sky, the smoke from the burning war materials captured at Hazlehurst Station drifted north along the railroad track and a drugstore on the main street was accidently set on fire by the soaring embers. Full rain barrels and the water tank at the depot made it easy to fight the fire, but two empty stores and a private home were demolished before the fire was extinguished. The depot had been spared for the express purpose of preventing such a disaster. It took townspeople working side by side with the "Yanks" to prevent the entire town from joining the cloud of smoke that could be seen for miles around.

The weary, smoke-covered men, soldiers and Southerners, completed their fire fighting by two in the afternoon. Some men from the Second Battalion found stored commissary supplies and ate what they could and left the surplus for the remainder of the column.

At the hotel that Kelly and Steadman tried to reach earlier in the day, three barrels of eggs and a quantity of flour, sugar and hams were prepared for the soldiers on a first-come, first-serve basis. Steadman was first in line. Kelly and the other Butternut Guerillas were shoved to the front by some of the men toward the middle. Someone yelled, "You guys get the most and the best food. We been eatin' horse ration so long we gotta watch somebody what knows how to eat proper."

Steadman roared, amid laughter, "You're right, doggone it. You're dead right!"

Most of the Second Battalion, except those north and south burning railroad trestles and those on picket, were at the hotel eating. They sat on the floor, they leaned against the wall, and they ate with their fingers, hunting knives, and any other instrument they could call into use. There was bragging about their actions that day and there was laughter. All in all, it was the closest thing to relaxation they'd had since leaving La Grange, Tennessee, ten days before.

Sergeant Surby sat on the porch in front of the hotel watching the men file in and out. He turned down a dozen invitations to eat, always making an excuse, but never the real one. He often yearned for moments like this, but seldom got them. He suspected that he was a true loner, but he had never gotten the chance to prove it. Sometimes, he wanted to plunge off into some remote wilderness and just live there in purposeless seclusion. Maybe after the war, he often told himself, I can go west.

Surby's mind drifted in and out of the goings-on. He'd watch the soldiers file in and out wondering who they were and sometimes being surprised by someone he'd known for a year or two. He couldn't get over the boots. There didn't appear to be a one of Grierson's men that had on a good pair of boots. Their clothing made them look more like Butternut Guerillas, he thought. They'd discarded Union blued for lighter "secesh" clothes when the rain and heat made the itchy wool unbearable. The only way anyone could tell they were soldiers was when a bugle called. The ranks would close up neat and straight as far as the eye could see.

Just out of town, the ammunition cars began to explode. Surby paid no attention, not even when dozens of soldiers burst out the hotel door to see what "all the shooting" was. A short time later, however, Colonel

Benjamin Grierson and the remainder of the column arrived. Again, like Newton Station, they heard the explosions and thought the Seventh was under artillery fire.

With Colonel Grierson was Captain Henry C. Forbes. Forbes was greeted roundly by all those able to get to him; then someone cleared the way for him to enter the hotel. Surby followed Forbes and finally decided to eat.

Surby watched Forbes eat and answer questions, then a soldier suggested that Forbes tell of his adventure to Macon. Forbes agreed and when he'd eaten, began telling his story of B Company's ride.

By and by, the soldiers quieted down to listen. They clustered about Forbes and hung on his words as if they were the last they'd ever hear.

"On our way to Macon," Forbes continued, "I had two scouts from my company, Robinson and Buffington, on the point. They found us a camp. 'Bout three miles from Macon.

"I ordered Robinson toward Macon about a mile to see what he could learn about the force at that place. When he'd gone about that distance and dismounted, he heard the tramp of horses. In a few minutes, a squad of six Confederate soldiers rode up.

"Well, when they's within fifty yards, he halted 'em. 'Who come there?' Robinson demanded.

"'Friends,' a voice answered.

"'Advance one and give the countersign,' Robinson called out.

"A Confederate captain advanced and inquired, 'You a picket here?'

"'Yes, sir; ain't you heard, the Yanks are comin'?'

"'Yes,' said the Reb, 'learned that they's about six miles from here, but I hadn't heard of any pickets stationed here.'

"Robinson answered him, 'Oh, yes. I was sent here and told to watch these crossroads.' Here Robinson referred to the crossroads between him and me and B Company.

"Well, now. The Reb captain, he asked Robinson, 'How many men are you?'

"'Only about sixteen of us,' Robinson told him.

"Says the Reb, 'What are your instructions about passing?'

"Robinson didn't hesitate, but repeated his instructions," Captain Forbes laughed.

"He says to the Reb captain, 'The orders from General Loring, the commander at Macon, are not to pass any soldiers, 'cept commandin' officers and citizens.'

"With that the captain perked up," Forbes stuck his chin out, "and said smartly, 'Well, my friend, I am a commanding officer and have permission to take a squad of men and scout around the country.'

"'I'll tell the sergeant of the guard,' Robinson warned him. He turned his head and yelled two or three times, 'Sergeant of the guard; sergeant of the guard!'

"Obviously, there was no answer. We were a mile away."

Captain Forbes hesitated and pulled a pipe from inside his pocket. One of his audience handed him a pouch of tobacco. He took it, nodded his thanks, and as he began to fill the pipe, he continued, "By this time the soldier with the Reb captain began to get suspicious that all was not aright. Two of 'em dropped back, soon followed by two more. That left only one, who turned around and wanted to know, 'What in hell do they mean leaving like that?' The four Rebs did not answer, but were soon on a gallop," Forbes laughed.

"Well, now," Forbes smiled, "Robinson tilted his head and twisted his face. To this captain, he said, 'Why, Captain, you must have queer men to leave in that way. I wouldn't give much for such men to look for Yanks.'

"The captain looked decidedly astonished and said to Robinson, 'I'll know what this means!' To his one remaining man, he commanded, 'You stay here. I'll bring back the rascals.' Or something like that. And away he went.

"Robinson figured this's his opportunity and he'd improve it. The Confederate sat on his horse with his double-barreled gun elevated, cocked and ready for blastin'. Robinson had on this long grey coat and under it, his carbine hung on a string. He slid his hand down beneath the coat, seized his carbine and cocked it silently."

Forbes' voice was nearly in a whisper. He paused. Suddenly, he blurted, "Then he unbuttoned the coat and in an instant had the carbine presented at the Rebel's heart — ordering him to drop his gun, ride forward and dismount, which he did. Robinson then draws his revolver, drops his carbine, breaks the shotgun, mounts his horse, orders the Reb to follow suit, and hurries him back to me.

"Well, I'm goin' to tell you, I made the poor fellow think that I would hang him if he didn't tell all he knew 'bout the forces in Macon. The man hadn't been long in the service; he's young and fast frightened. And as a result, he told me that there's about four thousand troops, mostly conscripts, stationed there, but that there had arrived that day nine hundred troops from Mobile."

Captain Forbes lit his pipe and inhaled deeply.

In a puff of smoke, he continued, "Needless to say, I found no advantage in visiting Macon and early the next morning, we headed back.

"After marching eight miles the scouts picked up a soldier belonging to the Second Mississippi Artillery. He happened to be one of those individuals that was opposed to the war, but rather'n be conscripted, had volunteered. This man, by the way, proved of considerable service to me since he had good knowledge of the country; just the man I wanted. And I used him to good advantage.

"I struck out towards the railroad, with the intention of cutting the telegraph and burning a bridge 'tween Macon and Enterprise, to prevent a force being sent from Macon to Enterprise; but as I neared the railroad I learned that the bridge was strongly guarded. I concluded to avoid it and destroyed the telegraph. Then we proceeded towards Newton Station.

"Now at Newton Station, I found that Colonel Grierson had gone to Enterprise."

Forbes paused and asked someone for a drink. He was given a canteen. After taking a short drink, he commenced again to speak.

"The trip to Enterprise was the most difficult. We traveled through swamps, swam streams, and rode through timber without any roads for hours at a time. There were Rebs patrolling the country in every direction," Forbes said, moving his hand in a sweeping gesture. "It was the only route we could take and avoid 'em.

"Within a mile of Enterprise, I learned that a force of three thousand Rebel troops was just gettin' off a train. I promptly raised a white flag and rode forward demanding the surrender of the town in the name of Colonel Grierson.

"The Rebel colonel that I made my demand to asked for an hour for which to consider my offer. Then he asked where he could find me at the end of that hour. I told him I'd be with my reserve."

Captain Forbes paused as if in deep thought, relit his pipe, then laughed aloud. "Well, I was with my reserve, all right. But in the next hour, we put both men and horses to the test. I doubt if there was any period when them horses pulled more ground under them. We had no intention stayin' so close by all them Reb troops."

Again, Forbes paused, shaking his head.

"Still don't see how we got out of that one," he continued. "Anyhow, we eventually got on your trail. I force marched my men as much as sixty miles a day. We swam streams where you'd burned bridges and — oh, yes, we were even taken into some fallen trees by a disloyal guide. He was goin' to trap us there for capture, but his scheme was discovered in time to avoid it."

Richard Surby interrupted, "What of Bill Buffington? We heard tell he was killed."

"Yes, yes, we lost Buffington. That was at Philadelphia," Forbes replied softly. "We arrived at Philadelphia a day after you men. Let's see, that was the twenty-fourth — Friday. Buffington, Private Robinson, and Corporal (Charles E.) Martin went ahead scouting into Philadelphia. The citizens no longer trusted any man dressed in butternut.

"At the edge of town, they shot and killed Buffington. Martin was wounded. It was three Reb soldiers that shot 'em. We didn't find 'em, but we did charge the home guard there and capture and parole thirty of 'em.

"Later on, near Raleigh, Robinson learned that a company of guerrillas was in that place. I ordered a charge there, too, and we took 'em by surprise; captured all of 'em. They said they thought that all the Yanks had passed. They were takin' dinner and 'fore they knew it, they were surrounded. There's twenty-nine of 'em.

"We destroyed their arms, took their horses and their captain and turned 'em loose.

"It was just after Raleigh that Lieutenant (William) McCausland suggested I send three well-mounted men to overtake Colonel Grierson. As you know, my brother Stephen and Private Wood completed that mission for us."

With that, Captain Henry Forbes slapped his knees and stood. He announced, "Boys, I'm tired. I want to rest these weary bones. Colonel'll be wantin' to move 'fore long," he added. Someone in the crowd asked a question and then the conversation became a general one.

Surby left the hotel. He found Wood and Robinson and talked to them for thirty minutes about Bill Buffington. Robinson told him that they didn't have a chance. The Rebs met them in a road, accused them of being Yanks, and commenced firing.

Surby said little, but thought about how sudden life had ended for the scout, Buffington. He concluded, to himself, that carelessness had been the cause. His mind raced trying to search out what Buffington could have done differently. He found no sure solutions.

At seven o'clock, when the column left Hazlehurst Station under the cover of the early dusk, Surby still thought about Buffington, but that was not all. The Butternut Guerillas and Grierson's command had passed within twenty-five miles of the capital of Mississippi. They had cut the railroad and telegraph lines of two railroads. Enemy scouts were out in all directions looking for them. For all he knew, they could be laying an ambush at this moment — an ambush which would burst upon them out of the black night's march ahead.

Couriers were flying in every direction with news of their movements. Forces were concentrating and being sent to intercept them and hem them in and annihilate them.

The thing that bothered Surby the most was that the enemy had every advantage. They knew the country — every inch of it. In our favor, Surby finally considered, we've got Grierson and his Colton's maps. He discovers the path; the scouts make sure it stays open long enough for the column to get through.

Just now, Colonel Benjamin Grierson ordered that the "path" would be Gallatin — southwest. At nine o'clock, the Sixth Illinois Cavalry, with Colonel Grierson leading, stormed impatiently into the quiet little county seat, routed a few guerillas, and cleared the path for the remainder of the column to pass unhampered.

A short time later, Sam Nelson, Richard Surby, and Isaac Robinson were on the point and clearing the way toward Natchez for the two regiments. They rode silently in the black night. Clouds still obscured the night sky and therefore, the stars.

A squeaking, wooden wheel in the darkness scared them, then alerted them to a wagon creeping along the road. They could not quickly decide, after halting in the road, what they had discovered.

Surby whispered to his two companions, "Let's get out of here!"

The three men led their horses quietly into a thicket of scrub pine and waited while the squeak grew louder. In minutes, they watched a train of oxen-drawn wagons pass. They could make out that it was a military train and what looked like a large gun.

Surby gave no command, but led his horse farther from the road, hoping the noise of the train would conceal the movement. Robinson and Nelson followed him.

When they were at a safe distance, they headed northeast, then doubled back onto the road. They lashed their horses toward the advance guard. Lieutenant-Colonel William Blackburn was the first officer they met. They told him what they'd found.

"Good job, Richard. Take your two scouts and report this to Colonel Grierson. We'll take care of the train," Blackburn responded.

With Grierson informed, Surby and the scouts caught the advance guard. The wagon train was already theirs. They had no casualties and for their trouble, they'd captured a thirty-two pound Parrott gun, fourteen hundred pounds of powder, two wagons, and some provision. All of it was headed for Grand Gulf, where in a short time General Ulysses S. Grant would be making an all-out attack to take Vicksburg.

Near Hargraves, at Thompson's Plantation, Sergeant Surby, the Butternut Guerillas, and approximately nine hundred Union soldiers lay down about midnight for what some would describe the next morning as "a good night's sleep."

None of the Butternut Guerillas thought about Bill Buffington; not even Ike Robinson who'd watched him writhe, cry and die; they were all too tired.

A Union trooper has dismounted and is firing in the heat of battle. This statue is located at the Vicksburg National Military Park. (Author's Collection)

Chapter 10

...Trafton's travels

While the sun streaked the dawn sky, Richard Surby and George Steadman plundered around Thompson's Plantation searching for food. They found nothing.

"Sarge, this place is what we'd call a starvation farm up home."

Surby only grunted in disgust. Obviously, he thought, cursing inwardly, somebody beat us to everything; or maybe these people are just poor like Northern folks is poor.

"Sarge, doggone it," George Steadman added, "if'n I don't eat 'fore long, I'm...."

"Yes, George," Surby interrupted, "I know. You're goin' to dry up and blow away."

"That's right, Sarge," Steadman answered. He was serious.

At least the rain had stopped. The horses fed well, and the southerly wind which brought so much rain and humidity the day before shifted and began drying the roads. The Sixth and Seventh Illinois mounted and moved at seven o'clock. It was Tuesday morning, April 28.

For three hours, the column wound west and then south toward Natchez. Occasional sightings of armed citizens and lone Confederate guerrillas did little to create diversions for Surby and the other scouts at the head of the marching column. They were expecting bigger trouble. Perhaps this would be the morning that they'd clash with Confederate cavalry. They were especially watchful and unusually jumpy.

At ten o'clock, Richard Surby was recalled to the column. The two regiments halted and a staff meeting was taking place as the other Butternut Guerillas returned to the advance guard.

While the scouts anticipated the outcome of the meeting, Surby and the others talked with the advance guard from the Sixth Illinois. Several members of the Sixth stood picket, but most sprawled under shade trees at the side of the road. Surby didn't know many men from the Sixth. Uncomfortable seconds passed until he spied Andy Standerfer.

The tall, long-faced Standerfer's eyes met Surby's and he called, "Surby, where you think we'll go from here?"

"Join Grant, I reckon. That's what I'd do, anyhow."

A voice from a rider on the road called "Seen any of the scouts?" It was Lieutenant-Colonel Blackburn.

"Here I am, Colonel," Surby yelled.

"Wanta see you, Sergeant."

"Take it easy, Andy," Surby said, striding toward the waiting Blackburn.

"You do the same, Sarge," Standerfer responded.

"Richard," Blackburn began when Surby was near him, "Colonel is sending four companies to Bahala, east of here on the New Orleans and Great Northern Railroad. It's below Hazlehurst so there could be trouble."

"You mean, Colonel, that the Rebs may be looking for us?" Surby said, sarcasm in his voice.

Blackburn ignored it and said, "That's right, Richard. George Trafton'll be acting major in charge of this detail; he asked for you to go along as scout."

"Fine, Colonel. Be glad to," he lied.

Surby's skin crawled. There'd been too many close calls; too much chance-taking. Buffington was dead. This wasn't the way they were supposed to work! All of them; together. All nine — except now there were only eight.

"Trafton wanted his own man, Sam Nelson, and you to go along," Blackburn continued, "but Colonel Grierson said if he's gonna take you, too, he wanted Nelson to stay with the main column."

"That's good, Colonel," Surby shrugged. Blackburn didn't notice. "Nelson's good a man as I got. He'll do the job."

"All right then, Richard. Get one of the others."

"Right, sir."

As Blackburn rode off, Surby walked into the trees. Robinson and Wood were on the Macon raid, Surby calculated. They've fought enough war for a while. Nelson'll need Corporal Kelly and where Kelly goes, Weedon always tags along. Fowler? Or Steadman?

George Steadman lay under a scrub pine; his mule stood by him nibbling the short pine needles. Steadman's hat hid his face. Steadman heard Lieutenant-Colonel Blackburn ask for the scouts, saw Surby walk onto the road, and hoped for a little more rest before moving again. I could sleep a day, he thought.

"Steadman!" Surby called. "Anybody seen George Steadman? He's a scout," Surby added to no one in particular.

Steadman rolled over, removing his hat with one hand and slapping at the mule's leg with the other, "Get outta here! Doggoned beast," Steadman mumbled. "Here I am, Sarge."

"C'mon, George. We're goin' for a ride."

"What's up?"

"C'mon; tell you later."

Surby and Steadman arrived at the Seventh Illinois' bivouac area just as Captain Trafton, A Company, and three others moved into the road. Surby found Charles Hunting, Captain of A Company, and asked him who the other companies were.

Hunting answered, "Well, let me see, Sarge. There's McDonald and F Company, Webster and H, and Jansen and M. All from Third Battalion," Hunting added, "'cept A."

Surby felt better with A Company along. He'd trained and ridden with most of the men in her. Steadman didn't know anyone in the battalion, but it didn't seem to bother him. Soon, they took their place at the head of the column and in minutes were out ahead finding a dry rout to Bahala.

"Steadman, when are you goin' to get rid of that mule?"

"Got a new one today, Sarge."

"A new one?"

"Yeh, traded the herders this mornin'."

"You goin' to ride a mule through this whole war?"

"Might. Doggoned, if we don't understand each other," Steadman laughed and patted the mule's cropped neck.

The two men rode on in silence. Each taking a turn on the half hour to return to Captain Trafton and inform him that everything was in order. There were no rivers to cross, just an occasional stream. Their route was a virtual wilderness, heavily timbered. The streams, generally mud free, forded easily.

Then, about a mile from Bahala and atop a thickly wooded hill, Surby halted abruptly. Seventy-five yards in front of him were two military tents. He slid slowly from his mount and signaled for Steadman, fifty yards behind, to do the same. Surby gripped his Navy Colt and peered through the low bushed in front of him trying to detect movement. Sweat rolled off his face and tickled his chin as it dripped off. The tents were Confederate.

Satisfied that no one stirred about, Surby got Steadman's attention and motioned for him to return to the advance column to warn Trafton of what lay ahead. Surby stared into the camp area for five more minutes; still no movement. Cautiously, he remounted and rode quietly back to the column that Steadman had halted. Surby met Trafton and explained, "Reb tents dead ahead."

"How many?"

"Two's all I could see."

"Abandoned?"

"Can't tell."

"Well, let's find out."

Trafton called for the company commanders. He ordered A Company to form a skirmish line. To McDonald, Trafton said, "Take your company and move to the right. Webster, take H and go to the left. Jansen, you back up A Company."

Surby and Steadman accompanied the skirmishers, leaving their mounts behind with Jansen's command. As they closed to within a hundred yards, all eyes were on the tents. It has got to be one of two things, Surby concluded. Either there's no one there, or they seen us. He wouldn't let himself think of that.

On the flanks, H Company and F Company were in position one hundred yards away. Slowly the companies converged on the two tents. Still no sign of anything. Suddenly, Steadman burst forward and jerked open a canvas flap. Contents: one sleeping black man.

Nervous laughter rattled through the trees as the men mounted and prepared to move closer to Bahala. Captain Trafton questioned the frightened slave. He was left behind by a squad of Confederate cavalry. They camped here and withdrew the previous day.

"Where to?" Trafton barked.

"Why, suh, they's goin' to Osyka. I's s'posed to watch the tents."

Trafton looked at Surby, "Sergeant, you go ahead and find out what's in that town. Stay out of sight."

Surby and Steadman hurried north along the ridge where the tents stood. Through the trees, they watched the town. Seeing no sign of military activity, they quickly beat a path back to Trafton and the others.

They reported their findings and Trafton asked, "Could we take the town in a charge?"

"Reckon so; couldn't be as much there as in Philadelphia."

"Then that's what we'll do," Trafton replied, nodding.

Ten minutes later, the little Mississippi town was in the hands of four companies of the Seventh Cavalry. The usual procedures began. The depot was burned, the water tank pulled down, trestlework fired, and a steam engine for pumping water and sawing wood was blown up. Captain Trafton captured a Confederate major named Weador and, after a short rest, the four companies and their captive headed west to the road they were to follow to catch Colonel Grierson and the rest of the column.

"Surby, you ever see a sidewindin' mule?" Steadman asked. The two men rode in and out of patches of woods. Steadman's were the first words spoken in over an hour.

"What kinda mule?"

"A sidewindin' mule!" Steadman said. He hated to repeat himself.

"No, can't say's I have."

"Look at this," Steadman screwed himself around in his saddle and pointed to the tracks his mule was leaving. "He don't track."

Surby looked back casually. Sure enough, Steadman's mount was leaving hind marks six inches inside the front hoof prints.

"I'd say you got an unusual mule, George."

"Figure he's a doggoned rarity?"

Surby was no longer interested in this conversation. He worried about rejoining the main column; nevertheless, he answered, "Might be."

"I think he is," Steadman remarked, still looking back at the tracks in the sandy, clay soil.

George Trafton had the four companies force marching. They were making good time. After a short rest at a plantation, they galloped intermittently for several miles and by eight o'clock in the evening, they were following the chewed up road left by Grierson and the main column. Surby reckoned that Grierson couldn't be more than thirty miles ahead. "If they go into camp by nine...let's see; we ought to join up by one or two o'clock," he said aloud.

"Hadn't we better find someone and check directions, Sarge?" Steadman asked. The black night was drawing down quickly now.

"Right, George. First house we see," Surby responded.

Fifteen minutes later, the two scouts approached a log house and drew up before it. Immediately, a lamp glided through the door illuminating its carrier.

Surby called to him.

An old voice answered clearly, "They's thievin' Yanks by here afore noon and hot on their tails was some of you boys."

Surby gulped, trying hard to conceal his surprise. He glanced at Steadman and then back to the man and the lamp. Thinking the old man was mistaken, he asked, "You mean Confederate troops, suh?"

"Cav'ry. Why? Ain't you with 'em?"

"Uh." Surby hesitated. "Uh, huh. We's sent over to Bahala to make sure them Yanks weren't goin' in that direction. I better tell the Major so we can get to catchin' up."

Surby mumbled a "thank you" to the old man. Quickly he and Steadman disappeared into the darkness and returned to report.

Excited, his voice breaking, Surby gave Trafton the news.

"He say how many Rebs there was?" George Trafton asked.

"No, sir. We'll have to try and find that out soon as we can."

"In the meantime, Surby, I'll pass the work to the companies to keep silent. You think we'd better do anything else?"

"Might not hurt to get a couple men from A Company spread out between us and the advance. Then if we spot the Rebs, we won't have to carry the word so far and'll be able to stay out front lookin' for a way to get around 'em just quick as possible," Surby answered.

"All right, Sergeant. I'll tell Cap'n Hunting."

Quickly, Surby and Steadman rode to the head of the column. At a distance of a half mile from their last stop, Surby glimpsed a distant flickering.

"See that light, Sarge?" Steadman whispered, fear in his voice.

"Yeh, I see it! Keep quiet!" Surby demanded. "Wait here; I'll go ahead. You hear shootin', don't come. Ride like ever'thing for Trafton and turn 'im off the road."

Steadman said nothing.

"You know what to do now, George?"

"R-right, Sarge."

"All right. Now I'm goin' ahead. You do exactly as I told you."

Surby sucked in a deep breath. His hand held the Navy Colt; he thumbed the hammer. His shoulders, then his arms twitched. He was uncertain what he'd find; he was scared.

Surby kicked the horse's ribs gently together, they walked down the road toward the dim light. As Surby got closer, he decided he was seeing a candle. A man held it. The candle-bearer shaded his eyes with his free hand and looked toward something to the side of his little cabin. The candle only made an eerie, glowing spot in the blackness, but Surby suspected that there was someone on a horse just beyond the fence.

Fifty yards in front of the house, a gate blocked Surby's advance. The man holding the candle still stood looking in the direction of the fence to Surby's left and within twenty yards of the front stoop of the house.

"Hello!" Surby called. "Step this way." The figure by the fence moved and Surby heard a horse snort.

"Who's there?" the man holding the candle yelled. His voice squeaked.

"A friend. Please step this way, suh. Want to ask you some questions."

Surby glanced about nervously, trying to see the rider in the dark while the candle and the man toddled toward the front gate.

When he could see Sergeant Surby, the man asked, shielding his eyes, "Ain't you a soldier?"

"Sure am. How long since troops passed?"

"You mean Colonel Adams, suh?" the quavering voice responded.

"Yes, and how many's he got with him?"

"Well, I don't know as I can tell. Can't see but a short ways, but there seemed to be a good many pass; then some cannon."

"How long ago?"

"Well, 'bout five hours, or it may be six."

That time must be right, Surby figured. Then he asked, "Who was that man that was talkin' to you when I came up?"

"Well, I really don't know." The old man glanced over his right shoulder. "He's a soldier and a stranger to me. He's inquirin' the way to Port Hudson."

"He leave?"

"Guess so," the man answered Surby.

"Well, good night. I got to be goin'. We got reinforcements for Colonel Adams." Surby hesitated, then added, "Oh, tell that man, if you see 'im, not to be alarmed. The Yankees're all ahead and we expect to overtake 'em tomorrow."

"Hope you do," said the old man. "They took two horses and a mule from me and my neighbor down here lost three mules and one horse, 'sides four of his best workin' hands."

That's nothing new, Surby laughed to himself, as he turned and rode back toward the head of Trafton's column.

In a few minutes, Surby was blurting all that he'd learned to Captain Trafton. Trafton made him repeat it, then started to speak.

"Rider comin'," interrupted Steadman in a whisper.

"Shhh!" Surby insisted. "Halt!" he yelled. "Advance one and give the password."

"I'm all right; I belong to the Confederate Army," a voice answered out of the dark. Then quickly, "Heard you talk with the man at the house."

"Advance and be recognized," Captain Trafton barked.

The rider prodded his horse forward at a lope. He's Confederate all right, Surby could see. Across the pommel, the soldier carried a double-barreled shotgun. Surby moved quickly.

"Ya'll must be worn out; let me have your shotgun."

The Confederate soldier grabbed for the gun, but relaxed when Surby added, "I'll have one of the boys carry it for you." Surby reached to his left and the soldier released the gun as soon as Surby had his hand on it.

Then Trafton said, "This man may be a Yankee for all we know."

"Oh, no, gentlemen; you're mistaken. I'm a lieutenant and belong to Port Hudson. I can tell you all about it and who commands there." He added nervously, "Then, Cap'n you...you can tell if I ain't all right."

"Well," Trafton dragged his words out, "I don't know."

"I'm on my way back to Port Hudson," the soldier replied quickly. "I've been on furlough."

"You just come down this road?" Surby asked.

"Yes, suh."

"See any Yanks?"

"No, but you'll find six men from Wirt Adam's Louisiana Cavalry at the next plantation. They're there on picket."

"All right. But you'd better ride along with us for a ways," Trafton insisted. "C'mon you can ride with these boys here."

Trafton led his prisoner to the head of A Company. The troopers there were all from Southern Illinois, Paris and Edgar County, many of them transplanted Kentuckians and Tennesseeans, one generation removed. They immediately struck up a conversation with the young lieutenant and he rode along casually at the head of the Yankee column, never suspecting that he had become a prisoner.

"This night is as black as...as...," Steadman began.

"As what, George?" Surby asked.

"It's as black as, doggone it, as...I got it! As licorice candy!"

"George Steadman, your mind is always on somethin' to eat," Surby shook his head.

"I can't help it. I's born that way. Say, did you used to eat licorice?"

"Why, sure. Ever' kid did."

"I used to like to get it and roll it up and put it in my pockets in the summer. It'd get real soft. Then I'd stretch it. Lasted longer that way," Steadman added.

Surby stopped his horse. They had not ridden far from where they'd captured the young officer. "You hear somethin', George?"

Steadman's mule stopped two steps later. Both men turned their ears to the side and stared into the black night. Now they could hear it plainly. A rider. They'd heard his saddle squeaking. Surby's revolver hammer opened, followed closely by the soft click of Steadman's.

Then the night rider said, "Hey!"

Surby answered him, "Be recognized!"

"Confederate soldier," he hesitated, then said, "and a lost boy." He laughed. Steadman and Surby moved closer to the rider. Behind him on the horse was a small boy.

"Where you headed?" Surby inquired.

"The boy's hidin' in the barn at the plantation up the road. Lieutenant told me to take 'im home. Lives 'bout six miles down the road, he says."

Surby asked, "That right, boy?"

The little boy said nothing. He appeared about seven or eight years old, the best Surby could make out in the dark.

"Says his name's Brett. Him and his ol' daddy had a run in. Least so that's what he tol' me."

Turning to Steadman, Surby ordered, "Take 'em back a way, Private. At least as far as the Captain. You understand?"

"Uh, oh, all right, Sergeant." Then Steadman spoke calmly to the soldier and the boy, "Follow me."

Soon, the sounds of Steadman and his prisoners faded and Surby clucked his horse forward again. He rode a short distance, slid down from the saddle and walked, leading his horse, for nearly a quarter of a mile. Then he heard Steadman returning. Surby led his horse to the side of the road.

Surby called, "Ever'thing all right, George?"

Instantly, he realized he'd made a mistake! It was Steadman all right, but the mule lunged forward nearly stomping Surby.

"Whoa!" Surby screamed. Steadman screamed too, but Surby couldn't make out what he said. Then Steadman stopped the mule a few yards down the road, dismounted and in seconds came leading the mule toward Surby.

Surby chuckled to himself, but Steadman ignored that and said, "Trafton had me take the doggoned Reb back to M Company. When he got there, I told him he'd have to join us for a spell."

"He su'prised?"

"Didn't say a word. The kid caused a little commotion, but one of them big Germans in M Company 'bout tore 'is ear off gettin' him settled. Ever'thing's all right now though."

"Well," Surby sighed, "we'd better get goin' and find out what we're up against."

"Hadn't we oughta wait for some help? Maybe a couple more guys from the advance? Don't you think?"

"No, George. We'll be better off handlin' it ourselves. Plantation should be just ahead. It's dark enough. Should be able to get as close as we want."

"Just five of 'em left, you figure?"

"If that Reb lieutenant was right." Surby paused, then added. "We ain't goin' to take chances though."

Surby and Steadman remounted and rode slowly into the night. Before they'd ridden more than five minutes, Steadman said, "Light up ahead."

Surby nodded. Soon they could see the light spraying from an open barn door. Then they heard voices.

"Looks like they're at the barn," Steadman said.

Through the open door Surby and Steadman saw three men busy feeding their horses. Then one of the three looked into the dark. He heard Surby and Steadman open the gate and ride into the barn lot.

A carbine and two shotguns stood propped against the fence near the gate. On the ground, in the light from the barn, lay three saddles. Surby pointed to the saddles and Steadman nodded. Only three men in the barn.

A soldier stepped to the door and spoke, "Ya'll just gettin' back?"

Surby looked at Steadman, then drawled, "Yeh."

"See any sign of them Yanks?"

"Same tracks we been follerin' all afternoon."

"They's sure runnin'," the soldier said. He turned and stepped back inside the barn.

Another of the men stepped into the doorway. Surby whispered to Steadman, "Get some men."

Steadman turned to ride away; the man in the door asked, "Where's he goin'?"

Surby ignored the question and called to Steadman, "Tell the Captain that ever'thing's all right and we'll be joinin' Colonel Adams pretty quick."

While Surby and the three conversed, Steadman ran his mule less than two miles to the advance guard. In a few minutes, Steadman and a dozen men from A Company were on their way to the plantation. Nearing the barn, Steadman told them to slow their horses. Casually, they rode up to the gate. The night was still black.

Keeping up a constant chatter about the weather, how tired they were, and their saddle-sore rears, the Union cavalrymen with Steadman dismounted in the road and tied their horses to the fence.

Surby stepped toward the fence and Steadman and two or three of the men with him climbed the gate into the barn lot to meet Surby. Together they walked into the dimly lit barn. Quickly, Surby announced that the three Confederate pickets were prisoners. At the same time, he pulled both Navy Colts from under his coat and punctuated his order by snapping the hammers back.

"What in hell's goin' on here?" one of the prisoners yelled, fear in his voice.

"Why, ya'll are our prisoners," Surby drawled, mimicking the captives.

"Well, I'll be," the youngest of the three Confederates exclaimed. "The Yanks has got us, boys."

Minutes later, after considerable loud cursing, the prisoners were escorted to Captain Trafton and the advancing column.

Six of the dozen men that assisted in the capture now followed Surby up a narrow lane toward the plantation house.

"Visitin' the ladies?" one remarked, smiling.

"Now, boys. They's a lot of shoutin' and cussin' goin' on at the barn. They may be waitin' for us at the house."

The lane from the house to the barn ran about three hundred yards. The men followed Surby through the gate, walking their horses quietly. Suddenly, a hundred yards from the house, Surby called loudly, lashing his horse at the same time, "C'mon men! You know what the captain's orders are. We got to find and bring along ever' man that is stragglin' behind. Ever' man is needed to whip those damn Yankees."

The cavalrymen raced forward, jumped off their mounts and ran through a gate and onto the veranda. They stood to each side of the door as the soldiers in the house, including a lieutenant, came through the front door to investigate the commotion. Immediately, each of the Confederates found his arms locked behind his back by the soldiers that rode in with Surby.

While waiting for Trafton to arrive, Surby sent three men inside the house. The ladies, as usual, were offended by the search. The soldiers chuckled at the ladies, but otherwise went through the routine methodically. The search was over by the time Captain Trafton and the four companies rode in.

The captured guns were stacked on the front porch. Surby told Steadman to destroy them. Sergeant James Vaughn of F Company offered to help Steadman and Steadman said that he didn't care.

Steadman was discouraged. He had ransacked the house for five minutes and found nothing to eat. "This place is what we'd call a starvation farm back home."

Vaughn said, "I'm from Vandalia. Where's 'back home', Steadman?"

"Why, that's...."

"Steadman," Surby interrupted.

"Yeh, Sarge."

"Make sure you unload them guns 'fore you do anything to 'em."

"Right, Sarge."

"Hey, Steadman," Vaughn called, holding a beautiful, hand engraved shotgun to the light. "Think I could keep this shotgun?"

"Sure, guess so. But you'd better ask Surby first."

Vaughn walked from the porch to where Surby and Trafton stood talking. "You should have seen our dandy lieutenant from Port Hudson," Trafton said, laughing.

"Why, what happened?" Surby asked.

"Well, when the prisoners from here were brought out to the road, he saw they were Confederate and asked one of the men what we were doin' takin' them prisoners. He said, 'They ain't Yanks'.

"'No, an' you ain't neither,' one of the men told him and then he cussed, 'Damn me, if I ain't sold!'" Trafton laughed aloud.

"Serves him right, trustin' Yanks," Surby said, shaking his head and smiling.

Vaughn stepped closer. He interrupted, "Surby, all right if I keep this shotgun?"

"Why sure, but you'll just get tired of it. Let me see it."

Vaughn handed the gun to Surby. Surby held it up, trying to look at it in the gleam of the lantern on the porch. Then handing it back to Vaughn, Surby said, "Awful heavy ain't it?"

"Yeh, but I been lookin' for one just like this. Shame to smash it."

"All right," Surby said and then turned to carry on his conversation with Trafton.

Vaughn smiled and walked to the porch. He picked up two of the shotguns that Steadman hadn't carried to a nearby tree where he was busy smashing the stocks. Vaughn handed the guns to Steadman.

"You keepin' that one?" Steadman asked, nodding to the gun Vaughn held in his left hand.

"Surby said I could."

Fifteen minutes later, the companies mounted and rode out the lane. As Surby neared the gate, a shotgun blast rocked the night. His first instinct was to jump down and lay flat along the fence.

Almost immediately, someone from the back of the column yelled, "Vaughn? You shot?"

Surby sped down the lane toward the house. Laying on the ground, one of the cavalrymen standing over him with a candle, was Sergeant James Vaughn. The broken shotgun lay by his side, the stock toward a tree.

"What happened?" Surby asked.

A voice in the dark said, "He's just goin' to get rid of that ol' shotgun; oh Jesus."

Surby shook his head and knelt. One barrel had gone off sending buckshot into Vaughn's thigh. The blood gushed from the torn wound.

Captain Trafton rode up and dismounted, "How is he?"

"Doesn't look worth a damn, sir. It's his leg," one of the men answered.

Trafton swore, then he said, "Well, take 'im to the house and make damn sure those girls'll take care of 'im. He can't travel like that."

Trafton assigned two of Vaughn's friends from F Company to see that he was settled in. They were to catch up as soon as possible. The column was ordered to continue their march in pursuit of Grierson and the main command.

Surby and Steadman rode silently for the next hour or so. The black night was lit some by a few stars that were showing through the thin overcast now. Both men thought of Vaughn.

"'Spect he'll die?" Steadman said finally.

Surby didn't answer.

At a crossroads, Surby and Steadman halted, allowing the column to catch up. They feared a wrong turn. Trafton soon joined them and while they discussed the direction they would take, five horsemen rode toward them on a trot. They were strangers. Without a word, they halted before Trafton and Surby.

Surby had his pistol cocked and the strangers no sooner arrived than ten men from A Company surrounded them.

Trafton spoke first, "Boys, you're our prisoners!"

One of the prisoners tried to wheel his horse, but Steadman had slipped in beside him and unknown to the man had a grip on his reins. Other than that, there was the usual surprise and swearing. As usual,

Trafton's command had taken more prisoners. Two more incidents of a similar nature took place a short time later.

At this hour, midnight, it seemed the countryside was crawling with Confederate soldiers, pickets and couriers. With a sort of impatience, George Trafton prodded his men forward. At the head of the column, scouting their path, George Steadman and Richard Surby poked their way forward avoiding trouble whenever possible. The serious air of determination that surrounded Surby was not matched by Steadman. Never, on other nights, had there been so much activity. Steadman was frightened. Time and again, he broke the quiet rhythm of the plodding mounts, "Sarge, I'm doggoned near scared to death."

Chapter 11

...Lawyer Mosby, the guide

No trees, no wind, no sound whispered in the black night; and if any noise would have exploded, Surby, and especially Steadman, would have screamed. They rode cautious. They rode scared. Both men yearned for information...a guide, if possible.

Finally, a few minutes after midnight, Sergeant Richard Surby decided he could stand the quiet no longer. He spoke softly to George Steadman, "I think we ought to try and get around 'em. Sooner or later, we're goin' to run into a patrol that's jumpy and they're goin' to shoot, then talk later. You stay up here, George; I'm goin' to talk to Captain Trafton."

"Don't stay away too doggoned long," Steadman muttered. He rode on as Surby left him. Intermittently, he held his breath and listened. Somewhere out there between him and Grierson was the enemy. But where? he wondered. Finally, he halted the mule and waited.

In a few minutes — it seemed longer to Steadman, Surby returned. The two men walked their mounts side by side as Surby said, "Captain wants us to try an' find out from somebody how many men there was with Adams' Cavalry."

"Think there's a plantation up ahead," Steadman remarked.

"Where?"

"Through there. There's a gate."

"Yeh, but where's the main house?"

The two men strained their eyes in the dim, starlit night. Finally, Surby added, "I see it. Just a one-room shack, looks like."

"Where?" Steadman asked, then, "Yeh, I see it, too."

The mule and the horse walked to the gate. Surby hopped down from his horse and told Steadman to get someone from the column. "Tell Trafton to stop when he sees our horses on the road."

While Steadman was gone, Surby stood looking at the house. No light; no sound. Then Steadman and another soldier were back. Surby explained, "I'll go to the door. You two stand to the side and don't let anybody get out."

The three men climbed the fence and walked the two hundred yards to the house. It was a neat little log house with a porch. Surby climbed the steps and knocked loudly on the door.

A voice from inside said, "Who's there?"

"A soldier. My captain sent me here to find out somethin' about the roads and how long since Colonel Adams passed. We're tryin' to overtake Colonel Adams with reinforcements.

"Come on in," the sleepy voice called.

Surby turned the knob; the door was unlocked. He kept his left hand on the butt of one of the Navy Colts under his coat. A dull glow from the fireplace lit the small room with its table, mirror, chairs, and bed.

"Light that candle on the table and sit down."

Surby did as he was told, taking the fireplace into close companionship. The man remained in bed. Then Surby bent forward, his elbows on his knees, and, first looking all around, said in a low voice, "Live alone here?"

"Sure do," he nodded. "I'm a lawyer. Bought this place a while back. Got little money, but someday I'll own everything hereabouts."

"You practice law here in Copiah County?" Surby asked, not sure if he was still in the county he named.

"Yes." The lawyer hesitated. He looked to be about thirty-five years old. Nice looking man, Surby thought. The man sat up in bed and said, "Well, you say you're a soldier and that your captain has sent you here to obtain information about Colonel Adams."

"And the condition of the roads," Surby broke in.

"Yes," the lawyer continued, "and the condition of the roads. But now, sir, before answering your questions, I'll ask you a few. To whose command do you belong?"

"Colonel Faulkner's First Mississippi Cavalry, stationed at Granada and sent by railroad to Jackson to assist in intercepting the Yankees at Pearl River," Surby spun the answer without hesitation.

"Is Colonel Faulkner in command of this force?" pursued the lawyer.

"No, sir. Major William's in command."

"What happened at the Pearl?"

"We arrived too late; the Yankees had crossed. We were ordered by a dispatch from General Pemberton to pursue the enemy and, if possible, fall in with Colonel Adams and report to him."

"What's your force?"

"We number about two hundred men, well armed and uniformed. Fought several battles with the enemy. Some of the men've captured Yankee clothing sufficient to clothe themselves with," Surby added.

The lawyer did not speak. Surby watched his eyes cautiously.

"One thing bothers me," he said, staring into Surby's eyes. "You don't speak like a Southern man," the lawyer suddenly blurted.

"That is easily accounted for. I'm from Missouri. Belonged to Jeff Thompson's command. When he disbanded, I came to West Tennessee and joined this command."

Surby paused, then starting to rise, added, "But I must not delay. Can you send a Negro along to guide us through to Union Church?"

"I have several blacks, but my horses and mules are not here. I received news that the Yankees are comin' this way and I didn't want to lose 'em. I'd go myself if I had my riding horse here. I'm acquainted with Colonel Adams and this reinforcement's a capital idea."

The lawyer paused and looked to the ceiling of the little cabin, his black, penetrating eyes rolled back in his head, his lower jaw swayed from side to side.

"Yes," he continued, "I would like to go — the Colonel stopped here half an hour and rested his column."

"Do you know, sir, how much force Colonel Adams had?" Surby asked quickly.

"About four hundred men, with six pieces of artillery. He left here about sundown. He figured he'd catch the Yanks and attack about three o'clock. There's a force from Port Hudson supposed to meet the front of the Yankee force on the Natchez road."

That settled it! Surby knew they had to have the lawyer now. He said calmly, "I would like it very much you would accompany us—I can mount you on a good horse."

With that the lawyer sprang out of bed, "I think that a capital idea. I will go." Pulling his pants on, he continued, "Be ready in five minutes. You'll find a saddle, bridle, and sheepskin on the door steps."

"What can I call you, sir?" Surby asked.

"My name's Mosby."

"Well, Mr. Mosby, I'll step out and tell the Major and have a horse brought up for you."

Sergeant Surby exited the house, picked up the saddle, and nodded for the men to follow him. "Watch the house," Surby said when he neared the fence. "Don't let him run out. He's goin' with us."

"We heard," Steadman said and snickered.

Shortly, Captain Trafton listened to Surby's good fortune, called for a man to get a horse, and asked another to get him a long gray coat and a gray cap. Many of Trafton's command wore Confederate clothes now. Their own Union blues were wearing out rapidly — and besides, the stench got more unbearable.

Everyone was ready and waiting when Mosby exited the house, strode to the fence, and jumped over. Surby introduced him to "Major Williams" (George Trafton) and the two men immediately struck up a friendly conversation about their mutual acquaintance, Colonel Wirt Adams. "Williams" declared that he knew both Wirt and his brother, Daniel, from when they "fit together" at Shiloh.

Surby left the two at the head of the column and resumed his position with Steadman on the point. As close as Surby could figure, it was twelve miles to Union Church. They must reach Grierson before three o'clock.

"Twelve miles in less than three hours! Near impossible," Surby calculated aloud.

"What's that?" Steadman asked.

"Oh, nothin', George; just thinkin' out loud."

Two more patrols were captured — and slowed their progress. Surby kept them off the road until Captain Trafton and Mr. Mosby had passed so Mosby would not detect what they were doing. After the second group was deposited with M Company, Surby rode alongside Trafton and Mosby.

At length, Surby interrupted their conversation by asking, "Mr. Mosby, where do you think Colonel Adams'll stop to feed and prepare before attacking?"

"Probably near the Fayette road on a plantation there. 'Bout four miles from here."

"Do you think it'd be possible for a person to get around his camp without being discovered? I mean, I was thinkin', if I could reach as near the Yanks as possible and find their position, then it'd be great advantage to us and Colonel Adams."

"No, that's impossible. You'd never get around Adams' camp and return in time. The land is too rough 'round here."

Mosby paused and then added, "But never you mind, I'm well acquainted with Colonel Adams and I'll go with you and pass you through the lines. Then you can have a good road to proceed on."

"I'll think about that." Then Surby asked Trafton, "Major Williams, sir, what time is it?"

Without looking at his watch, Trafton answered, "About one."

"Mr. Mosby, I'll return if I conclude to go through Colonel Adams' camp."

Ahead of the column and nearing the added scout that was riding between the advance and the point, Surby said aloud to himself, "I've got to go—Grierson's got to know."

The scout in front of him stopped and when Surby caught up, he informed him of his plans. "Me and Steadman are goin' ahead. We want to look at the Reb camp 'bout four miles up the road. If we can get through to Grierson, we will."

"Sure you will, Sarge."

"Ditto? Is that you?"

"Yeh, Sarge. Ross got sick; I took his place."

The two men rode together a ways. Surby talked about what a "fix" they'd gotten themselves into. Ditto sensed Surby was depressed, "C'mon Sarge. We'll get out of this."

"Yeh, Ditto, but I've got a funny feelin' I'm not goin' to."

Ditto didn't respond. Then abruptly, Surby said, "Well, I gotta get goin'. If I don't come back, tell Colonel Blackburn that I...," Surby lapsed into thought.

"Forget it, Sarge. You'll make it," Ditto interrupted moments later. "Hell, your own men couldn't even kill you the other night. No damned Reb goin' to get you." Ditto laughed and wondered about his own possibilities of surviving this raid.

"Yeh, well," Surby began, "I gotta go, like I said."

"See you, Sarge."

"Sure."

Not far ahead, Surby found George Steadman. "C'mon, George. We're goin' for a ride."

"Sarge, just as soon you didn't say that any doggone more."

"What's that?"

"Just goin' for a ride. Ever' time you say that we get in a mess."

Surby shook the reins and gently touched up his horse. If we get caught, he thought, they'll shoot us! These stinking rags will get us shot. Surby shook his head, then his mind continued, what would my folks think? And my brothers? Wonder what—

"If we don't get to Grierson, you expect he'll be able to hold them Rebs off?" Steadman asked, interrupting Surby's thoughts.

"They'll be awful tired to fight at three o'clock in the mornin', even if we get to 'em in time. Pickets prob'ly be half asleep too."

It was pitch black in the tunnel of trees the two men rode through. Steadman's mule had one white stocking. Steadman said, every time he looked at it, "Ain't that weird?"

But now, as Surby looked down, he didn't see the stocking. It was too dark even though Steadman rode in the wagon track to his right.

"We ought to be gettin' to Adams' camp in 'bout half a mile."

"Gonna talk your way in?" Steadman asked.

"Don't think so. Rather get around 'em."

In the road ahead, both men heard something. Both scouts' mounts stopped. They stood motionless. Surby and Steadman listened to the night. In front of them in the tree-covered lane several riders approached, laughing and talking. Should they run or stand their ground? Could they get off the road without being heard? Steadman could hardly breathe. His heart pounded.

When the riders drew within what seemed twenty-five yards, Steadman was startled by Surby's steady command, "Halt!"

The talk and laughter broke off abruptly. The light from a break in the trees over the riders' heads let Surby see movement. Their horses were in a line across the narrow road. There was a glint of what had to be their weapons. The sharp clicks of hammers locking, ready to kill, confirmed it.

"Who comes there?" Surby called.

"Friends," a voice drawled.

"Advance one and give the countersign!" Now Surby's voice was not so steady and Steadman contemplated running.

There was silence for a few seconds and then one of the riders drawled through his nose, "Ain't got no countersign!" At the same time, a horse and rider moved. He was coming closer to Surby and Steadman.

Another span of uncomfortable seconds passed. The rider who closed on Surby and Steadman stopped and called, "Who are you? You alone?"

"I'm a scout. Got a man with me. Column'll be up in a few minutes. We been tryin' to catch Colonel Adams. Been ridin' all day," Surby volunteered, the fear gone from his voice again.

"All right! Ya'll found 'im. We belong to ol' Wirt Adams' Cav'ry and tomorrow we intend to give the Yanks hell. Ain't that right boys?" he called to the others in his group. They laughed, relieved that it wasn't the enemy they faced.

The one that spoke with a nasal drawl asked, "What force ya'll with?"

"Major Williams is commandin' the column. We's from Faulkner's Fust Miss'sippi. Tried to catch the Yanks on the Pearl," Surby said, his drawl thick now.

The third man said, "Them Yanks had 'em a fight last evenin' at Union Church. Ol' Wirt's gone to get troops from the river. Gonna take them Yanks 'tween Fayette and Union Church in the mornin'. They're tryin' to make Natchez, but they's gonna get slipped up."

"What you doin' here then?" Surby croaked.

"Left us behind so's we could tell anybody where to join up with the Colonel."

"Well, I'd better go tell the Major that ya'll's here. Else, might be an accident or somethin'."

"Right smart idea. We'll wait for ya'll."

Ditto and the others were surprised to see Surby, but after a quick explanation, they rode to where Steadman waited with the three. As soon as Surby and the others arrived, they informed the Confederates they were prisoners and disarmed them.

Quickly and quietly, Surby led them off into the timber by the road side. In a few minutes, the column — and Mr. Mosby — passed and the prisoners were turned over to M Company.

Surby and Steadman rode past Mosby on their way to the front of the column. Mosby called out, "Sergeant, who were those men that you had beside the road?"

"Just some Yanks. They were stragglin'. Probably plunderin' the homes her'bouts. Said they got lost. But I don't believe it."

"They ought to be shot. I think that a capital idea. Men like that shouldn't be allowed to live. Imagine, lootin' and plunderin' these poor folks."

"Oh, I agree, Mr. Mosby. Where's Major Williams?"

"He rode ahead a piece. You'll find him up there," Mosby said pointing.

"See you later, Mr. Mosby. Oh, by the way, Adams has gone to Fayette for more troops," Surby said as he and Steadman headed into the night looking for Captain Trafton.

They found Trafton talking to one of the scouts from A Company and by the time Surby and Steadman arrived, Trafton had the information about Adams.

Trafton was overjoyed. The Reb force with Wirt Adams no longer lay in their path. An hour before, he was worried, like Surby, that all was lost. Now it would — or at least, should — be clear all the way to Grierson and the others.

Mosby soon joined the group. He asked Captain Trafton. "Do you intend to join Colonel Adams or follow up the Yanks?"

"Why, Mr. Mosby, that question is one I've thought a great deal about," Trafton answered, his head cocked quizzically.

Mosby seemed puzzled, but asked, "And what is your decision, sir?"

"I think I'll send a courier through to Colonel Adams and tell him that we'll support his frontal attack with an attack to the rear ourselves."

Mosby clapped his hands, "Oh, Major. I think that a capital idea and I must be the one to take the message to Colonel Adams."

"No, Mr. Mosby. I couldn't let you do that," Captain Trafton said, shaking his head dramatically.

"But I must, Major," Mosby insisted, smiling.

"It is far too risky, sir," said Surby to Trafton.

"Sergeant, you're right." Addressing himself to Mosby, Trafton said, "Sir, I just can't permit it." Then again to Surby, Trafton said matter-of-factly. "Sergeant, you send a courier to Colonel Adams. Please return when you've sent him and report to me."

"Yes, sir, Major," Surby responded as he whipped his horse back along the column.

After riding for a time with H Company, Surby returned to the head of the column, Mr. Mosby and George Trafton.

"Your order's been obeyed, sir," Surby reported and without hesitation continued on his way to where Steadman scouted for the column.

Near Steadman, Surby called out, "George? Hey, George?"

"Yeh, Sarge?"

"We made it!"

"You're right, Sarge."

"What's first thing you're goin' to do when we get back?"

"Eat! Man, I'm pig hungry and sow mean."

Surby laughed loudly and said, "I should've known."

Surby and Steadman were almost giddy in their conversation. The long hours without rest, the fear and tension, and the hunger had drained their strength. Most of the soldiers in the column had suffered the same hardships, but the loneliness of riding the point could never compare with the companionship in a marching column. The worry of whether one's manner of speech was sufficient to fool the enemy and, even worse, the constant knowledge that the safety of two hundred or more men depended on how well the job of advance scouting was done, caused tension to build in the scouts that nearly caused collapse.

A brisk gallop brought Steadman and Surby in sight of the twinkling light of the camp just as they broke over a rise. The Sixth and Seventh Illinois Cavalries lay just ahead. "I'm goin' ahead to warn the pickets we're comin' in, George. Be back in a few minutes."

When the first call of "Halt!" was issued and the password offered, the men of B Company of the Sixth Illinois went wild. "Trafton's back; Trafton's back!" they yelled. By the time Surby reached the main camp, several men were up and looking into the darkness trying to see who had ridden in. They wanted news of their friends.

Sam Nelson was one of the first to get to Surby. Surby told him to pass the word that there was a Confederate guide, a civilian, with the column that thought he was "rendering valuable service to the Confederate States of America."

Surby continued, "Be sure and spread the word to the rest of the men. They should watch themselves until the head of Trafton's command passes."

"Uh, huh, Sarge. Ever'one — uh — make it back?" Sam inquired.

"We had to leave Vaughn from F Company. Accident. Took a load of buckshot in the leg."

"We — uh — got shot up here last night," Nelson said.

"I heard. Anybody killed?"

"No — uh — nothing serious."

"Don't forget to tell ever'body to keep quiet 'til the advance moves by," Surby said. "I've got to get back."

"All right — uh..., Sarge. I'll tell 'em," Sam called as Surby rode away.

Surby warned the pickets on his way back to the column. He then rode briskly to where Mr. Mosby and George Trafton were. Surby wanted to see how Mosby would react when the pickets came into view.

As the first picket was passed, Mosby, somewhat startled, said, "I didn't know that there was a Confederate force near."

"Oh, Mr. Mosby. It's only one company. They were sent down the east side of the railroad. They were expecting us."

"Well, Sergeant, that is a capital idea," Mosby replied.

George Trafton fished his watch from his pocket and looked at it in the first light of day in the quiet, little village of Union Church, Mississippi. The sun would soon focus on a beautiful white church overlooking rolling hills and forest. Sprawled on the grass were the men of Grierson's raiders, most sound asleep in the warm, pleasant morning air.

Captain Trafton's men dismounted and began feeding their horses, while Trafton tied his horse and reported to Colonel Grierson.

"Come with me, Mr. Mosby," Surby requested. Then he led the lawyer-guide near the veranda of the town house that served as Grierson's headquarters. There, the two men sat for a while discussing the weather and "what a fine day it was for killin' Yanks."

In a short while, Adjutant Sam Woodward stepped onto the veranda and called for a guard to bring the prisoners to sign their parole papers.

A table was placed on the porch and a chair brought out of the house. In a few minutes, the prisoners lined up at the opposite end of the veranda.

Surby watched as Mosby's face turned from hatred and contempt for the "damned Yankee" prisoners to one of puzzlement — and then amazement. "Why — why, Sergeant. I think I know one of those men. May I go see?"

"Why certainly, Mr. Mosby," Surby answered and then added, "that would be a capital idea."

Mosby glared at Surby and then at the prisoners and then back to Surby. Then he stood and walked toward the men, now crowding around the table to get their names on the parole papers. One of the prisoners turned and looked at Mosby when he walked up. He smiled and said, "Why, friend Mosby. You here? I didn't expect to see you a prisoner."

Mosby smiled and said, "Why? Explain. What do you mean?" Mosby looked around the grounds; fear wiped the smile away. "Are these not our troops?"

"Our troops? Oh, no," the soldier said laughing. "I wish they were; I'd feel a damned sight better than I do now. No sir. They are the genuine Yankees, but they'll not do anything with you. You're a citizen, not a soldier."

The prisoner paused while Mosby, hands on hips, surveyed the scene in the yard. Mosby said, "I don't believe it. I just don't believe it."

"I am surprised, lawyer Mosby, that you had not noticed the difference," the prisoner commented.

Mosby, a scowl spreading over his face, looked across the veranda at Sergeant Surby. Dropping his hands to his sides, Mosby walked briskly toward Surby. Two feet in front of Surby he stopped and shouted; his eyes blazed fire and hatred, "this is a damned Yankee trick."

Surby slapped his thighs, bent forward, stumbled backward, and nearly ended up on the ground laughing. He regained his composure and shuffled back to where Mosby stood, his face flushed now. Surby put his hands on Mosby's shoulders and said solemnly, "Mr. Mosby, you are sold, but it is all fair in war times. And don't you think that is a capital idea?"

The blood left Mosby's face; he had ample time for reflection. His mouth twitched a little. At first he was full of revenge, but as he got cooler, that didn't seem to him a project worthy of a gentleman. He shrugged his shoulders, "Sergeant, you have done well. But for God's sake, don't ever mention this to any person."

"All right, but it'll be awfully hard to keep."

Then the two men had a good laugh, Surby explaining the events of the previous ride. Finally, Surby asked, "How are you goin' to get home?"

"Well, it's too far to walk."

"I'll speak to the Colonel and see if I can get you a horse. We generally turn loose several each morning."

"Fine, that would be a capital idea!" he added, laughing.

Surby got the necessary permission from Grierson, had a horse saddled, and presented it to Mosby. "Keep this horse as a remembrance of the Yankees," Surby offered.

"That I will do, Sergeant. And thank you, sir. Yours was not quite the equal of Southern hospitality, but it will certainly do."

"And I thank you, Mr. Mosby."

The Sixth and Seventh Illinois Cavalry regiments exited the little village of Union Church as Mosby rode back along the road toward Hazlehurst Station. It was six o'clock, a beautiful morning, and Sergeant Richard Surby was glad to be alive.

While George Trafton's special detachment had been traveling thirty more miles than the main column during the previous twenty-four hours, Grierson's command had its share of trouble, too. In the course of their march the previous day, their direct route toward Union Church had been an easy one. But two miles from the quaint village nestled around the beautiful church atop a hill, the column met the enemy.

Surby learned that Companies A, C, and D of the Sixth Illinois, with Captains Alonzo D. Pierce, James D. Angley, and First Lieutenant Joseph Coker commanding, were in the advance and met one hundred and fifty Confederate soldiers. A, C, and D were able to drive the enemy through Union Church to a point a mile west of the village. Several confederate prisoners were taken and at least two wounded. The Union companies had one man wounded.

The Confederate force held off for the remainder of the night. Obviously waiting for Wirt Adam's reinforcements, Surby knew.

The plan for ambushing Grierson's column was being thwarted now as Surby and the Butternut Guerillas checked the path ahead. The direction led not to Natchez — as Adams expected, but toward the southeast and back to the railroad.

For the first three or four miles out of Union Church, the riders dodged through pine forests avoiding any signs of life that might give away their whereabouts or purpose. First, Surby led the column south, then west, southwest, southeast, and, at times, even north. The compass pointed in all directions, but the tendency was always toward the southeast and Brookhaven on the New Orleans and Great Northern Railroad.

When Surby, as per instructions from Lieutenant-Colonel William Blackburn, felt the column was out of danger from spies, he led them onto the main road to Brookhaven and valuable time was gained in their race for life. They discovered a Rebel military train hauling commissary supplies and pulled by oxen and mules and it slowed the advance of the column, but supplied the men with needed food. The train was destroyed.

Within four miles of Brookhaven, Steadman and Nelson easily coerced five Confederate guerrillas into letting them examine their weapons. Then they took them prisoners. Surby was ecstatic that they'd worked the trick so well when they were outnumbered five to two.

A short time later, a house was searched. Steadman and Nelson turned up eight shotguns and rifles and three revolvers. The inhabitants knew they were faced with "Yanks" from the outset of the encounter. Surby and the Butternut Guerillas had no time to play a game. They moved quickly.

The extent of their foray into enemy territory was turning their earlier bravado into caution. Besides, speed was becoming a necessary tool if Grierson and the column was going to escape through Mississippi without extreme losses.

About two miles from their objective, Brookhaven, Blackburn overtook Surby. He halted the Morgan in a cloud of dust and said, "Richard, want you to go ahead and see what's in Brookhaven. Don't want to take a chance on a Reb concentration of troops there that could strike the column with the men the shape they're in."

"Right, Colonel. I'll take Nelson and the others and leave Steadman."

"Fine, Richard, but remember: use caution!"

"Right," Surby nodded.

Within minutes, the seven scouts galloped toward the town of fifteen hundred population. The early afternoon sun beat down on them and hot dust rose from the hooves of their mounts as they drew to within a mile of Brookhaven.

Just ahead in the road, Surby spotted several men walking. Their civilian "uniforms" and lack of weapons belied the fact that they were indeed regular army troops.

"Where ya'll headin'?" Surby inquired.

One, a tall, lean boy of nineteen or twenty, drawled, his voice high pitched, "Why, Port Hudson. Gonna help Gen'ral Pembe'ton 'gainst them Yanks what's tryin' to take ol' Vicksbu'g."

"Why that's right nice ya'll," Surby responded and then to Fowler, Surby ordered, "Private, take these here boys to the Captain and see they's fed proper."

"Follow me, boys," Uriah Fowler smiled, turning his horse back toward the column. There were eight more prisoners this time and Surby sighed relief, then wondered how much longer their luck was going to hold.

As the Butternut Guerillas rode out of a wooded area and down a long sloping hill, they had their first look at Brookhaven. The sun shone from the shimmering rooftops and here and there in the streets they could see small groups moving about — apparently civilians. South of town in the distance, there were a number of tents glaring white through the trees on a rise. The scouts waited, scanning the area for several minutes. Satisfied that there were only civilians scattered about town on this sunny Wednesday afternoon, Surby returned to the head of the column and reported his observations.

Within four hundred yards of town, a shot rang out from a clump of trees to the left of the column. Immediately an officer gave the order for the column of fours to charge and in minutes, the Seventh galloped through the streets of Brookhaven. The Sixth rode off south, the direction of the tent-covered hill.

In town, the citizens were alarmed at the sight of the Union soldiers, their guns blazing and swords flashing in the hot sun, and fled into their homes. There was no resistance. The shot from the woods was merely a signal to alert the citizens of the enemy's approach.

South of town on the hill, the Sixth found nothing but tents and a few guards and convalescents. The Confederate soldiers were outnumbered and showed no desire to fight. A force of fifteen thousand Confederate soldiers could have bivouacked in the facilities there. To the Sixth's relief, their dashing charge into the training camp was in vain. The last of the trainees were ordered away the day before, Grierson's men found later.

As the Sixth rested their horses under the trees shading the abandoned camp, the Seventh destroyed a dozen freight cars, a railroad bridge, and the depot. A short time later, E and F Companies of the Sixth, under the command of Captain John Lynch of Olney, Illinois, set out to destroy railroad trestles for one mile north of town.

There were still some Confederate soldiers in town, but all were from a hospital and eager to be paroled so their service would end. Some civilians offered to surrender themselves to the "Yanks." Once captured and paroled, the Southerners felt they could avoid the hated conscription into military service.

Lieutenant-Colonel Blackburn busied himself with other matters. He had an overstuffed pocket of Confederate dollars captured earlier. He set out to organize a party for the First Battalion of the Seventh Illinois.

At a hotel, Blackburn convinced the owner that he could feed two hundred men in the short time Grierson planned to remain in Brookhaven. The owner recruited additional help from the streets, bought extra food and in a short time, was serving Blackburn's First Battalion. The honored guest turned out to be none other than the head of the Butternut Guerillas, Richard Surby.

The meal was the first hot food many had eaten in days. Sergeant Surby stood, with encouragement, attempted a speech, but gave up when two hundred men applauded and cheered, and sat down in favor of another plate of fried sausage, eggs and hot bread.

An hour later, as Surby exited the hotel with Blackburn, the hotel owner mopped his brow and called after them, "I wish you Yanks'd come ever'day."

Blackburn swept his hat off in a gallant gesture and said, "My dear man, for the delicacies which your establishment is now noted, I would return from Hell to feast with you."

Surby began laughing, grabbed Blackburn by the belt from behind, and said, "C'mon, Colonel. Let's get outta here 'fore he thinks we're candidates for an asylum."

"Right you are, my good man," Blackburn smiled through his heavy black beard.

That night, six miles south of Brookhaven, the general topic of conversation was the hospitality shown the soldiers during their stay in Brookhaven. Everyone agreed that Brookhaven was no Philadelphia.

"Why doggoned if they didn't treat us jus' like we's folks," George Steadman remarked as he slid the saddle from his mule for the first time in thirty-eight hours.

Two hours after sunset, the camp of Colonel Benjamin Grierson's column was sound asleep. A few pickets somehow stayed awake; but the stamping horses, the occasional barking of the dog which followed the commissary wagon, and the hooting of a distant owl disturbed no one on the grounds of Gill's Plantation.

Chapter 12

...the balm of a thousand flowers

Sergeant Richard Surby, his eyes open, lay on his back staring. He saw a large oak tree, but only dimly in the first streaks of dawn. Where am I, he wondered silently. Then it came to him. Gill's Plantation — in Mississippi. Nearby, he detected movement. Somewhere someone dipped a sock filled with coffee into boiling water. The aroma caused him to raise his head and shoulders from his saddle-pillow.

A small, but blazing fire ten yards away cast its light over George Steadman. Another dozen or so flowing fires sparkled and danced throughout the campgrounds. Then Surby looked back into the sky. It was time to get up. He stood and flapped his arms several times trying to drive the stiffness from his back and shoulders. This is the thirteenth day since we left La Grange, Tennessee, he reckoned.

"Sarge, that you?" Steadman called, staring into the shadows.

"Yeh, George."

"Want some coffee?"

"It done?"

"Just about."

Surby felt around on the ground, then walked toward the fire. "Sure got the makin's of a pretty day," Surby said, approaching Steadman, boots in hand.

"Awful quiet too, this mornin'," Steadman continued. "Think we'll try and join Grant?"

"Don't know. Colonel Blackburn thinks we'll go there if we get word that Grant's attackin'," Surby yawned. "Wouldn't be any good otherwise. We'd never get 'cross to the west side of the Mississippi, if he's not."

"Where we goin' to go then? New Orleans?"

"Might be," Surby yawned again, rubbing his eyes.

Steadman poured two tin cups of coffee and set one beside Surby who was busy pulling his boots over his damp and swollen feet.

"Hey, Sarge?" Sam Nelson called, sleepily.

"Time to get up, Sam," Steadman responded.

"All right, I'm comin'. Uh, pour me some of that coffee."

Within a few minutes, it seemed the entire camp began to stir. A lamp lit the window on the right side of the veranda of Gill's plantation house. The men of the Sixth and Seventh Illinois knew what that meant. They hurried to eat breakfast and prepare to move out within twenty to thirty minutes.

Just a while later, Lieutenant-Colonel Bill Blackburn stepped off the veranda. He walked straight toward the Butternut Guerillas. Surby watched the big man take long strides, speaking an occasional "Good Morning" and "How you boys today?" to the men of his First Battalion, Seventh Illinois Cavalry, as he approached.

"We're gonna move 'long the railroad again this mornin', Richard."

"How far to the next station?" Surby asked.

"Be about three-, maybe four-hour ride. Real small town — Bogue Chitto."

"When's the column movin'?"

Looking at the eastern sky, then at his pocket watch, Blackburn said, "Colonel wants us movin' by sunup. Be about twenty-five or thirty minutes."

"All right. Me and the boys'll be fed and movin' by then."

"Good, Richard." Blackburn paused, then studied the campground. "Oh, Richard. If I's you I'd keep a fresh horse under me as often as I could change."

"Could you have herders bring horses closer to the front?"

"Think we can do that. Colonel'll want the two regiments to change more often now too. Maybe we can run 'em between the regiments."

"That'd be fine."

"We'll see you then. Take care yo'self," Blackburn added as he turned toward the house.

By the time the Butternut Guerillas finished breakfast, coffee and crackers, the Sixth Illinois was forming in the advance for the day's march. Surby sent Nelson to the veranda to tell the officers that the scouts were riding out.

On the veranda, the owner of the plantation spoke to Colonel Grierson, Major Starr, and Lieutenant-Colonel Loomis.

Nelson stood at the steps and heard him say, "Well, boys, I can't say I have anything 'gainst you."

"Glad you feel that way, sir," Grierson said.

"You haven't taken nothin' of mine 'cept a little corn for your horses and that you're welcome to. I been hearin' 'bout you from all over the country. You're doin' the boldest thing ever done."

"Well, thank you."

"But you'll be trapped though. You'll be trapped, mark me."

"Why, Mr. Gill," Mathew Starr said, "with the best corn in southern Mississippi, how can you think our horses could ever fail us." Starr laughed.

"Major, it's a hundred miles to Yankee forces. Ever' five miles, you're goin' to run into Confederate forces." Turning to Colonel Grierson, Gill continued, "Suh, I've nothin' against you, but you've performed an insult on the South. Your column is marked. You'll be trapped, I tell you. It can be none other."

"Perhaps so, Mr. Gill. We'll see, won't we?" Grierson wheeled and walked briskly from the porch.

Nelson caught Grierson's eye.

Grierson asked, "What is it, Nelson?"

"We're...uh...fixin' to move out; the scouts, I mean, sir."

"Fine. The column'll follow in five minutes."

Sam Nelson led his horse to where Surby and the scouts sat mounted and waiting. He climbed into his saddle and it wasn't long until they were ahead of the Sixth — the advance — and moving cautiously along the railroad track.

The promise of the dawn held true. It was a beautiful day. It would be hot, but for the next few hours, the yellow-brown dust that rose from the horses' hooves was mellowed by the dew that soaked the earth during the night.

Black, spiraling smoke marked the path of the column southward along the tracks. Trestles were kindled by the advance and fired by the rear guard.

About nine o'clock, the two tracks ran into one, forming an iron arrow pointing at the dozen or so buildings that marked the next objective of the cavalrymen, Bogue, Chitto. Minutes later, they arrived unmolested. The depot flamed and collapsed quickly, but a long, high railroad bridge and two hundred and fifty feet of trestlework were not so swiftly conquered.

The main column continued on its way while this job was completed. The Butternut Guerillas captured two couriers, but they were taken with little drama and yielded the usual information. Little.

The sun crept higher in the sky and beat down on the weary, bearded dirty, sunburned troops as they neared Summit, Mississippi. Steadman remarked, "Fifteen more miles and we'll be in Louisiana."

Steadman said it like he meant safety and Kelly added quietly, "Aye, but that's not exactly home, you know."

Summit, Mississippi was a quiet and peaceful town. The war had taken away the majority of its three thousand inhabitants and those that were left yielded quietly to the Union soldiers marching in their streets. Sergeant Surby suspected Brookhaven had somehow passed word of the "Yanks" to Summit. It was obvious that Summit was not cringing in the face of the "murderous Yanks."

"Better to humble ourselves before the enemy than ruffle his feathers," someone remarked. But Richard Surby couldn't buy that. Again, as at Brookhaven, the Union soldiers were treated humanely.

Large quantities of sugar, salt, molasses, and meal, all of it government property, were found, loaded into freight cars, and moved out of town to be burned.

"Want us to burn the depot, Colonel?" Sergeant Surby asked Blackburn.

"No, Grierson says it's too close to private homes. Men have fought enough fire."

While the officers decided a safe course from Summit, the cavalrymen prowled the streets. Summit was one of the larger towns they'd taken.

Food was abundant and the men ate well. Some of the townspeople even served basket lunches to the men.

Company L Quartermaster Sergeant Aaron Lambert of the Sixth Illinois sat on a board walk, gorging himself with a picnic lunch, complete with linen napkin.

Surby and the scouts whistled and guffawed as they passed Lambert. He shook a chicken leg at them and invited them to "set a spell and eat a bite," but they rode on, aimed at two shade trees farther down the street.

Several of the scouts struck up conversations with local citizens. They talked of the war, when it would be over, why the fighting continued, and generally, agreed that little good was coming from it.

"Strange, this game called war," one elderly gentleman remarked.

While many cavalrymen were so engaged, some searched for other pleasures. About a mile from town, in a swamp, word spread that thirty or forty barrels of Louisiana rum had been found. A steady stream of horses and riders in that direction prompted several officers to become suspicious. Grierson sent an officer and squad of men to the happy gathering. The squad went armed with axes.

Shortly, they arrived at the party. The officer announced his intentions and his squad unwillingly began to perform their duty. Protests rang out through the cypress trees as the swingers shattered the barrel heads. A burly sergeant form the Sixth Illinois cried out in an Irish brogue, his voice rolling through the trees, "Would you be allowin' the balm of a thousand flowers to mingle with the stinkin', foul swamp water? Lads, have you no respect for art?"

Tears streamed down his ruddy cheeks and he added, "Please, lads, spare just one wee barrel for the likes o' me."

But it was no use. The Colonel had commanded and the squad obeyed. The officer, sitting astride his horse and looking down on the old sergeant, was trying to console him, "Sarge, the stuff is too dangerous to keep. We've come a long way without it and we've got still further to go. Why that stuff is guaranteed to kill further than any rifle in Uncle Sam's service."

"But, laddie, sir, you're not understandin' the need for such bliss as this," the sergeant pleaded.

The young officer was befuddled. Never had he seen such a display of emotion.

Wiping his eyes, the old sergeant made his final plea, "We'll be a needin' it for medicinal purposes only."

"Sorry, Sarge." Turning to his men, buy wielding their axes, he grinned and said, "Dispatch that demon rum, men."

Then he looked around spying a corporal nearby in the crowd of mourners, he motioned for him to come nearer. He ordered the corporal to go to town for a jug. "Make it a big one," he added. "The Sergeant may be right. We'll take some for an emergency."

A cheer went up amid joyous shouts of praise. The Irish sergeant scooped his hat full of Louisiana rum and swamp water. Up and onto his head went the concoction. More cheering and laughter accompanied the group back to Summit.

Thirty minutes later, the big Irish sergeant rode up and down in front of his company shouting orders and inspecting his men for the ride which would take the column to their resting place for the night.

Before marching, there was a hurried inspection to redistribute ammunition. Some of the men had nearly forty rounds left, others less than ten. It was not time for a fight. Grierson needed only one thing now. He must join Union troops — and soon. The verdict of the officers' meeting was issued and the column marched toward Liberty, west of Summit.

The scouts departed twenty or thirty minutes before the main column and rode only a short distance before George Steadman made contact with a Confederate officer.

It was a beautiful sunset Steadman rode into and he remarked to the rider that he hoped the weather held.

Careful questioning revealed that Steadman was speaking with Second-Lieutenant Bill Wren, a courier.

"Where you comin' from?" Steadman asked.

"Osyka Station."

"How's that?"

"Just hit this road goin' east back a ways."

Satisfied, Steadman asked, "Many forces there?"

"Yeh, we're ready for the Yanks," Wren said matter-of-factly. "Three regiments and some artillery," the young lieutenant boasted.

"Any cavalry?"

"Oh, sure. One regiment; two of infantry."

"'S that right?" Steadman said, thrilled with his information.

"Yeh, got 'em ready for them Yanks what's comin' down the railroad. Goin' to trap 'em 'fore they can go farther."

Steadman invited the lieutenant to relate this information to his captain. "We're chasin' them Yanks, too. Maybe we can swing over to the railroad and help out," he added

"Why? Didn't you come from Summit?" Wren asked suspiciously.

"Uh...no, we just passed west four or five miles 'bout an hour ago."

"Oh. Is that it?" Wren said and smiled.

The click of Steadman's revolver hammer signaled an end to the game and the lieutenant was his prisoner. Steadman returned him to the column. And the scouts continued running into Southern soldiers. Soon others were captured and sent to the rear to join the Rebel lieutenant.

Steadman and Surby, Nelson and Kelly, and Fowler and Weedon shared the point for the next three miles. They met little opposition, but when a Confederate soldier or anyone who might give them away appeared, they were quick to grab him. Finally, Grierson's command began filing off the road into the cedar-dappled lawn of Spurlock Plantation.

The Butternut Guerillas made a quick search of the surrounding country, found nothing of unusual concern, and returned to find themselves a camping spot close to the plantation house.

As they untied the gear from their saddles, Art Wood joined the group.

"Where you been, kid?" Charles Weedon asked.

"Around."

"That right?" Weedon muttered.

"Yep," the short blond Wood answered, throwing his blanket on the ground near a fire Steadman was struggling with.

"Hear anything?"

"Like what?"

"Like where we go from here," Weedon said, his manner impatient.

"Louisiana."

"Louisiana? You sure?" He shifted his tobacco to the other jaw.

"Sure. Head Grierson say so."

Richard Surby and Sam Nelson joined the group. Weedon said, "Hear that, Sarge? Wood says we're headed for Louisiana."

"What I heard too," Surby acknowledged. "Two or three days and we'll be home."

"Home?"

"Sure. We got troops at Baton Rouge," Surby replied, stripping the saddle from his mount.

"Baton Rouge?" Kelly interrupted, surprised.

"That's what they're sayin' now. Course, we got to get by any Rebs 'tween here and there," Surby replied.

"Two or three days! Can you believe it?" Fowler muttered half to himself, half to the others, smiling.

"It's not all that doggone far either," Steadman said.

"Yeh, but you just watch somethin' mess that trip up. Ain't goin' to be a picnic," Charles Weedon protested.

Sam Nelson flapped his blanket down over his ground cover and said, "Now, Charlie. 'Spect we'll make it now we come this…uh…far."

A short time later, the group sat or lay on blankets surrounding Steadman's cool fire. The twang of a banjo became audible through the sagging cedar branches. A cool breeze from the north caused the fire to flick its fingers about. One by one, the Butternut Guerillas laid their heads back and found the solace of deep sleep.

Thirty minutes after Richard Surby began snoring, a big, weary man found the scouts' fire. He stepped into the circle looking for quiet conversation, found the men asleep, smiled at his sadness, and retreated to the big plantation house.

Lieutenant-Colonel William Blackburn was uneasy this night. The solemn reports of confederate forces closing from all directions frightened him. His thoughts wondered back to his native Ohio, and then to Paris, Illinois, and finally his family. Elizabeth, his wife; Anna, Jennie, Eliza, and Billy. He would sleep little and light this Thursday night, the last day of April, 1863.

Chapter 13

...hell on the Tickfaw

Before first light on Friday, May 1, the Butternut Guerillas shuffled about in the glow of their campfire checking their gear for the journey to the Mississippi River. There were still suspicions that the regiments might head toward New Orleans. Others insisted that Baton Rouge was their objective. Port Hudson was definitely out since it was a Confederate stronghold.

Looking around him, Richard Surby sensed the condition of his men. The Butternut Guerillas got progressively more difficult to arouse in the mornings. Shouted orders rang through the other companies — followed by angry curses, then more shouts. The Sixth and Seventh Illinois were weary.

Just as the first rays of sun sneaked across the sky, Lieutenant-Colonel William Blackburn, at the head of the First Battalion of the Seventh, raised his hand and barked the command that moved the advance guard away from Spurlock Plantation, cool and quiet under the beautifully trimmed cedar trees.

The march was slow at first, through wooded terrain without benefit of roads. As the sun rose and lit even the wooded paths that the scouts, the advance guard, and the Seventh and Sixth Illinois Cavalries traveled, the pace quickened. Soon, the regiments were making four miles each hour, then five. All in all, it was a pleasant ride.

The Butternut Guerillas flanked out from the paths and moved steadily to the sides of Sergeant Surby. Surby could see them from time to time through the gently fluttering leaves on the smaller trees. A whistling, a Mockingbird trilling his morning notes, startled Surby and the others on several occasions.

About half past eight, Surby halted his horse on a narrow, dirt road which crossed the thick timber through which he was leading the column. A creaking sound alerted him. As he stood in the road, a sutler's wagon and a rider on a fine horse appeared. Both wagon and rider headed southeast toward Osyka.

"Mornin'. Seen any Yanks?" Surby drawled.

"Not nary one. They're movin' on 'nother road, I hear."

"Seen anything of Wirt Adams?"

"No, can't says I have. Why you ask?" the rider said, sensing something amiss. The column closed on the crossing and there was considerable noise coming from the horses and men as they neared the edge of the woods.

Sergeant Surby raised his hand from his side. In it, he held the Navy Colt, hammer thumbed back. He smiled, "'Cause I'm a Yank and was just wonderin'."

The rider with the wagon did not appear startled. He only shook his head calmly at the sutler, who with wagon halted, looked up at Surby and said, "Well, I never...."

"What you haulin'?" Surby said to the sutler.

"Just some toback."

"Good," Surby exclaimed as Blackburn came out of the woods and onto the road.

"What you got, Richard?"

"Some smokin' for the men."

"You go on ahead then," Blackburn ordered. "I'll take care of this. They see anything up the road?"

"Said not. Asked about Adams, but they ain't seen nothin'."

"All right, then."

"Oh, Colonel, he did say he thought we were on another road."

Blackburn glared at the rider, then at the sutler. The advance guard gathered around the wagon taking tobacco. "I'll talk to 'em. Hurry it up, men!"

Surby looked for an opening into the woods on the south side of the road, found one, and prodded his horse. Soon he was followed by the entire command. The woods got thicker as the Butternut Guerillas traveled south and the flankers returned to a single file with Surby leading the way.

At ten o'clock, Surby was suddenly on a road. "Must be the Liberty-Osyka road," he said aloud. Then he whistled softly. Nelson answered the whistle and was soon in the road, dismounted, and standing by the kneeling Surby.

"Look at this, Sam."

Nelson knelt, "Gosh, what...uh....do you make of it, Sarge?"

"Rebs! A half hundred or more."

Piles of fresh horse dung dappled the road. The tracks in the road had not been made long before.

"Probably just ahead of us then...huh, Sarge?"

"Maybe an hour," Surby said as George Steadman, riding a horse, exited the woods. Surby looked up, started to ask how come Steadman wasn't on a mule, but said instead, "George, get Blackburn."

Steadman saw the tracks and the dung and concluded the same thing as Nelson and Surby. This was trouble. His horse loped through the trees, dodging limbs, Steadman clinging to his back, hat in hand. When he spied the advance, he called for Blackburn to come forward. Grierson and Blackburn rode together and both men, hearing the call, urged their horses ahead. They followed Steadman toward the road.

When they were in the road, the Butternut Guerillas and the two colonels re-examined the ground. No more than one hour, and fifty or sixty riders with no artillery was their combined conclusion.

Surby posted Uriah Fowler and Lycurgus Kelly up and down the road to be sure they did not have visitors as they conferred in the road. Grierson then spoke, "Well, Sergeant, we're headin' in their direction." Grierson pulled a map from his shirt. He unfolded it, took out his compass, studied both, and concluded, "We've got to cross that bridge south of here. No other way."

The early morning breeze picked up a little and rustled the leaves at the tops of the trees. Grierson removed his hat and wiped his forehead on his sleeve. The others watched his every move. Finally, the bearded colonel spoke, "Here's what we'll do. Now I sent Newell and a squadron from F Company east earlier. They're supposed to meet us at Wall's Bridge in about two hours. If they can't get to the bridge by then, that's all right. They'll pick us up from behind anyhow."

The column was almost to the edge of the woods now. Grierson looked into the woods, then back to Sergeant Surby, "You stay a half mile in front; no more, understand?"

Surby nodded.

"Put your scouts out to flank. We don't want an ambush. Chances are, they don't know we're back here. But don't let a thing go unobserved."

"Be cautious, Richard," Blackburn interrupted.

"That is the word, Sergeant. Caution! If you see anything or even hear anything, report back. The whole command depends on your judgment," Grierson added firmly.

"Yes, sir, Colonel. A half mile in front and report ever'thing."

"That's right. Now follow those tracks. And, Sergeant, tell your other men about Lieutenant Newell. We want no unnecessary shootin'."

"Right, sir."

The blood throbbed in Surby's temples as he walked his horse along the road. His information ran through his head. Tracks — hour old. Fifty men — God, fifty! They'll be noonin' soon...have to watch for pickets.

All the time his eyes searched the huge oak trees along the narrow road. Perfect for ambush, his senses told him. Brush too thick for flankers.

Two miles down the road, Surby caught a glimpse of white to his right. He stopped his horse. By standing in the saddle and peering through the thick underbrush, he could see a two-story, frame plantation house. It was nearly three hundred yards from the road. The live oak trees and silver poplars hid the house almost completely from sight as he walked his horse farther down the road, occasionally standing in his stirrups and looking in the direction of the house.

Finally a road entered the trees to his right aimed toward the house. It was a winding road and Surby couldn't see anything but trees from the entrance. Signaling for the string of scouts behind to keep quiet and motioning that they should not go to the house, Surby continued on, passing the road to the house.

Suddenly in front of him, at a distance of about three hundred yards, something moved. Horses! Their heads were hidden from view, but their rumps extended into one lane of the road, their tails swishing.

Surby made no move to warn the others. He was sure they'd see soon enough. Besides, Surby saw only three horses now, all saddled and riderless. That'll be a picket guard, Surby calculated. Twisting in his saddle. Surby motioned Charles Weedon closer. Pointing to the horses, and holding up three fingers, Surby whispered, "Tell Grierson." Weedon nodded, spit a stream of tobacco juice, and rode away silently.

As decided several nights before, Surby and the Butternut Guerillas rode at night with their pistols drawn. Today, they agreed to the same procedure, since the risks were great. Surby watched Weedon walking his horse quietly down the road. As Weedon passed George Steadman and then Art Wood, Surby saw them prod their horses at a quicker pace toward where he stood waiting.

Without speaking, Surby moved ahead, Wood and Steadman following. Their squeaking saddles made the only noise. Near where the horses stood, a tree had fallen with the trunk extending to the edge of the road. On the log, two soldiers of the Confederate army sat, dressed very much like the Butternut Guerillas. Another man lay on the ground staring through the clearing at a dazzlingly bright, high sky.

Surby, at first, paid them little attention and as he was almost parallel with them, he turned his head toward where they sat and said, "Hello, boys. On picket?"

"Yeh. Been on about an hour and feel devilish tired," the soldier nearest the road drawled.

The other one on the log took a straw-like weed from his mouth and added, "Been travelin' night and day after the damned Yanks." He shook his head and before anyone else could speak, he added, "And I'll bet my horse they'll get away yet."

"That's just our case," Surby remarked, "but where's your command?"

"Over in the bottom; resting," he pointed south and west toward an open field of cotton. "Couple ol' boys with us is back at the plantation gettin' us some dinner. You see 'em?"

"No," Surby said, puzzled. He glanced at Steadman and Wood. Then turning to the three Confederates, he asked, "Whose command you boys with and how many of ya'll?"

Before Surby could get his answer, two shots, followed by the ring of carbine, came from the direction of the plantation house to their rear and west of them.

The man on the ground, alert now, put both hands on the shotgun that rested across his waist. He exclaimed, "What the hell?"

Surby stiffened his right arm and aimed at the man's chest, "Lay that gun down 'fore I blow a hole in you, boy!" Wood and Steadman convinced the other two to do the same.

"Get mounted," Surby yelled. The three walked cautiously toward their horses and Surby added, "Double quick!" They responded and the scouts herded them quickly to where the column was halted near the narrow, winding road that led to the plantation. The prisoners were taken to the rear. Blackburn rode up from a meeting with Grierson. They had been at the middle of the column.

Surby asked, frowning, "What in hell happened?"

"I don't know," Blackburn blurted angrily. He looked around and spotted Bill Stiles, a lieutenant in G Company of the Seventh Illinois. All the men were looking in the direction of the firing, the plantation house.

"Stiles," Blackburn yelled.

"Yes, Colonel?"

"What in Sam Hill is goin' on here?"

The thirty-five year old Stiles dropped his head, then said, "Lieutenant Gaston took a dozen men to the house, sir."

Blackburn frowned and shook his head.

Stiles continued, "Guess they got trouble. He left me in command, but since there's only a shot or two figured he'd handled the problem."

"I 'spect he did, all right. Whole Reb army'll know we're here." Blackburn continued to Surby, "Richard, get out on that scout — and be careful!"

"Stiles," Blackburn ordered, "take a squad and get Gaston out of there!"

The eager lieutenant commanded, "First squadron! Column of twos! For-ward!"

And off along the winding path, Stiles and his men disappeared as Surby, followed by Steadman, Fowler, and Wood, returned up the road to the cotton field.

At the downed tree, all eyes stared into the open cotton field, the direction the Reb soldiers pointed. As the four scouts exited the woods alongside the field, they saw two men sitting on horses. They were a fourth of a mile away.

There was a road going back into the woods, probably a second entrance to the plantation house.

The field fell away to a tree-covered bottom. That would be the river bed. Ahead, the road led a quarter of a mile south and then turned sharply to the right. Another quarter of a mile took it by where the two men were astride their horses staring in the direction of the Butternut Guerillas.

"Weedon, stay here and stop the column. Fowler and Wood, go down this road in the woods and see if it's not another entrance to the plantation house."

Surby motioned for Steadman to go with him and walked his horse into the cotton field on a diagonal in the direction of the two men still standing at the opposite corner of the field.

When Steadman and Surby were about a hundred yards into the field, one of the two Confederates called out, "What in hell does all the firin' mean?"

Surby cupped one hand around his mouth and answered, "Reinforce-ments comin'. Your picket fired on our advance." Surby paused, then added slowly, "Thought we's Yanks."

"Anybody hurt?"

Shaking his head, Surby called, "It's all right."

The man who asked the questions laughed aloud, "Is that all?" Then he put spurs to his horse and started toward Surby and Steadman at a gallop, leaving his partner standing.

Surby continued in his direction and without looking at Steadman, said, "Let 'im ride between us. I'll take 'im." Surby eased the hammer back on the Colt.

The rider came close, a smile on his face. Surby, with Steadman on his left, halted his horse and let the rider close on him.

"How're you, boys? How much force you got?" the rider said, riding between Surby and Steadman.

Surby turned his horse to the left so that the big Colt in his left hand could not be seen by the other man at the far corner of the field. Slowly and calmly, Surby spoke, "See this?" nodding his head at the revolver. "Don't speak or move. Don't want to blow you through. Give 'im your gun," Surby nodded to Fowler. Fowler and Wood had retreated from their trip on the road to the plantation when they heard the shouting in the field. The man handed his shotgun to Fowler easy and without a word.

Now for the other one, Surby thought. He turned to see Steadman walking, leading his horse, toward the other man who had come within a hundred yards. Steadman didn't have his revolver in his hand! Before Surby could move, Steadman met the rider. He was twice Steadman's size. Steadman suddenly dropped the horse's reins, and grabbed the reins of the Confederate soldier's horse. At the same time, Steadman jumped to the side and grabbed the rider's holster so he couldn't pull his pistol.

"Who and what in hell are you?" the big soldier screamed. The horse and rider were twisting and turning with Steadman being dragged alongside, still grasping the reins and the holster.

"Wood!" Surby yelled. Instantly, Surby and Wood spurred their horses and in seconds were helping Steadman and the lunging horse and rider.

Surby grabbed the officer with one arm, Wood settling the horse, and with the revolver placed at the side of the rider's head, Surby yelled, "Surrender, or I'll blow your brains out!"

Rider and horse calmed simultaneously. Steadman lay on the ground nearby, flat on his back. Wood asked, "All right, George?"

George Steadman got to his feet and limped to his horse, retrieving his hat on the way. Wood laughed and Surby ordered the prisoner to join Fowler and the other captive.

"We're Illinois boys. You'll be treated well," Surby added, trying to put the captive officer at ease.

"I'm not afraid, suh. But I would not be yo' prisoner had it not been that I was deceived in yo' dress."

"True, sir. What can I call you?"

"Scott, Captain E.A. Scott."

"Well, Captain Scott, come along. Our colonel'll want to see you."

Out of the tree-covered road at the corner of the cotton field, Lieutenant-Colonel Blackburn and his big bay Morgan appeared. Seeing Surby,

Blackburn turned his horse and galloped toward the Butternut Guerillas and their captives. Blackburn was alone.

"Sergeant, bring along your scouts an' follow me," Blackburn called before he reached Surby. "I'll see where those Rebels are now," Blackburn added, dashing by, the Morgan's black tail flying.

Surby yelled at Weedon, who had ridden down when the excitement started, "Take these men back to the column."

Kelly and Nelson now galloped down the slope from the advance of the column which had begun exiting the woods and moving into the cotton field toward Surby and the others. Steadman was on his horse, but leaning over rubbing his sore foot. Wood and Fowler sat staring, slack-jawed, at Blackburn riding alone toward the corner of the field where Surby had first seen the Confederates, Captain Scott and the other soldier.

Surby, for the first time, realized how far in advance Blackburn was. He mumbled to himself, then screamed to the others to follow him. "Double quick!" he added, his voice breaking.

The Butternut Guerillas caught their colonel as he halted the Morgan at the road twisting into the woods toward the river, the Tickfaw. The scouts looked at Blackburn and Blackburn eyed the heavily timbered bottom. The Tickfaw River brawled its way swiftly through the marshy woods. A little to their left, they saw the bridge. It looked to be about fifty feet long and they could see that the current in the stream would never allow them to ford.

Blackburn, Surby by his side, stood in his saddle and surveyed the scene coldly, with no expression on his face. As he settled back down, he gently kicked the big bay forward. The scouts followed.

The road had never been made except by the travel over it, and at this season, it was a way of ruts cut in the black soil, and of fathomless mudholes. The horses picked their way carefully through the mud.

Nelson's chest throbbed; the sweat flowed from his brow. His eyes darted from bush to tree, stump to drift pile. His ears strained, reaching out for any sound of anger — a cylinder rolling in a revolver, a hammer snapping open, a curse, heavy breathing. His nostrils sensed his lathered horse, the dung of many horses, and the stench of the black, sticky gumbo along the river's banks. Beside him, Steadman thumbed the hammer back on his Navy Colt. Sam Nelson heard the scouts behind echoing Steadman's action, then he realized he'd done the same. The wind rustled the leaves softly and sunlight danced in the road ahead.

The Morgan with Blackburn erect in the saddle, pranced closer to the bridge. The scouts awaited the instant when the clammy hands and sweat-streaked faces would suddenly dry; the cold breath of death sweeping the heat of excitement away. Blackburn's saber was out. It's shining death gleamed in spots of sunlight.

A lone explosion from a hidden carbine shattered the air. The trees echoed the blast. There was a scream and Blackburn and the big Morgan lunged onto the bridge, the planks thundering. Then the deadly rumble of nearly a hundred muskets and carbines crashed, fire spewing from their muzzles.

Close behind Blackburn: Surby, Nelson, Steadman. Then Wood, Fowler...where was Kelly? Pistols blazed, onto the bridge they charged...and into a wall of enemy bullets! The enemy? Where are they? Invisible? the air breathed whistling, whining death. Skipping, careening bullets tore wildly toward man and beast. Leaves and limbs shuddered. Slowly, so slowly, the ambush became reality!

Blackburn's beautiful Morgan, his black mane and tail shimmering, twisted, screamed and crashed — dead! Blackburn felt a burning, tearing jerk at his thigh as he was slammed in the face with a wooden plank — only his head was on the bridge floor now. His eyes blurred, flashing red, then white. He struggled to lift himself. Almost instantly his head exploded and slammed again onto the bridge. Everything went black.

Elsewhere Richard Surby was nearly torn from his saddle. Then the fire in his leg burst forth. He grabbed for the gushing wound without letting loose the reins and so, spun the horse around and fled back across the bridge and up the brush-lined road and away from that place of death.

Steadman and his horse waited and watched the scouts burst past him and go hurtling into the cotton field. He wailed, "They got the Colonel!"

"Where in hell's the column?" Nelson yelled.

Galloping toward them, dirt flying, Lieutenant William Stiles rode, a dozen men from G Company chasing after him. At the corner, Stiles didn't hesitate, but led his men down the lane, horses blowing, men yelling, sabers waving. In seconds, their hooves thundered over the bridge...the lightning death of carbines and muskets split the air! Again, the pounding hooves and suddenly there were only seven men riding into the glaring sunlight of the field.

"My God," a voice cried.

"Where's George? What happened to George?"

"You see Hughes go down?"

Everything happened very fast. A bugle call announced the arrival of the remainder of the column. Grierson shouted orders to Prince and Prince repeated, "A and D; Dismount! A, form skirmishers to the left. D, take the right!"

Grierson, his horse prancing about, told a frightened private, "Get Smith's Battery up here. Dammit, hurry!" he screamed.

Nelson and Kelly moved along the tree-umbrelled road on foot to look for the enemy. As Captain Jason Smith and one section (a two-pounder gun) came rolling up, Nelson ran from the woods, shouting, "To the left, 'bout a hundred yards!"

On the ground nearby, Surby lay watching the commotion. His hand clasped at his thigh, the blood oozing between his fingers. He feared he'd bleed to death.

Kelly ran from the woods and directly at Colonel Grierson. Grierson leaned down from his horse to take the Irishman's report. Kelly screamed that Blackburn was on the bridge, pinned under his horse. Another group of wounded and screaming horses lay near the approach on the opposite bank. There was a man lying among them. He looked dead.

"Kelly! Hey, Kelly!" Surby yelled.

Kelly took his leave from Grierson and ran to where Surby lay in tall weeds at the side of the road.

"Colonel alive?" Surby asked, squinting into the sun.

"Think so; he's on his back, but I think I saw a hand move," Kelly smiled, adjusting a blanket someone had placed under Surby's head.

"God, we gotta get 'im outta there! Help 'im, won't ya?"

Just then, Smith's two-pounder exploded into action. Amid shouts of "Fire!" the whump of the shell could be heard and then the clanking reload and again, "Whump!"

"Take that you sons o'bitches!" someone cursed, half crying.

In the woods, carbine and musket fire slowed and then stopped. Someone yelled, "They're runnin'. By God, they're runnin'. We licked 'em!"

Shouts roared throughout the trees. Smith elevated his guns and began lobbing projectiles across the wooded bottom. Then after a minute, he commanded, "Cease fire!"

Immediately, Grierson ordered the bugler to blow "Boots and Saddles," then "Charge!" as the Sixth rushed across the bridge in pursuit of the fleeing Confederate force.

Someone lifted Surby onto his horse. He felt faint. The high, noon sun blazed. Then Surby was in the cool, dark woods and shivering. At the bridge, a grizzled soldier offered him a canteen. He drank, water dribbling from his chin. His eyes focused and he could see Nelson and Fowler. they were prying a horse off a man's leg? Surby shook his head and moved closer. Blackburn? Alive?

Then a familiar voice called, "Richard? Richard you all right?"

"Yes...yes. And you, Colonel? How you?" Surby asked. His voice sounded weak and far away.

"Shot up a little," Blackburn answered, staring at his leg. "But all right."

Blackburn winced. Surby rubbed his eyes and thought. You can't be all right! The blood. Look at the blood — on the bridge...your hip...your head. Then Surby shook his head and said, "Get you anything?"

"No, R...Richard. You go ahead now," Blackburn's face twisted in pain as Nelson and Fowler tugged at his leg. "I'll see you ahead," the big man added through clenched teeth.

Surby felt better now. The leg was numb; the wound had clotted. He took a deep breath, wiped downward across his face with his lift hand, exhaled and said, "No, Colonel, I'll stay."

Suddenly Nelson and Fowler heaved Blackburn's leg free of the horse's dead weight.

Richard Surby slid from his horse and sat carefully beside Blackburn. Nelson stood and looked about. At the far end of the bridge, several troopers knelt with men from Stiles' squadron who had been wounded in the charge. One of the kneeling soldiers motioned for Sam to join them.

"Stay...stay with 'im, Bud," Nelson said to Fowler. "I'm gonna see who's over there."

"Go on, Sam. I'll stay with these two 'til the ambulance gets here."

Sam Nelson walked to the end of the bridge where his way was blocked by a dead horse. He climbed slowly over the animal's back.

"What you want?" Sam asked.

One of the soldiers looked up shyly and pointed to Sam's left. Nelson stared at the man and turned his head slowly, fearing what he finally saw. It was George Rinehold. He lay beside the ramp on the mud bank, partially hidden from Sam's view.

Quickly, Sam ran, slipping, through the mud to Rinehold's side. He knelt and asked softly, "Georgie?"

Rinehold's eyes stared straight into the trees and sky overhead. He's dead, Sam thought.

"Georgie, can you see me? It's Sam."

Rinehold rolled his head groggily to the side. Looking at Nelson, he smiled, "I got it, Sammy. My belly's on fire; my legs won't move."

"Now, Georgie, you hold on, hear?"

Rinehold continued, uninterrupted, "Sammy, you ever see my boy; you ever see him, Sammy? God, he's spunky one. I can most hear 'im now." The glazed eyes quit Nelson in favor of the sky. "He's just there, Sammy. See 'im; see my boy, Sammy?"

The dying man's voice grew in pitch and excitement gathering power and his last sentences were spoken with scarcely a perceptible pause. With an effort he had raised himself almost without assistance to a sitting position. But now the fire faded out of his eyes and he fell back exhausted.

"See 'im. My boy...." The voice died out in a whisper; the sentence never finished. After a few seconds there was no sound but soft sobbing, the gurgle of the stream, and the quiet rustling of the new leaves high in the trees.

Sam stared at his friend through moist eyes. Slowly he rolled his thumb across George's eyelids, then wiped his own eyes with his sleeve. He slid his hand inside the dead man's jacket and shirt and came out with the letter addressed to Rinehold's wife. Sam's head slumped; then with a deep breath, he blew himself upright, stood, and stumbled to the bridge.

Minutes later, the two-wheeled ambulance arrived and George Douglas and August Leseure climbed down to help Nelson and Fowler get Blackburn loaded. Blackburn was comfortable and complained little. By this time, Surby felt much better and protested when Dr. Erastus Yule insisted that he join Blackburn in the ambulance.

Finally, Surby consented, but wouldn't permit anyone to help him over the tailgate. Inside the little wagon, Rees Hughes and Bill Roy lay stretched out. Roy was conscious and smoking. Hughes appeared to be asleep.

Surby found a space large enough to accommodate sitting down and stretched his wounded leg in front of him. Blackburn cursed and grabbed hold of a crosspiece behind the driver's seat, pulling himself into a sitting posture.

Surby watched Blackburn, thought how terrible he looked, then asked, "Colonel, Grierson'll want Nelson to head the scouts, don't you 'spect?"

"What do you think, Richard?"

"He's the only man for it."

"Tell 'im then."

To the driver, George Douglas, Surby said quickly, "Get Sam Nelson back here 'fore he rides off!"

Nelson sat astride his little horse Shawnee at the end of the bridge, staring down at George Rinehold's lifeless body. He heard Douglas calling, but did not immediately respond. Then, he slowly turned his mount and clucked him back across the bridge to the ambulance.

"What's matter?" Nelson asked the drive.

"Sarge wants to see you," Douglas said, nodding his head backwards.

Nelson went to the back and looked in, "Yeh, Sarge?"

"Colonel Grierson'll want to see you, Sam...'bout takin' over the scouts."

"Figured I'd see 'im up ahead," Nelson answered, taking a deep breath.

Surby noticed that Nelson looked dazed by all that had happened. He twisted his head to the side and asked, "Sam, you feel all right?"

Nelson sighed and said, "I...I'll be okay." Without added comment, Nelson turned his horse away from Surby's view and rode indifferently onto the bridge.

The ambulance rocked along the road for a mile before pulling into the lane at Newman Plantation. The Sixth and Seventh were already there. A Company of the Seventh escorted the ambulance and several of the Butternut Guerillas went ahead to scout.

Sam Nelson had arrived ten minutes earlier, found Colonel Grierson, and been given command of the scouts. He was already on point by the time the ambulance pulled to a halt before the pillared veranda.

Inside the plantation house, the wounded were made comfortable and soon, the two regiments prepared to move. Dr. Yule had no encouragement for Grierson when he inquired about the wounded. Hughes, Roy, and Blackburn were almost certain to die. Several men asked to stay behind and tend their wounds. Richard Surby could not be moved and was bound for a prisoner of war camp. George Douglas, one of Blackburn's men from A Company, and Sergeant Major August Leseure insisted on staying and were given permission. They were both old friends of Blackburn. Dr. Erastus Yule, on loan from the Second Iowa Cavalry, wouldn't leave either. So the bridge over the Tickfaw had its final tally. One dead, two mortally wounded, two seriously wounded, and several destined for Confederate prison camps.

Colonel Benjamin Grierson stopped by to make certain the wounded and those that were staying behind had everything they needed. He tried to cheer one of his favorite officers, William Blackburn, "Should've seen them Rebs run, Bill. They scattered blankets and gear from Wall's Bridge to the Mississippi, I bet."

A faint smile crossed Blackburn's lips.

Surby asked, "Are the scouts out, sir?"

"Sam Nelson's on point, Sergeant. Don't you worry; he's learned his lessons well. Had a good teacher," Grierson said, patting Surby on the shoulder.

Colonel Edward Price burst into the little room. His face was flushed, his breathing noticeable short. "Colonel," he addressed Grierson, "my officers and me think it wise to bivouac here. We need the rest."

Before Grierson could answer, Blackburn blurted, "That'd be a damn fool thing to do, sir. They're runnin'; keep 'em runnin! Stop now, they'll get time to lay another ambush."

"But what about these wounded? Are we just goin' to leave 'em?" Prince pleaded, his mouth drawn.

Surby laughed, trying to ease the tension, "Look at it this way. Me and Colonel Blackburn rode across that bridge with nearly a hundred guns target shootin' at us. Nothin's goin' to happen to anybody that lives through that kind of hell."

Blackburn agreed and added, "Don't you worry none 'bout us. We're all Paris boys and we'll be back there 'fore you boys. You'll probably be in Baton Rouge 'til the war ends. Some Reb officer'll have us sign a parole paper and they're liable to escort us out of here, us bein' Grierson's raiders!"

Prince laughed nervously, walked to his second-in-command, Bill Blackburn, knelt beside him with his hand on his shoulder, and dropped his head. As he stood to leave the room, he said, "See you in Illinois, Bill."

The two regiments moved quickly from Newman Plantation and were making six miles each hour on approaching the Mississippi-Louisiana border about two o'clock in the afternoon. Sam Nelson rode point. He did not relish the responsibility he was harnessed with, but muttered to himself philosophically, "Someone's got to do it."

Flanked out on his sides and taking turns on point were the other scouts: Wood, Robinson, Steadman, Weedon, Kelly and Fowler.

The narrow, tree-lined road they followed out of Amite County, Mississippi was steaming in the sun now. Sam's horse was blown and hot and from time to time, Sam dismounted and walked him for a short distance. When the advance guard, the Sixth, got close enough for him to hear the clanking of metal, Sam would remount and ride for a while.

Just before crossing into Louisiana, Nelson heard a rider. Shifting his position, his eyes fell on a man coming through the woods to his right. He lead the spent horse to the side of the road. Should be one of the flankers, Kelly or Fowler, coming in, he reckoned, too tired to consider anything else or care. In a few seconds, both Kelly and Fowler rode out of the timber twenty yards up the road.

"Sam, 'bout forty Rebs comin' up a side road," Fowler called, his breath stumbling in spurts from his lips.

"How far off?" Nelson asked matter-of-factly.

"Should be 'bout two hundred yards. They'll hit the main road there," Fowler said, pointing a short distance up the narrow road. His breathing was steadier.

Nelson mounted and whipped his jaded horses forward. At the intersection, he turned in the saddle and looked back down the road from where he had come. The advance of the Sixth was not over four hundred yards away, he calculated.

Satisfied the advance was close enough, Nelson prodded Shawnee forward, his pistol in hand. Fowler and Kelly followed closely behind. Steadman loped up the road from his position between the advance and the point. He'd found another mule to ride. He arrived just as Sam and the others moved into the center of the intersection — in full view of the Confederate soldiers. The Butternut Guerillas saw them at about the same time. Their revolvers came up and fired almost as one.

This scattered the Confederates and before they could reorganize, the advance of the Sixth was in the intersection and dismounting. If the enemy charged, they would break it with a smashing volley.

Colonel Grierson, on hearing the pistol shots, ordered Captain Jason Smith to get one of his guns forward. In a little over a minute after the Sixth dismounted, Smith and his battery entered the intersection. Sam Nelson pointed down the road and the two-pounder creaked into position, the eye of the barrel searching out the enemy. Smith's Battery lobbed a half-dozen shells into the trees, sweeping the little woods with a storm of leaden hail, tearing the trees and sending thunder after the Rebels. Before the smoke settled, horses and men made a hasty retreat.

Colonel Grierson, satisfied that the danger had passed, said more to himself than Sam Nelson, "Good work. Now let's get drivin'. It'll be dark before we cross the Amite River — and it's just as well."

"That's...uh...Williams' Bridge, right, Colonel?"

"That's it, Sam. Greensburg in two hours, then the bridge."

Sam watched Jason Smith's Battery being congratulated and rode away thinking: If only they'd handled it this way at Wall's Bridge. In his mind, artillery was the answer.

By four o'clock, Sam Nelson, still on point, entered the little town of Greensburg, Louisiana, sixteen miles northwest of William's Bridge. Less than fifty yards into the town, Sam's path was blocked by a wide-hatted, mounted civilian. Across his saddle lay a shabby old shotgun.

"Uh...afternoon."

"Howdy," the man responded, looking Sam over carefully.

"Who're you?" Sam inquired.

"I'm County Clerk, St. Helena County. Who're you?"

"What you...uh..doin' here?" Sam asked, ignoring the question.

"Waitin' for a courier to come up; tryin' to get some news."

"Uh...you know...uh...who you're talkin' to?" Sam asked.

"Don't know your name, but you're a soldier from Port Hudson, ain't you?"

"Uh...no sir. You're mistaken 'bout that. Why you're talkin' to a live...a live Yankee and here's some Yankee whiskey," Sam said, offering the man the spare canteen he'd deftly extracted from his saddlebag.

Sam raised his pistol and extended the canteen in the same movement. The man took the disc shaped canteen. Instead of fear in the man's eyes, Sam saw only surprise. After taking a long drink, the man lowered the canteen, wiped first his mouth, then his eyes. Returning the canteen, he exclaimed, "Sure do thank you."

"Why, you're welcome, sir. Any soldiers in town?" Sam added.

"Can't says I seen any for sev'ral days. Most's out chasin' you north of here."

"That's good."

The Sixth and the main column soon rode into view, Fowler and Kelly just ahead of them. Sam ordered Fowler and Kelly ahead to check the rest of the town and turned his prisoner over to the Seventh when they marched through. As Sam clucked his horse ahead, the prisoner, the County Clerk, called out, "How 'bout another nip of that Yankee whiskey?"

Nelson turned, fell in beside the column, and handed over the canteen. Again, the man took a long slow drink. Wiping his eyes, he said, "Sure's good. Thank you 'gain."

"'S all right."

Lieutenant George William Newell, who had signed on at Harrisburg, Illinois, caught up with the column while they rested in Greensburg. Newell and F Company had fallen on hard times in their search for food and horses and Grierson was disappointed. It meant the final march to Baton Rouge would be even more difficult on spent horses and hungry bellies.

A half hour later the Sixth and Seventh marched from Greensburg, leaving the little town and its complacent inhabitants with all their buildings and most of what little food they had.

Sam Nelson and George Steadman talked about the weather, the good road, and the beautiful landscape. For nearly an hour, there was little else to do. Then four miles from Greensburg, about half past five, they encountered two uniformed riders.

"Where you...uh...boys headed?" Sam inquired, his eyes darting about.

"The railroad," a tall, lean, smartly-uniformed soldier answered.

Sam motioned to their well-lathered horses and said, "Kinda hurryin', ain't you?"

"We're couriers," the other, the younger of the two, said proudly.

That was enough for Sam. He raised the Navy Colt and with a wave of the barrel ordered, "Hand 'em over."

Both couriers gave Sam their leather pouches. Steadman took their guns. Sam opened the pouches and found identical messages: The Confederate force at Osyka was supposed to stop the Yanks at Williams' Bridge — by order of General Franklin Gardner at Port Hudson.

The prisoners and messages were passed back to the column and Nelson and Steadman rode on until dusk turned to dark. The clear sky was domed by a million stars and plantation houses passed by, some noticed, some ignored, others not seen. The two regiments snaked along the road, running for their lives, but the life was nearly gone from them. They needed sleep. By eleven o'clock when the moon rose, big and bright, dimming the light from the stars, Grierson's once dashing raiders were little more than a column of plodding horses and nodding riders.

Within a few miles of Williams' Bridge, a messenger found Sam Nelson slumped in his saddle, sound asleep. Sam figured he had slept for only a few minutes, but the fear of what he could have walked into in this condition surged though him with the same effect as a dunking in a cold stream. Even Sam's numb, saddle-weary rump began to tingle.

The rider carried a message from Colonel Grierson, "Get word of the bridge." Nelson, Steadman, Wood and Fowler hurried ahead and inquired at two shacks and one plantation house. Carefully worded greetings, small talk, and then questions, supplied them with the basic information. There were guards on the bridge, but most slept at night on the south side of the river at a plantation house. Only two guards remained at the bridge during the night.

Minutes later, Sam Nelson reported to Colonel Grierson. Grierson, at first, was overly elated, then he sobered and added, "Sam, be careful. This might be what these people are supposed to say. If General Gardner at Port Hudson knew we were comin' this way, then these guards might."

"Right, Colonel. I'll...uh...make sure."

The column came to a halt a mile from the bridge. Grierson brought Jason Smith's Artillery Battery to the advance, just in case. Ahead, Sam Nelson and George Steadman found the roads muddier, the closer to the Amite they rode. Finally, directly in front of them, in the glow of the moon, the river and bridge appeared. The road, canopied by trees and thus out of view of any sentries that might be at the bridge, led into a splash of moonlight.

In the moonlight now and exposed to anyone that might be watching from the other side, Steadman and Nelson walked their mounts cautiously in the sticky mud, their Navy Colts ready — the hammers cocked. Senses strained for a telltale sign that they might be watched; they slid from their saddles and stepped onto the long bridge. The rush of the water several yards below roared. They could barely hear the planks in the bridge knocking under the hooves.

Halfway across the bridge and one hundred yards from the other side, Sam jerked his head quickly around. He thought he saw something and stopped abruptly. Steadman stood motionless for a full minute, then slowly and carefully they continued across.

Soon, they neared the end of the bridge, Sam took a few quick steps and jumped off the approach of the south side. A shuffling noise to Sam's left alerted him. He squatted quickly, his Colt ready. A clicking sound came from some trees ten yards in front of him. He waited and then began to crawl toward the sound. It was a man, a guard! Sam crawled to a big cypress, slipped to another and was, at once, behind the Confederate soldier. Carefully, he looked about for the other guard. He could see none.

Nelson slipped his left hand behind the soldier's head and around his mouth, then jerked the head back on his pounding, heaving chest. "Not a sound," Sam whispered, placing the Colt to the man's cheek. Steadman appeared silently.

"The other guard?" Nelson demanded, whispering.

The Confederate guard pointed into the dark.

Again, Sam whispered, "Call him!" Nelson held the man's collar with one hand and placed the muzzle of the Colt at the nape of his neck.

The frightened guard spoke softly, "Jed! Hey, Jed!"

Out of the shadows, a voice answered, "What's matter?"

"Two couriers just come up."

"Didn't hear anybody," the other guard said as he came into the moonlight adjusting his belt.

Steadman and Nelson prodded their prisoners across the bridge in front of the two Navy Colts. Nelson questioned them about more guards, was convinced there were no more, and speedily returned the two prisoners to where the other Butternut Guerillas waited. Steadman stayed behind watching the bridge until the other scouts rode forward.

Word passed to the column that the bridge was secure and within fifteen minutes, the two-hundred-yard-long bridge trembled under the weight of the column of twos that crossed in the bright moonlight. It was midnight and soon would be the sixteenth and final day of Grierson's Raid.

Chapter 14

...the long ride

During the next few hours on Saturday morning, May 2nd, as Grierson's raiders moved through Louisiana toward Baton Rouge, Sam Nelson fought the urge to sleep. He wished for sleep. Sleep would heal his body. His very soul would be cleansed by sleep. More than once he resisted the temptation to turn from the road, dismount, and curl up beside a tree to slumber away the weariness of the past two weeks.

Finally, another of the scouts joined him. It was Art Wood.

"Keepin' awake, Sam?"

"Almost."

"Know what you mean. Some officer just flailed hell out of me with his saber," said Wood.

"What happened?"

Wood laughed, "I don't know. Must've gone to sleep and fell off my horse. Next thing I knowed somebody standin' over me cussin' and flailin'."

"What'd you...uh...do?"

"Got out of there! Decided I'd come up here. Whole damn army is asleep, best I can tell. There's stray horses ever' place you look."

"Who's ridin' rear guard?" Nelson asked.

"Forbes and B Company."

"They'll roust 'em out."

The conversation ran itself out with those words and in a few minutes, Sam Nelson nodded in the saddle, his body twisting from side to side with each movement of his horse.

"...Them guns at Port Hudson. Sam, hey, Sam! Wake up!" Nelson heard Wood say.

"What's that," Nelson said, shaking himself like a wet dog.

"I's sayin', sure good to hear them guns at Port Hudson."

"Yeh? Boy, I must of fell off to sleep again. You better keep talkin'," Nelson said, shaking his head vigorously.

From there, the conversations drifted smoothly and pleasantly along from the bridge crossing to sleep, from sleep to weather, from weather to the guns at Port Hudson, from the guns to the Mississippi River, from the river to Baton Rouge; then took a wild jump to women. With that Wood unloaded his heart, but Nelson could think of nothing but his wife, Meg.

Meg and the kids would be asleep now. The kids'd be anticipating their trip to the store. Saturday was the day. Meg would ride the old plow horse; the kids would walk by her side. There was never enough money at this time of year. She'd buy flour, molasses, and a treat for the kids; all in exchange for the butter she'd carry in a sack to the little store at the crossroads.

Neighbor women would be there. They'd talk of any letters they'd received from their husbands. In the store would be a few men too old to go to war. They'd listen to the women, then get up and walk to the front porch and sit among empty boxes cursing their old age, then remember other wars and when they were young.

Then, as the sun fell from the sky in its journey toward night, the women would say their good-byes and return to the solitude which sustained them — their homes and their memories of how it was before the war when their families were complete, when their men were there to do the work of two men and scratch a living from the soil.

"...Yes, sir-ree. Can't wait."

"What's that," Sam asked, hearing but not comprehending.

"Can't wait for ol' Baton Rouge and the ladies," Wood repeated.

"Yeh, well...."

Again, the two men found nothing to say to each other. Their horses plunged on slicing the black night while sugar mills and beautifully draped, moss-covered, live oak groves slid by unnoticed. Nelson and Wood rode on; their path to Baton Rouge was clear. Soon, they thought, all the weariness will be rewarded. But there was yet another obstacle — Sandy Creek.

As the night wore on, Wood returned to the advance guard. He was bored with his companion and looked for someone to talk with — and stay awake with. Then George Steadman came forward. He brought the bad news.

"Sam, accordin' to Grierson's maps, there should be a doggone creek ahead. Sandy Creek he called it. Wants you and me to go ahead and scout it."

Nelson said nothing. Disgust and depression shrouded his tired mind and body. He was so sure that nothing obstructed the route. Now a sick feeling spread over him; he wanted to scream, cry, curse, and quit the march. It would be so easy to disappear, then catch up tomorrow, he told himself.

In the column, the word spread quickly. Riders began nudging their comrades awake in anticipation of the crossing. Some shook themselves awake; others did their best, but fell back into the grip of sleep.

Out in front, Sam Nelson and George Steadman rode quietly forward. Before long, they approached the bridge through a thick grove of trees. Rays of light from the rising sun nipped at the tree tops as they advanced within yards of the bridge. Carefully, they scanned the east approach to the bridge. It was not protected. But across Sandy Creek, it was a different matter. Nelson sighed and shook his head. Long rows of Confederate tents stood as a barrier between Grierson's men and their refuge at Baton Rouge.

Sam motioned Steadman to stay east of the bridge while he crossed for a closer look. The camp lay at least 200 yards away, he figured. In a few minutes, he returned.

"See any guards, Sam?" Steadman whispered as Nelson walked from the bridge.

"Uh...no. But it worries me. There's two slaves building a fire. They didn't see me." Nelson paused. Looking back across the creek, he said, "What do you think?"

"Could be ambush; could be they don't know 'bout us."

"Could be," Sam agreed. "You...uh...tell Colonel Grierson what we found. I'll stay an' watch out; see what happens."

Sam Nelson stretched out on the cool ground, staring at the bridge while Steadman reported their findings. The two Negroes on the opposite side of the bridge near the camp fed the blazing fire. Soon they sat, their knees drawn to their chests, their backs to the bridge, and warmed themselves.

A noise above startled him. He lay very still for several seconds, then rolled on his side. Looking overhead, he saw nothing. Then a squirrel sprang from a small limb to another tree, making a whooshing sound. That was it. Sam rolled back on his stomach.

God, I'm tired, he thought. He shook his head vigorously. With his knuckles, he tried to cleanse his tired, bloodshot eyes. Mosquitoes swarmed about his face. Earlier he rubbed mud on the back of his hands, now he did the same to his face. He placed the Navy Colt on a clump of weeds and with his right hand, scratched a welt on the thumb of his left hand. He was miserable.

Looking at the enemy camp, Sam watched the two blacks. They continued to take the fire into close companionship. Troops should be here soon, Sam reckoned. He pushed himself to his knees, picked up the Navy Colt, then stood beside a tree, looking toward the edge of the grove for any sign of Union cavalry.

The wave of a hand startled Sam. Then he recognized Captain Samuel L. Marshall. Marshall was clad in an old and tattered duster. He led over two dozen men. They were dismounted and moving straight toward Sam through the trees and mud.

When Marshall was within ten yards, he mouthed silently, "Anything?"

Sam Nelson shook his head, then pointed toward the campfire and the two Negroes. Marshall waited for his men to draw close together, then with a hand signal began toward the bridge. Silently, half-crouched, Marshall and H Company of the Sixth Illinois stepped onto the bridge. Two hundred yards in front of them, the Negroes were still sitting, their backs to the bridge. Beyond, the tents for six hundred men sat silently.

Across Sandy Creek, Marshall and H Company spread along a dirt bank and prepared for battle. They were now less than one hundred and fifty yards from the Confederate tents. Their carbines rested, ready to fire in support, as E Company and Captain John Lynch stepped onto the bridge, mounted. The horses' hooves were mute. The short, sturdy bridge concealed their movement.

Sam Nelson hurried to the edge of the grove and retrieved his horse. He assured Lieutenant-Colonel Reuben Loomis, commanding the detachment, that all was in order. Still not a sound from the camp.

"What's their force?" Loomis inquired, staring into the woods, trying to spot the tents across the river.

"Uh...'nough tents for, I'd say, five- or six-hundred men. But, but...uh...there's not many horses," Sam added.

"Infantry," Loomis blurted. "And asleep."

The two men hurried forward, making their way to the head of the company led by Captain Lynch. Within one hundred yards of the rows of tents, Loomis raised his hand and yelled. E Company charged through the rows of tents, their sabers flashing, and pistols exploding from one end of the camp to the other. By the time they re-formed at the west end, H Company approached the opposite end of the camp on foot.

Slowly and carefully, a few tent flaps opened and crippled and bandaged Confederate soldiers emerged, their hands, when possible, raised in surrender. There were only forty convalescent soldiers in the entire camp.

Quickly, the Confederates were questioned. They were what was left of C.C. Wilbourn's Cavalry. Wilbourn was ordered away the day before. He was to intercept the Yankees moving south from Brookhaven! Grierson was overwhelmed.

Their luck still held. Again they had moved past the enemy with such speed that they had thwarted them. Now Baton Rouge was certainly possible. A jubilant Grierson ordered, "Prince, take the Seventh forward. I'll keep the Sixth here to destroy the camp and parole the prisoners."

For Colonel Prince, the Seventh, and the Butternut Guerillas, the road to Baton Rouge lay wide and easy to advance upon. Their speed surprised them. On their left, the land was flat. There was low, swampy ground to the right. In this type terrain, it was near impossible for the enemy to lay an ambush.

Sam Nelson's mud-covered face streaked with sweat. The bright sun grew hotter as the scouts rode closer to Baton Rouge. An occasional plantation house slipped by, but generally, there was no need to stop. The drowsy column had only visions of Baton Rouge and safety. It had been so long since they had a good sleep.

But the march was interrupted less than two hours later. Two shots, followed by another and then another, startled the Butternut Guerillas.

Steadman halted first.

Someone yelled, "Where's the shootin' comin' from?"

Kelly and Fowler rode fifty yards behind the others. They reined their horses to a halt and looked to their rear along the road. Kelly called, "Back here. There's a rider comin'."

Nelson, Steadman and Weedon saw the rider now. A cloud of dust rolled along behind him. Then two hundred yards to his rear was another cloud of dust. There were several riders there.

Kelly and Fowler hurried forward joining the others to await the lone rider. Then he was on them. He skipped his horse to a halt in the middle of the Butternut Guerillas, his pistol in hand.

"Get outta here, boys! The road's full of Yanks to our rear!" he cried.

Sam Nelson rolled his head to the side and said, "Yes, and you are...uh...right among 'em now."

The Confederate officer's jaw dropped; Steadman took his pistol, grabbing it from his hand, before he could react.

"Where you...uh...headed?" Nelson asked calmly.

"Damn Yankees!" the officer said and then, turning his head away, spit.

"Now, doggone it. That's no way to act," George Steadman said while Nelson shook his head, making a clucking sound with his tongue.

Four riders from A Company arrived. They were the ones pursuing the Confederate officer. One laughed and said, "Ran 'im right to the ground, huh, boys?"

"Sure did," Sam said smiling.

"C'mon, where you going in such a rush? You can tell us," Nelson assured his prisoner.

The young lieutenant was in no mood to talk. The scouts rode on, the prisoner remaining with them. Nelson continued his questions.

Finally, the young officer blurted, "Heard shootin' from Sandy Creek; 'bout daylight."

"That was us," Nelson responded, nodding.

"Thought I'd go to the Comite and warn the pickets there."

"What's your name anyhow?"

"Joseph Hinson."

"Glad to make your acquaintance, Joe Hinson. I'm Sam, Sam Nelson," Sam said, pumping the Confederate officer's hand.

"Be seein' you," Sam continued. "George, take him back." Nelson added, "I'm goin' to ride on ahead. Catch up when you...uh...can."

"Quick as a flash. C'mon Joe. They'll parole you so you can go home, or somethin'," Steadman said.

Sam Nelson rode on with his thoughts for nearly three miles. Suddenly a lone man appeared on the road in front of him. Sam couldn't tell if he had stepped from the swamp or what. He was dressed in civilian clothes and showed no sign of being armed, so Nelson approached him casually, his Navy Colt in his belt.

"Mornin', soldier," the stranger greeted Sam.

"Uh...mornin'. Any soldiers 'round here?" Sam asked, getting right to the point.

"Up the road," the man pointed, "'bout a quarter mile, at a house."

"How many?"

"Just one; an officer."

"Fine, suh. Thank you," Nelson said, touching the brim of his hat to the man. Nelson hurried off down the road; the man did the same in the opposite direction.

When Sam Nelson reached the gate twenty-five yards from the front stoop of the low log house, he halted and dismounted. The front door stood open and as he raised his hand to knock, a young attractive lady rose from a table where she and others were eating and stepped toward the door. Sam Nelson did not speak; he did not have to.

"Why come in, suh. We's just sittin' for a bite. Won't ya'll join us?" Her eyes twinkled. She said her name was Melissa something, but he didn't catch it all. He had other worries.

Sam looked by her trying to focus his sun-blinded eyes on the table to see if the Confederate officer was present. He could see only forms and nodded his appreciation at the lady, removed his hat, and stepped into the room. At the table, two more women stood, as did the Confederate officer, and greeted him almost in unison.

The lady from the door flitted about preparing a place for Sam at the table. Sam refused the officer's hand and said, "Excuse me, suh. I best wash up a bit. The mud and all," Sam said, holding his hands up to all present.

"Certainly, by the stove out in the kitchen," the young lady who had met Sam at the door apologized.

The house was built humbly, but the furnishings were better than some that Sam had seen in plantation houses in Mississippi. Sam ducked through a low threshold and into the kitchen.

Beside the stove, near a back door, he found a dry sink. The wash pan was half full of dirty water an Sam picked it up and stepped through the door to empty it. A bare, damp spot on the ground was the dumping place. Only one horse stood among the trees and it was not saddled. Everything looks all right, Sam figured.

Back in the front room, his hands washed, Sam seated himself. On the table was the usual service, but somehow not as tired as what he'd been used to. Heavy stoneware and sugar bowls with zinc teaspoons sticking out partially hid the drab tablecloth. Steaming biscuits and two discouraged plates of butter sat carelessly among bowls and platters of food. Sam's mouth watered.

He ate heartily, interrupting himself only often enough to respond to the small talk being made by the ladies and the Confederate officer. When he was stuffed, he pushed the plate back, refused a cigar offered by the Confederate officer and asked, "Anymore soldiers in the area?"

"'Bout two miles down the road; there's a company."

"They stationed there?"

"Have been for sev'ral days, so they told me this mornin'," the young lieutenant answered.

"Is that all we've got on the Comite crossin', Lieutenant?" one of the ladies asked, frowning.

The Confederate nodded, then smiled, "That's all's needed. We're holdin' the Yanks in Baton Rouge and Port Hudson."

"You...uh...from Port Hudson, suh?"

"No, my command's at Natchez."

"Well, in that case, suh, you may...uh...consider yourself my prisoner," Nelson said without emotion.

The lieutenant's head jerked up abruptly, his hands slapped down on the table, and he glared at Sam. Nelson slowly moved his hand on top of the table, the big Navy Colt, hammer cocked, pointing directly at the officer's chest.

The officer's anger left instantly on seeing the big pistol staring at him, but the anger was not replaced by fright, rather indignation.

"I am an officer, suh, and will start for my command in the mornin'," the lieutenant began. "Besides, suh, you have nothin' to do with me if you're a conscriptin' officer."

One of the ladies, standing ready to slice a berry pie, watched the scene unfold, returned to the table by the officer's side and said indignantly, her eyes blazing, "He ain't no officer and can't conscript you."

Sam Nelson paid her no attention, not wanting to take his eyes off the officer. He stated calmly, "Do you...uh...know who you are talking to?"

The Confederate officer, puzzled, responded, "I suppose you're a soldier, suh."

"Yes, sir. And a live Yankee and you may just consider yo'self my prisoner."

That did it. All three ladies jumped to their feet. There were cries of disgust. There were screams and foul oaths coming from the ladies. Sam Nelson could hardly believe some of the ways in which he was being described. They doubted him and screamed more oaths to add emphasis to their doubts.

One complained, "He ain't nothin' but a common soldier!"

Another agreed, but added, "He ain't even that!"

On and on they ranted. Sam sat calmly, saying nothing, watching them grow angrier and angrier. He only grinned.

Finally, one of the three said, "You can't fool us!" The fire still in their eyes, she turned to the young lieutenant and shouted, "Don't you believe him!"

Patiently Sam waited. Their insults did not offend him. Occasionally he looked out the front door toward the road. Finally, a broad smile crossed his face. He shrugged his shoulders and pointed out the door.

As one, the ladies and the officer became silent. Four heads turned, four pairs of eyes stared, and four mouths sagged open in amazement.

On the road, starting toward the house was a column of twos, Company A, Seventh Illinois Cavalry.

Tears and screams burst from the three ladies as they huddled around their officer. They wanted to console him. "Oh, my dear," they began. They hugged the young, handsome officer saying, "They'll kill you! They'll kill you!"

"Now, now, ladies," Sam Nelson interrupted. "Ain't nary a hair on his fair head goin' to be touched. Don't you worry none now."

Sam motioned for someone to come inside. Two sergeants and Colonel Prince walked toward the house.

Calming themselves, the ladies began, in turn, to kiss the young officer good-bye. Each good-bye took a little longer than the last.

Colonel Prince stepped through the door, revolver drawn, "What have you here, Sam?"

"Don't rightly know, but I think I got...uh...a prisoner, sir."

Prince called to a sergeant from A Company and informed him to escort the lieutenant to the rear. Then to Nelson, he asked, "Any word on the Comite crossing?"

"One company of soldiers is all I found out," Nelson answered.

"Tell Colonel Grierson then. We'll finish up here and wait on you. Give the men a chance to rest," Prince added.

Nelson nodded and turning to the three ladies, now drying their tears, said, "Like to thank you ladies for your hospitality."

They glared, said nothing, and Sam replaced his hat, grinned, and strode toward the road and his horse.

He belched loudly as he went through the gate and ignored the comments of the troops in A Company as he rode back toward the column, only three-fourths of a mile away and approaching on the flat, treeless road.

In fifteen minutes, Nelson was back at the head of the advance probing for any sign of Confederates between the command and the three to four miles to the river. Taking no chances, he relayed Grierson's orders to the other Butternut Guerillas and ordered them to the front with him. Nelson cautioned Steadman, Wood, Robinson, Weedon, Kelly and Fowler: "No mistakes this time boys. You know well as I do, we'd never...uh...stand up in a fight after the hell we been through."

The flat, open road fell away to the Comite River bottoms and the scouts rode to within three hundred yards of the river crossing. Then they dismounted and walked into the trees. Continuing on, they stayed in the trees until they could see the other bank. There were pickets, but no tents.

"What you think, Sam?" Charlie Weedon asked.

Nelson remained silent only shaking his head. Still staring across the river, he motioned for another of the scouts to come forward. Steadman and Wood responded.

"You two move down river on foot. Should be pickets this side too," Nelson ordered.

Steadman said, "C'mon." Wood followed.

Before they'd walked twenty yards, Nelson saw them stop, crouch, and motion for him.

At their side, Nelson looked through the trees. The puzzle was solved.

Sunlight danced off a group of tents, not on the other side of the Comite, but on the same side the scouts were on! The Confederate camp was guarding against the Yankees in Baton Rouge and at Port Hudson. The campsite was opposite the approach of the enemy! Union forces should arrive from the west — but not today.

"Let me go ahead," Art Wood said to Sam Nelson.

"Uh...all right, Art."

Nelson quickly changed his mind and held up his hand for silence. Something moved between them and the river.

From the Comite, little more than a creek at this point, a Confederate soldier rode straight toward the scouts.

Quickly Sam told Wood, "Go on Art. He's spotted us, but...uh...he don't seem too upset. Get your horse and go on down the road."

Wood mounted and rode toward the creek, riding on an oblique from the slowly approaching Confederate picket. The remaining scouts walked back to the road and to their horses.

Still in the woods, the Confederate rider spoke, paying no attention to Wood, "How're you, gentlemen? Ya'll come to relieve us?"

"Yeh. Company'll...uh...be up in a few minutes," Nelson drawled.

"Well, it's 'bout time ya'll come up. We been here now four days." On the road now, he halted in front of the scouts, then added, "Just 'bout outta grub."

No sooner had the soldier halted than George Steadman walked his mule alongside and twisting and turning his head, drawled, "Well, just look at this, won't you?"

Steadman looked at Nelson, then at the Confederate soldier's gun laying across the pommel of the saddle, "Hey, Samuel. Ya'll ever see a shotgun like this one?"

Nelson stared, "No...uh, can't says I ever have. Where'd you get it?" Sam said, admiring the dog-eared shotgun.

"Why, have a look. Becky Sue (his gun) has been with me nigh onto two years now. Right fine gun," the Confederate picket said proudly, handing the shotgun stock-first to Nelson.

The instant Nelson held the gun, Steadman cocked the hammer on his single-action Colt and spoke quietly, grinning, "Blow you through if you make a sound."

The young soldier was noticeably frightened and Nelson quickly added, "Won't hurt you none, boy. Just do's you're told."

Steadman added, "Let's me an' you take a little ride." He motioned the Confederate ahead and together they rode toward the column as Art Wood returned from viewing the camp close-up.

"Well, Art?" Sam asked.

"Well, you know the camp's on the east side of the creek. Right at the end of the lane leading to the ford. Dry ground and trees all through the tents. And fenced!"

"That rules out much of a charge. Uh...you check the flank?" Nelson interrupted.

"Might get some men in there on foot. This fence runs on for another two hundred yard and then turns south. Just up ahead an old fence starts and runs nearly to the creek. Camp's boxed in; fence on two sides, creek on one."

"Can we...uh...get there any way 'ceptin' the road?"

"Main charge'll have to be straight down the road and the road's wide open, the way I see it," Wood said, wiping the sweat from his face. The trees blocked what little breeze there was. Even with the clear, sunny sky, the air was humid and sticky.

"Art, you...uh...stay here. Keep out of sight. Rest of you go back a piece with me."

Seeing the Seventh in the distance, Nelson spurred his horse toward them, leaving the others. Grierson and Prince rode at the head of the column.

"Looks like a company, sir. Just as we expected."

Grierson nodded and said, "We talked to the prisoner Steadman brought back. That's what he told us too. Find anything else?"

"Camp is...uh...boxed in. Fences and the river make it impossible to get more'n a column of fours in there."

Grierson shook his head, tugged at his dusty beard, then threw his hand in the air, halting the column. "Ed," Grierson said to Colonel Prince, "let 'em rest."

While Prince passed the word, Grierson, Nelson, and Lieutenant David Bradshaw knelt in the road sketching the layout of the camp, the creek and the fences.

Grierson ordered, "Lieutenant Bradshaw, you take A Company and flank to the south of the camp on foot." Turning to Lieutenant-Colonel Loomis, who had come up from the Sixth to inquire about the halt, "Reuben, you know Will Ashmead in Company I. Get 'im for me."

Captain William Ashmead soon joined the circle and Grierson filled him in on the plan. Ashmead would take D, E, and I Companies down the road in a column of fours.

Then Grierson warned, "Hit 'em hard. We want to run 'em like cattle if we can. Less chance gettin' shot up that way."

"I understand, Colonel," Ashmead nodded.

"Prince," Grierson said, "let's move."

With the Butternut Guerillas in the lead, Companies D, E, and I rode down the road with A following. Colonel Grierson and the remainder of the column followed several hundred yards back. Captain Jason Smith's Artillery rode beside the head of the column with Grierson in case they were needed.

Three hundred yards from the camp, Company A and Lieutenant Bradshaw left the road and proceeded into the field to take up their position for their flanking attack. When they appeared to be in position, Captain Ashmead gave the order for the three companies with him to charge.

Sam Nelson yelled, squeezing several shots into the trees as he rode headlong into the Confederate camp on the Comite River. In seconds, the calm, early morning camp was a shambles. Soldiers ran in every direction.

Sam Nelson had little time to think of it, but it appeared to him that the Rebs were scared as much as surprised. They didn't anticipate such an all-out attack, particularly from the east, their rear.

Camp kettles and steaming stew were scattered throughout the camp. There were shotguns and a few carbines propped against trees; none fired. There were coats, blankets, and hats strewn throughout where earlier a busy owner had been standing. Men chased stampeding horses through the trees trying to take that one sure method of escape. Most failed.

Thirty minutes passed. The Sixth rode by the camp and forded the creek on their way to Baton Rouge. The Seventh collected fleeing Confederates from the surrounding woods. One cavalryman from I Company discovered sixteen Confederate soldiers hiding in a hole that water in the stream had washed from the bank. They surrendered without hesitation.

Three more Rebs were caught hiding in the fork of an oak tree. All in all, forty-two prisoners were taken in thirty minutes on the morning of May 2nd.

Besides the shots fired by Grierson's men, only a half dozen or so Confederate bullets split the air. At nine o'clock, the Seventh splashed into and swam the little river and rode out to catch the Sixth and the Butternut Guerillas.

Three miles beyond the Comite River, at a plantation house, first, the Sixth, then the Seventh, called a halt. The worn and tattered men of Grierson's two regiments dismounted to dry their equipment. It had been thirty hours for some, and more for others, since they had taken any kind of extended rest.

The saddle-sore cavalrymen sprawled on the ground, many half naked, their clothes draped from trees. The ford on the Comite was deeper than expected. Many, especially those riding small horses, were soaked through.

Not long after dismounting, men started talking about Baton Rouge. It was close. Six miles, some had it. Someone figured the two regiments had traveled eighty miles in the last thirty hours. Another added, "Hell, that ain't nothin'! We done rode eight hundred miles in sixteen days."

Everywhere there was a certain giddiness. Troopers that had caused trouble and been failures all their lives now had something of which to be proud. They were already speculating that what they had accomplished would be one of the greatest events of this "damned, confounded, entire war," as they called it.

The officers had other things for which to be thankful. Inside the large plantation house, Colonel Benjamin Grierson sat quietly. He had directed a minor miracle. About nine hundred men had left Tennessee; he'd lost about twenty, as close as he could calculate. Some were captured because they straggled. Others were left with the wounded. The wounded and the dead created his deepest ache. With luck the captured would be paroled, the wounded tended, and the souls of the dead received in a happier, less war-weary world. Grierson relaxed.

Now, as the morning wore on, the plantation grounds looked like a battlefield. Sleeping soldiers and beaten, jaded men trying to sleep littered the grounds. Sam Nelson, just back from a short ride toward Baton Rouge, joined them. He'd already reported to Prince. The road was clear to Baton Rouge, as far as he could tell.

Sprawled on the ground, Sam Nelson's legs twitched and kept him awake. Too long wrapped around a horse. Sam thought. He rolled on his back, switched to his stomach, brushed away an ant that crawled onto his hand, and sat up when he heard a mumble grow into a roar from the area where the prisoners were held.

Sam raised himself on his elbows. Around him a few others did the same, but all in all, most of the men were now in deep sleep in the shade of the huge trees draped with long clusters of the beautiful Spanish moss.

The guards surrounding the prisoners started across the plantation grounds and toward a road that curved south away from the plantation entrance. An open field made over a mile of road visible. It disappeared into a heavily wooded area. Some of the prisoners stood and cheered now. Sam Nelson's heart pounded. Rebs!!

He jumped to his feet and looked toward the road. Sure enough, exiting the woods was a force of mounted soldiers. The dust rolled into the trees. Running to the first horse he could find, he jerked the girth strap tight and mounted.

Riding by George Steadman, he yelled, "Tell Grierson. Cav'ry comin'!"

"Huh?" Steadman asked groggily.

"Cav'ry comin'! Tell Grierson!"

Steadman nodded and Nelson sped out the main gate. As he rounded the curve in the road, he slowed the horse to a lope and horse and rider, both near collapse, made their way to meet the column which looked to be no more than one or two companies.

But what would two companies of alert, well-rested, well-armed Confederate cavalry do to Grierson's groggy, sleepy, and collapsing command? Sam asked himself.

He sorted his plan in his mind. He wanted to slow them long enough for Colonel Grierson to form a defense and meet their attack. He feared this time they would not believe his disguise, so he decided he could cross the field and lead them away from the plantation first, then turn them in that direction. His horse was tired, but a short run might work.

Now Sam Nelson walked the horse. His muscles were taut. He figured he would gouge his heels into the bone-weary horse's flanks, lash the tired mount across a shallow ditch, and into the run for his life — and that of Grierson's raiders. Keep low in the saddle, he reminded himself.

The sun beat down on Sam's head and sweat blurred his vision. In front of him, five hundred yards away, the column of twos came closer. He swiped at the sweat. Any second now, Nelson thought. Suddenly, a rider burst forward toward Sam. Stunned, Sam stopped his horse and waited. What now?

Four hundred yards (I'll let him close and wait for the column to give chase.), three hundred yards (Sam cocked his Navy Colt), two hundred yards...the rider's dressed in Union blues!!

Aloud, Nelson exclaimed, tears in his eyes, "By God, he's a Yank!"

Sam let the hammer down on the old Colt and slipped it inside his belt. The rider slowed his horse and walked carefully, his carbine resting on his right knee, toward Sam.

"Don't shoot! Don't shoot!" Sam Nelson shouted.

"Hands up, Reb!" the soldier commanded.

"I'm not a Reb. I'm Seventh Illinois!"

"Yeh, and I'm Jeff Davis. Face your horse the other way; keep your hands in the air!"

As Nelson followed the Union sergeant's orders, skirmishers from the sergeant's unit moved in the woods along the fence. Down the road, a lone rider came from the plantation.

Colonel Grierson, his blue uniform dusty and ragged in the bright sun, sat his horse proudly. The big bay's head was held high; his tail shimmered in the sunlight. Again, tears rose in Sam Nelson's eyes.

From behind Nelson, the Union sergeant asked, "Who's that?"

"That...uh...rider's my Colonel. Ben Grierson, commanding the Sixth and Seventh Illinois Cav'ry."

The sergeant clucked his horse closer to Sam. He stopped and then continued on toward Colonel Grierson. The Union skirmishers drew near the fence on Sam's left. Each rested his carbine on a tree, taking aim at the Colonel.

Grierson waved a white cloth. The Union sergeant rode up to him. The carbines slid from the fence.

Sam watched as the Union sergeant and Colonel Grierson faced each other, talking.

"Well, I'll be damned!" the sergeant exclaimed loud enough that Sam could hear.

Then Sam watched the sergeant slip his carbine into its scabbard, remove his hat, and ruffle his carrot-collared hair.

Shaking his head, he repeated, "I'll be damned!"

An hour later, at eleven o'clock, Captain J. Franklin Godfrey's First Louisiana Cavalry escorted the Sixth Illinois, Jason Smith's First Artillery, the Confederate prisoners, the Seventh Illinois, the Negro horse herders, and about thirty vehicles of every description from the plantation and toward Baton Rouge, six miles away. The force stretched for two miles.

Less than a mile from Baton Rouge, Grierson's command was now accompanied by Colonel Nathan Augustus Munroe Dudley and his staff representing General Christopher C. Auger, commanding Baton Rouge, soldiers stationed there, and most other curious persons in the city. The street thronged. Thousands welcomed the long column with shouts and cheers. Banners waved, flags flew, and music played.

The men of the Sixth and Seventh groaned and sat erect in their dusty uniforms — those who had uniforms left — on their starved, beaten and exhausted horses. The procession wound through the public square and down to the Mississippi River where their horses watered. Then, a short time later, the raiders mounted and rode the two miles outside Baton Rouge to Magnolia Grove.

It was after sunset when the troopers in Grierson's command slid from their horses. They stripped the saddles off and collapsed onto the ground without benefit of food or blankets. The One Hundred and Sixteenth New York and the Forty-Eighth Mississippi Infantry Regiments brought food and other provisions, but too late. The ride was over, the Sixth and Seventh Illinois slept.

Sam Nelson tossed and turned for over an hour before he slept. Finally, he fumbled in the dark, found the Yankee whiskey, drank, and replaced the canteen. Again and again in his mind, as he listened to the breeze rustling the heavy magnolia leaves, he saw an old black man and a small boy standing in the street in Baton Rouge. The old man's words came to Sam:

> You must look at them people with respect, child. They's the great warriors what come from the North. They travel without sleep and they stop the railroads and cut up the track.

Finally, Sam Nelson slept. The nightmare was over. The story of the Butternut Guerillas was done.

Harper's Pictorial History of the Civil War caught Grierson and his raiders entering Baton Rouge, Lousiana. (Author's Collection)

Aftermath

During the nearly two years remaining in the Civil War, the men who participated in the story of the Butternut Guerillas met different fates.

Colonel Benjamin Henry Grierson cooperated with General Nathaniel Prentiss Banks during the siege of Port Hudson in Louisiana. On one occasion, at Clinton, Louisiana, on June 3, 1863, a month after his successful raid, he stood off a force more than double his own. On that same day, Colonel Grierson received appointment by President Abraham Lincoln to the rank of Brigadier General of Volunteers. He commanded the First Cavalry Division of the Sixteenth Army Corps under General Stephen Augustus Hurlbut. Later, his commands included a Cavalry Corps of the District of Western Tennessee; a cavalry division of Western Tennessee, Army of the Tennessee; and the cavalry corps of the Military Division of Western Mississippi. He was promoted Major General of Volunteers on May 27, 1865 and remained in the U.S. Army as a commander of the Tenth U.S. Cavalry, the famed "Buffalo Soldiers," until his retirement in 1890.

Grierson's "Ol Homestead" in Jacksonville, Illinois. (Courtesy Fort Davis National Historic Site, Fort Davis, Texas)

Lieutenant-Colonel Reuben Loomis of the Sixth Illinois Cavalry remained with the Sixth to his death on November 2, 1863. His place of residence at the time of enlistment was DuQuoin, Illinois and he served his regiment well through the six months following Grierson's Raid. He was killed by Major Thomas G.S. Herod in Memphis, Tennessee.

Major Mathew H. Starr, of the Sixth Illinois Cavalry, was promoted to the rank of Lieutenant-Colonel after Loomis' death and then to Colonel of the regiment on July 19, 1864. The Jacksonville, Illinois, colonel was with the detachment that was attacked in Memphis by Nathan Bedford Forrest's raiders on the morning of August 21, 1864. The wound he received in that raid was fatal; Colonel Starr died of his wounds on October 1, 1864.

Major Thomas G.S. Herod of the Sixth Illinois Cavalry continued with his regiment until he killed Lieutenant-Colonel Loomis on November 2, 1863. The native of Shawneetown, Illinois, was sentenced on February 13, 1865, to ten years in prison where he served until released May 2, 1866, by order of President Andrew Johnson.

Colonel Edward Prince of the Seventh Illinois Cavalry was a lawyer in Quincy, Illinois, before entering the service. Clashes with Colonel Grierson following the raid led to Prince's dissatisfaction with the military, but he served the Seventh with distinction until he was mustered out of service by the order of General C.C. Washburn on October 15, 1864. In Quincy, after the war, he became one of the leading citizens.

Lieutenant-Colonel William D. Blackburn of the Seventh Illinois Cavalry remained at Newman's Plantation after the battle at Wall's Bridge on May 2, 1863. His wounds were too severe for him to be moved and the loss of blood he suffered caused him to slip into a coma and die on May 17, 1863.

Richard W. Surby, the first leader of the Butternut Guerillas, a resident of Paris, Illinois, was moved from Newman's Plantation to a Confederate hospital in Magnolia, Mississippi, twenty miles away. His condition improved and he was moved to Libby Prison at Richmond, Virginia. Almost immediately, he was exchanged and permitted to return to Illinois. He rejoined his command in Tennessee on October 13, 1863. On February 10, 1864, he re-enlisted as a veteran and was promoted to Hospital Steward on the Field and Staff of the Seventh Illinois Cavalry. He was mustered out of service on November 4, 1865 and discharged two weeks later at Camp Butler near Springfield, Illinois.

Samuel Nelson, the second and last leader of the Butternut Guerillas, entered the service of his country from New Haven, Illinois in Gallatin County. He continued in service with Company G of the Seventh Illinois Cavalry Regiment until he was mustered out of service on October 15, 1864.

Isaac E. Robinson, a native of Elkhorn Grove in the north-west corner of Illinois, remained with B Company of the Seventh Illinois until mustered out of service on October 15, 1864.

George W. Steadman, the short, wiry private from C Company of the Seventh, followed the lead of several of his fellow scouts and was mustered out of the service on October 15, 1864.

Charles K. Weedon of , Illinois was promoted corporal and mustered out of service as a member of Company E of the Seventh on February 4, 1865. Weedon was a recruit and had not joined the Army until February of 1862.

Uriah Fowler of Company H, Seventh Illinois Cavalry, remained in the Army as a private. The Shelbyville, Illinois, resident was mustered out of the Army on October 15, 1864.

William Buffington, the only Butternut Guerilla killed on the raid, was from Rock Creek area of Carroll and Whiteside Counties in northwestern Illinois. He was a private at the time of his death near Philadelphia, Mississippi at noon on April 24, 1863. He was buried near where he fell.

Arthur S. Wood from Wysox in Carroll County, Illinois, did not complete the war with his companions. Records show that the private from B Company of the Seventh was taken prisoner by Confederate forces. Subsequently, his name was dropped from the Regiment's rolls. His fate is not known.

Lycurgus K. Kelly, the corporal from , Illinois, re-enlisted in February 1864. After a furlough, he returned to Mississippi and while recruits in the Seventh Illinois were fighting at Brice's Crossroads in Mississippi, a Union Army guard mistook Kelly for an enemy and fired several shots, killing Kelly instantly.

Sixth and Seventh Illinois Cavalry Regiments
May, 1863 - December, 1863

The Sixth and the Seventh Illinois Cavalry Regiments remained at Magnolia Grove outside Baton Rouge for several days following their successful raid through Mississippi.

About May 20, the Sixth and Seventh were ordered to Port Hudson with General Christopher Colon Auger. On June 3, the Sixth, on an expedition to Clinton, Louisiana, was engaged in a fight with the enemy. There were two killed, four wounded, and three taken prisoner. On June 4, they returned to Port Hudson. Privates William P. Wycoff and George L. Fitch died of wounds.

From June 23 to July 9, both regiments were involved in laying siege to Port Hudson. After the surrender of the fortification and on July 19, the Sixth and Seventh boarded the steamers *Planet* and *Imperial* bound for Memphis up the Union-held Mississippi River. A few days later, they rejoined General Grant's Department of the Tennessee.

Their base camp was at Germantown and it was from there they moved to Collierville to do battle with Confederate Generals James R. Chalmers and Nathan B. Forrest. Horace T. Dort and Levi D. Vinson from

Cottonwood, Illinois were captured on October 11 and assumed dead. The following day, Lieutenant Henry Nicholson was killed and Lieutenant William McCausland seriously wounded. McCausland recovered, but Lieutenant Charles F. Lee died of his wounds.

Off and on during the next month and a half, various companies from the Sixth and Seventh were engaged. At Quinn's Mill, Mississippi, Francis T. Davis was wounded and died shortly thereafter on November 6.

In November, the Sixth and Seventh joined with Colonel Edward Hatch on an expedition to Covington, Tennessee. Nathan Bedford Forrest engaged them on November 29 near La Grange. It was a running fight and not decisive for either side. At one time Forrest almost had the brigade surrounded, but they slipped away.

On December 4 at Moscow, Tennessee, there was sharp clash with Forrest. The Sixth had five killed, six wounded, twenty taken prisoner, and two reported missing. The enemy was routed and driven fifteen miles. Among the dead were William Hendrix of McLeansboro, Illinois and Harvey Yewell of Golconda. Private Yewell was reported missing in action and assumed dead. The Sixth rejoined the brigade at Germantown to continue their operations against Forrest and General James Ronald Chalmers.

1864

During 1863, the Sixth and Seventh had their glory, but also their grief. Too often, the grief came in the form of another great cavalry leader, Nathan Bedford Forrest. Eighteen hundred and sixty-four, the third full year of the war, was to be no different. It seemed to many of the men in the Sixth and Seventh that Forrest was everywhere!

An expedition to West Point, Mississippi, from February 10 to February 25 had the Sixth and Seventh under command of General William Sooy Smith. At West Point, Nathan Bedford Forrest struck again. He inflicted losses on the retreating regiments all the way to Okolona. Privates Davis D. Andes, Azro B. Bliss, James Churchfield, John Waber, Edward More, Wiley Jackson, and Charles W. Gallentine of the Sixth and Seventh Illinois were lost. The regiments licked their wounds at Germantown.

The end of March was the happiest day the Sixth and Seventh had known since the day in May 1863 when they settled under the pleasant Magnolia Grove trees near Baton Rouge. It was re-enlistment day and it meant most would be returning home to Illinois on furlough. Over half the officers and men of the Seventh re-enlisted, while nearly as many did the same in the Sixth. Through April and the early part of May, Illinois was filled with the heroes of Grierson's Raid. Many had not seen their families and friends since late December 1861. It was a happy time.

At Mattoon, Illinois on May 11, 1864, the men of the Sixth Illinois Cavalry rejoined in preparation for the journey back to Memphis. The Seventh also returned and in a few days the Sixth and Seventh were together again in the little Tennessee village of Germantown.

General Samuel Davis Sturgis took the Seventh, mostly recruits, with him to attempt to block Forrest's drive into Tennessee. At Guntown, or Brice's Crossroads, 3300 dismounted troops under Forrest turned back and soundly defeated Sturgis' force of 8000. When the battle was over and Sturgis' force was fleeing for their lives, it was found that Joel B. Smith and Washington Clow of the Seventh were missing. They were never found.

A short time after, Forrest feinted toward southwestern Tennessee. Sherman feared that Forrest might somehow disrupt his drive toward Atlanta and ordered General Andrew Jackson Smith toward Guntown. Seven companies of the Sixth were sent to Collierville, ten miles east of Germantown, to protect the railroad and thus support Smith's campaign. On July 10, George W. Savage died. Private Joseph H. Hardin of Eldorado, Illinois, died at Memphis of wounds a week later. Lieutenant Edward Bell was killed on the 22nd and two of his men were captured while they patrolled the railroad. Private Henry C. Echols of McLeansboro, Illinois, died of wounds three days later.

Smith engaged Forrest and was then ordered toward Oxford, Tennessee. Again, Smith was joined by the Sixth and Seventh. On August 5, Private Leman E. Hayes of the Seventh was killed. On August 13, at Hurricane Creek, Forrest struck again. This time it was Privates John Dial,

Richard W. Solomon, and Jacob Smith who were Forrest's victims. Three days later, Charles T. Brumfield and Abraham Robinson of Mt. Vernon, Illinois lost their lives.

A detachment left behind in Memphis while Smith drove toward Oxford was made up of several companies of the Sixth and seven companies from the Seventh. Still, Forrest found them. He and his raiders slipped through the fog late on Saturday night, August 20. When the excitement was over Colonel Mathew H. Starr of the Sixth lay mortally wounded. Lieutenant Thomas W.H. Miller and one of his men were captured, but several others from both regiments were not so lucky. Privates Samuel H. Huston, Robert Waddle, James W. Mitchell, and Chetal Clark did not see the dawn burn the fog away on Sunday, August 21. James C. Clendenen and William L. Harris died of their wounds nearly two weeks later.

Somehow regaining their composure after this attack, the Sixth and Seventh chased Forrest and his Confederates to the Tallahatchie River. General A.J. Smith on hearing of the sneak attack returned to the vicinity of White Station, Tennessee, in order to protect against another such occurrence.

While at White Station, the men with Smith from the Sixth and Seventh continued to take losses. Joseph B. Lindsay was killed on September 18 and four days later, Privates Abner Earnest, Waheau Oliver, William D. Ramsey, and Richard Douglas were all mortally wounded.

Since Atlanta had fallen on September 2, it was decided to drive toward Clifton in anticipation of any Southern drive into Tennessee. General Edward Hatch took the Sixth and Seventh to protect General Cadwallader Colder Washburn's Infantry toward Lawrenceburg, Tennessee. Washburn decided to remove his infantry and Hatch continued on to Savannah, Tennessee, and then back to Pulaski. On this ride, they were intercepted by Confederate General John Bell Hood who was beginning his Tennessee Campaign. After some limited skirmishes near Florence, Alabama, Hatch got the cavalry out and headed back toward Pulaski.

With the Seventh ordered to Pulaski to anticipate Hood's next moves, things slowed for few days. Then, on November 8, the Seventh found themselves doing picket duty along Shoal Creek. On the Duck River near Shelbyville, the Sixth contented themselves with sporadic forays against the Confederate forces in the area. On November 20, James E. Evans was killed and two days later, First Lieutenant George Anderson of Kinderhook, Illinois met the same fate.

The Seventh operated around Campbellsville and was nearly surrounded by Forrest. They narrowly escaped to Columbia on the 24th. On November 29, the Sixth became engaged in a five-hour battle near Lawrenceburg, Tennessee. They too retreated to Columbia.

Raids toward Shelbyville, Pike's Ford, and a return toward Columbia led to participation in the Battle of Franklin. Both the Sixth and Seventh were in the battle for this little Tennessee town on November 30. The Seventh captured several soldiers of a division of Confederate infantry and then the Sixth and Seventh, together, retreated toward Nashville to shore up that city's defenses.

While Hood's Army drew near Nashville, the Sixth was sent toward Glasgow, Kentucky. On December 13, they were back at Nashville and joined with the Seventh and Hatch's Division. Before the day was over, the Seventh had carried three redoubts, captured thirteen pieces of artillery, and a large number of prisoners. The Seventh suffered thirteen killed.

The Battle of Nashville continued the next day with the Seventh involved in the attack on the works at Brentwood Hills. Major John M. Graham was seriously wounded, Captain William McCausland did not survive his wound, and Captain Uriah Brant suffered severe, but not fatal wounds. The Sixth captured two redoubts and nine pieces of artillery. They took a number of prisoners and lost two, one from Captain Dan Maulding's H Company, Private Mike McCarty. On the 15th, the Sixth struck mounted, then on foot, and with the Seventh later in the day, pursued Hood's forces toward the Tennessee River and later to Florence.

Privates William Low, Charles P. Carver, Daniel H. Shanks, Axle F. Wahlgrane, and George B. Butler died on the 15th and 16th at Nashville. They were all members of the Seventh. Two men from the Sixth, Henry A. Henson of Cairo, Illinois and Leonard Denson of Shawneetown, Illinois, died of wounds during the following week.

With the Battle of Nashville over, Hood retreated. The Sixth and Seventh pursued. The retreat by Hood was marked with dead from the two Illinois cavalries. Private George Martin was killed near Franklin on December 16. Royal Cockrell died near Franklin the next day. John H. Mansly was mortally wounded near Murfreesboro. Louis Stenger was killed in action at Buford, Tennessee on the 24th. On Christmas Day, 1864, Andrew J. Phillips was killed in action near Pulaski.

1865

The last year of the Civil War began quietly for the men of the Sixth and Seventh Illinois Cavalry Regiments. Back in Nashville, the wounded were still suffering and on January 1, just as the New Year dawned, Private George T. Pool died of wounds received two weeks earlier. Francis M. Smith of Paris, Illinois, joined him on January 14.

On January 13, the Seventh rejoined the Sixth at Gravelly Springs, Alabama near Florence. Skirmishes took the lives of Marion J. Reader, Charles Steele and John J. Smith on the 25th, 26th, and 27th of January. Then in February, the Sixth and Seventh moved to Eastport, Mississippi. They remained there until May when the Department of Alabama and Mississippi surrendered.

During the next months, the Sixth and Seventh were at times together, at other times separated, and sometimes serving detached duty without their own units. The Seventh spent the bigger part of May and June in Okolona, Mississippi.

Five days after the cruiser *Shenandoah* fired the last shot of the war in the North Pacific on June 28, the Sixth was ordered to Nashville and after a short time, back to Decatur, Alabama with the Seventh. They did not remain there long. While the Seventh remained in Decatur during August and September, the Sixth moved to Montgomery. In late August, they were ordered to Demopolis. In September, six companies were detached to Montgomery, two to Opolika, and one to Tuskegee.

All the moving around and false hopes of home harassed the soldiers in the Sixth and Seventh during these months. Many had been home for only one furlough during the entire period of the war. They had fought at Bird's Point in Missouri, formed Sherman's Corps' advance to Granada, Mississippi, in 1862, and fought in innumerable other engagements during both guerrilla and conventional warfare. Occupation duty six hundred miles from home was not the glory and the reward that they deserved. They were ready to go home!

Finally, the word came. On October 20, the Seventh marched for Nashville and the Sixth was ordered to Selma, Alabama, two weeks later. On November 4, the Seventh was mustered out of service. The 5th of November turned out to be the same glorious day for the Sixth.

Two weeks later in November, the Sixth and the Seventh were at Camp Butler near Springfield, Illinois, going through the long lines for the last time. They received their final pay and on November 20, 1865 were discharged from their service with the United States Army.

THE END

SIXTH CAVALRY REGIMENT

FIELD AND STAFF.

Name and Rank.	Residence.
Colonel.	
Thos. H. Cavanaugh	Jacksonville
Benjamin H. Grierson	Jacksonville
Mathew H. Starr	
John Lynch	Olney
Lieutenant Colonels.	
John Olney	DuQuoin
Reuben Loomis	Jacksonville
Mathew H. Starr	Jacksonville
John Lynch	Olney
William D. Glass	Golconda
Majors.	
Benjamin H. Grierson	Jacksonville
William L. Caldwell	
Arno Voss	Chicago
Adjutants.	
John Wood	Quincy
Isaac Gibson	DuQuoin
Battalion Adjutants.	
Reuben Loomis	
James D. Stacy	
John J. Ritchey	McLeansboro
Mathew H. Starr	Jacksonville
Thomas G. S. Herod	Shawneetown
Charles W. Whitsit	DuQuoin
John Lynch	Olney
William D. Glass	Golconda
Alonzo D. Pierce	Pope county
Elijah T. Phillips	Cairo
Lucius B. Skinner	DuQuoin
Thos. H. Cavanaugh, Jr	Harrisburg
William H. Beck	Pope co
Will Yates	Golconda
William H. Beck	Jacksonville
Haney R. Parker	DuQuoin
Sylvanus Gard	Albion
William H. Boicourt	Olney
Joseph T. Janes	Metropolis
Samuel N. Docker	
Henry C. Jaques	
Nelson B. Newman	Metropolis

Name and Rank.	Residence.
Quartermasters.	
John M. Snyder	
John C. Grierson	
Mathias K. Busick	
Battalion Quartermasters.	
James D. Stacy	
Thomas P. Stacy	
George N. Hubbard	
Surgeons.	
John N. Niglas	Peoria
Archibald B. Agnew	Anna
First Ass't Surgeons.	
James S. Whitmire	Metamora
Archibald B. Agnew	Anna
Josephus R. Corbus	Mendota
Second Ass't Surgeons.	
Joseph H. Everett	
Madison G. Nixon	Waterloo
Chaplains.	
James F. Jaques	
Augustus DeFoe	
John H. Aughey	
Commissaries.	
George T. Redfern	Metropolis
William Pollard	
NON-COMMISSIONED STAFF.	
Sergeant Majors.	
Axel Nyburg	
Firth Charles Worth	
James David Angell	
Thomas Burns	
Robert Bradley	
George W. Halladay	
George W. Morey	
Q. M. Sergeants.	
William A. Beck	
John J. Clark	
Mathias K. Busick	
William Riley	
Commis. Sergeants.	
George Redfern	

Name and Rank.	Residence.
William Pollard	Massac co
Robert F. Glass	
Hospital Stewards.	
Edmond W. Tyler	
Ignatz A. Niglas	
Louis Oberhauser	
Thomas A. Lovelady	
William A. Duer	
Chief Buglers.	
George Bammell	
Gottworth Eileinstein	
Saddler Sergeant.	
David M. Fligor	
COMPANY A.	
Captains.	
George W. Peck	Metropolis
Alonzo D. Pierce	Pope co
Alexander Vickers	Massac co
First Lieutenants.	
Thomas Baker	Pope co
Alexander Vickers	Massac co
Nicholas Robinson	
Second Lieutenants.	
Jacob E. Vaughn	Pope co
J. H. Benham	
Thomas J. Raphael	Massac co
First Sergeant.	
Alonzo D. Pierce	Pope co
Q. M. Sergeant.	
Firth Charles Worth	Pope co
Sergeants.	
Zebulon P. Thompson	Pope co
Thomas Spencer	
Alfred W. Canfield	
James Babb	
Corporals.	
Albert Babb	Pope co
John F. Hamlirg	
William Brush	
John F. Mann	Massac co
William J. Henley	Pope co
Alexander Vickers	Massac co

Name and Rank.	Residence.
Thomas M. Thompson	Pope co
Alvin B. Hawkins	
Buglers.	
Julius H. Benham	Pope co
George T. Redfern	Massac co
Farrier.	
Martin Edwards	Massac co
Blacksmith.	
Martin Edwards	Massac co
Privates.	
Atkins, Samuel	Massac co
Beesley, William	
Brown, Henry	Pope co
Cravens, Orien R	
Cravens, Solomon T	Johnson co
Campbell, John D	Pope co
Cooper, Samuel H	Massac co
Conner, Torrence	Massac co
Depue, Josiah W	Metropolis
Detterline, King H	Pope co
Dean, Frank M	Massac co
Evans, James	Pope co
Edwards, Daniel T	Massac co
Edwards, James R	
Faughn, Enos	
Green, Benjamin F	Pope co
Golightly, Francis	Massac co
Gibson, Joseph A	Pope co
Glenn, John	Pope co
Holden, Green	
Holderfield, Thos. F	
Holderfield, James H	Massac co
Holderfield, Wm. A	
Herreld, Isaac N	Pope co
Herrell, John P	
Habie, John	
Harris, Edward	
Hodge, John	Metropolis
Jones, H. Jasper	
Kibbler, William E	
Liggett, Thomas	Massac co
Lott, Jonathan	
Madden, Marcus	
McGregory, Joel	
McMullen, John	
Mitchell, John	

Newbury, Jacob	Pope co.
Neill, Jesse	Massac co.
Noel, John D.	Pope co.
Noe, Edgar S.	Massac co.
Perrin, James Z.	Pope co.
Paisley, Joseph T.	
Paisley, A. Jackson	
Paisley, John H.	
Paisley, George H.	
Paisley, William H.	
Pollard, William	
Paine, C. Manning	Massac co.
Raphael, Thomas J.	
Ruble, Nathan	
Ruble, John S.	
Robinson, Nicholas	Massac co.
Senton, Greenbury	
Sexton, William A.	
Smith, William E.	
Smith, Thomas	
Suris, James H.	Pope co.
Spencer, John	
Shaw, John W	
Suris, William C.	
Stafford, Samuel L.	Massac co.
Stafford, Henry D.	
Stepter, William R.	
Smith, George L.	
Steele, Alonzo	Massac co.
Tuten, John or Rob't C	Pope co.
Upjohn, Charles	
Vincent, Newman	
Wilkins, Henry J.	
Whitelock, John C.	
Wells, James	Massac co.
Yates, Benjamin F.	
Yates, Abraham S.	

VETERANS.

First Sergeant.

Alexander Vickers	Golconda

Sergeants.

Nicholas Robinson	Golconda
Albert Babbs	
William Brush	
John F. Mann	
Samuel Atkins	

Corporals.

Thomas Raphael	Golconda
Benjamin Yates	
Mark D. Madden	
John C. Whitelock	

Privates.

Beasley, William	Golconda
Cartwright, Thomas	
Dean, Francis M.	
Faughn, Enos	
Golightly, Francis M.	
Glenn, John	Massac co.
Garvey, Thomas B.	
Harrell, John P.	
Holderfield, Wm. A.	
Holderfield, James	
Holderfield, Thos. F	
Kibbler, James	Pope co.
Kibbler, William E.	
Lott, Jonathan	
Liggett, Thomas	
McMullen, John G.	Golconda

COMPANY B.

Captains.

John C. Fite	Johnson co.
William B. Peterson	
Wm. B. Peterson	Johnson co.
William H. Holly	Crittenden co, K

First Lieutenants.

John C. Fite	Johnson co.
William B. Peterson	
William H. Holly	Crittenden co, K
John C. Fite	Johnson co.

Second Lieutenants.

Lemuel L. Lawrence	Reynoldsburg
William B. Peterson	Johnson co.
John C. Fite	

Noel, John D.	
Perrin, James Z.	
Pollard, William	
Stafford, Henry D.	
Upjohn, Charles S.	

First Sergeant.

Benj. F. Lawrence	Johnson co.

Q. M. Sergeant.

Fountain Lay	Johnson co.

Sergeants.

Hiram H. Wise	Golconda
Isaac Britten	
James M. Clark	

Corporals.

Hugh P. Robinson	
Jackson Ivy	Johnson co.
John W. D. Wommack	
John Latta	
Joshua Simpson	
Charles S. Maelers	
Matthew J. Murphy	
Joshua H. Ramsy	

Farrier.

George W. Chapman	Johnson co.

Blacksmith.

Cornelius A. Shew	Johnson co.

Privates.

Angel, James H.	Johnson co.
Boozer, George W.	
Bratten, Henry	
Bonner, Robert H.	
Clendenen, James C.	
Cole, Samuel L.	
Choat, George W.	Pope co.
Choat, William C.	Johnson co.
Clendenen, Thomas J	
Choat, Andrew J.	
Colbaugh, Carroll H.	
Crain, William S.	
Datson, Robert B.	Johnson co.
Gregory, Harry	Williamson co.
Grant, Thomas J.	Johnson co.
George, Pierce	Williamson co.
Gown, Francis M.	Pope co.
Gay, Jordan	Johnson co.
Handley, Richard A.	Johnson co.
Herron, John R.	Pope co.
Harris, Van Buren S.	
Handley, Samuel	
Harris, Robert J.	
Jones, James Fen. J.	Johnson co.
Jackson, William H.	Pope co.
Jones, David L.	Pope co.
Lay, Levi	Pope co.
Laney, Joseph	Johnson co.
Lawrence, Thomas N.	Pope co.
Mounce, William R.	Johnson co.
Murphy, James F.	Pope co.
Mabary, William	Johnson co.
Mabary, Frederick	Pope co.
O'Neal, George	Pope co.
Pendergrass, William	Williamson co.
Perry, George	Johnson co.
Phelps, William L.	Williamson co.
Robinson, John	Johnson co.
Reagan, John	Pope co.
Reagan, James	Pope co.
Rose, Micajah	
Reagan, Josiah F.	Johnson co.
Russell, Christopher M	Williamson co.
Ross, John C.	Johnson co.
Snyder, James B.	
Sullins, Madison L.	Pope co.
Smith, Samuel H.	Pope co.
Stone, Tilmon	
Stone, Joseph	
Solomon, Thomas J.	Johnson co.
Smith, James H.	
Smith, John W.	
Tapley, John S.	
Tapley, William H.	
Warren, Starling I.	
Westbrook, Benj. B.	
Warren, Robert W.	Williamson co.
Wooten, Edward E.	Williamson co.

VETERANS:

Q. M. Sergeant.
Hiram H. Wise.... Reynoldsburg

Sergeant.
William H. Holly.... Salem, Ky.

Corporals.
William S. Crain.... Marion
Samuel J. Smith.... Golconda

Bugler.
Joseph Laney.... Reynoldsburg.

Privates.
Colbaugh, James F.... Reynoldsburg.
Choat, Andrew J....
Harris, VanBuren S.... Golconda
Harris, William L....
Handley, Samuel E.... Reynoldsburg.
Hutchinson, Nath'l B.... Ballard co. Ky.
Ice, James W.... Reynoldsburg.
Jackson, Orange.... Golconda
Lawrence, Thomas N.... Reynoldsburg
Murphy, James F....
McGowen, Francis M.... Golconda
Ogdon, Daniel J.... Marion
Pendergrass, William.... Golconda
Smith, David.... Reynoldsburg.
Shaw, Cornelius A.... " "
Tapley, William H.... " "
Tapley, John S.... " "

COMPANY C.

Captains.
David P. Foster.... Jacksonville.
James D. Angley.... Golconda.
Robert Bradley.... Manchester

First Lieutenants.
William L. Edwards.... Jacksonville.

William L. Edwards....
Charles H. Hazzard....
George Anderson.... Kinderhook.

Second Lieutenants.
John Bradley.... Manchester
William P. Rigg.... Athensville.
William H. Short.... Ashland
Charles H. Hazzard.... Jacksonville
George Anderson.... Kinderhook.
William P. Rigg.... Athensville.

First Sergeant.
David K. Spencer.... Greenfield.

Co. Q. M. Sergeant.
John Landers.... Jacksonville.

Sergeants.
March H. Smith.... Manchester.
Archa McDonald.... Jacksonville.
Robert M. Smith.... Athensville.
Joseph Hoglen.... Jacksonville.

Corporals.
Thomas A. Jackson.... Beardstown.
James Rolertson.... Virginia.
Joseph Parker....
William Rigg.... Athensville.
Thomas Lawson.... Johnsonville.
John C. Bradley.... Manchester
Chaplen Schooly.... Virginia.
David W. Ford.... Prentice.

Bugler.
George Bammel.... Jacksonville.

Farrier.
John Barber.... Jacksonville.

Blacksmith.
John J. Snyder.... Arcadia.

Wagoner.
William F. Clark.... Virginia.

Privates.
Allen, Hiram C....
Anderson, George A.... Jacksonville.
Beck, William A.... " "
Brown, George.... Murrayville.
Buck, James W.... Manchester.
Bradley, Robert.... Franklin
Boone, Thomas B.... Virginia
Brady, William....
Brinim, Peter....
Barker, Craton.... Cooperstown
Carthight, Samuel.... Jacksonville
Carpenter, Charles L.... " "
Carpenter, Edward M....
Craig, Andrew J.... White Hall.
Clenham, James C....
Cowles, Frank.... Kinderhook
Conlin, Paul.... Jacksonville
Currin, James....
Durfee, Munroe.... Lagrange.
DeWitt, James B.... Mt. Sterling.

Foley, Michael.... Jacksonville.
Flynn, Patrick.... Springfield.
Gilbert, Joseph.... Rushville.
Gratehouse, Major.... Glasgow.
Holly, Martin W....
Harmond, Edward V.... Time.
Huggard, Charles A.... Jacksonville.
Holladay, George W.... Greenfield.
Jackson, Joseph.... Rock Island.
Jackson, George.... Beardstown.
Kinney, Patrick.... Jacksonville.
Lanhand, Pleasant.... "
Lewis, William C.... Winchester.
Lustick, William.... Jacksonville.
More, Robert B.... Virginia.
Milsha, Silas.... Jacksonville.
Murphy, Stephen....
Montgomery, Samuel.... Springfield.
McEvert, Henry.... Glasgow.
Mullen, Barney.... Ashland
McDonald, Josiah N.... White Hall.
McMahan, Patrick.... St. Louis, Mo.
Nagle, Patrick.... Jacksonville.
Nagle, James....
Osborn, James M.... Orville.
Ohler, William J.... Exeter.
Peterson, John.... Manchester.
.ullum, William E.... Greenville.
Poland, Peter.... Murrayville.
Sinclair, John.... Jacksonville.
Sinclair, Thomas....
Stout, William G.... Manchester.
Smith, John W.... Ashland
Sweeney, Paul H.... Jacksonville.
Urteker, Joseph....
Voss, James.... Beardstown.
Waters, Patrick.... Jacksonville.
Wilkerson, George.... Manchester
Wilkerson, Cana....
Weken, Frederick....
Watson, M. Nathaniel....
Zillion, Frank.... Virginia

VETERANS.

Q. M. Sergeant.
Robert Bradley.... Manchester.

Sergeants.
Peter Poland.... Murrayville.
Clayton Barker.... Coopersville.
Hiram C. Allen.... Bath.

Corporals.
Robert L. Yancey.... DuQuoin.
Henry McEvert.... Glasgow.
John Peterson.... Manchester.

Bugler.
George Bammel.... Jacksonville.

Saddler.
Nicholas M. Watson.... Prentice.

Privates.
Bradley, John C.... Manchester
Brady, James Jr.... Ashland
Bockewitz, William.... Springfield.
Buck, James W.... Murrayville.
Conlan, Paul.... Jacksonville
Curtis, Charles L.... Mulkeytown.
Durfee, Munroe.... Legrange
Flinn, Michael.... Rushville.
Hoglen, Joseph O.... Jacksonville.
Hite, Samuel S.... Delavan.
Jackson, Joseph.... Rock Island.
Lawson, Thomas.... Jacksonville.
Lanham, Pleasant.... " "
Landers, John.... " "
Lewis, William C.... Winchester.
Murphy, Stephen.... Jacksonville.
Nagle, James.... " "
Nagle, Patrick.... " "
Rigg, William.... Athensville.
Robison, James M.... Virginia.
Silkwood, Nathan.... DuQuoin
Werner, Christopher.... Springfield.
Zillion, Frank.... Virginia

COMPANY D.

Captains.
Hosea Vice.... McLeansboro
Joseph Coker....

First Lieutenants.
William L. Stephens.... McLeansboro
Joseph Coker.... " "
James H. Dailey.... Mt. Vernon.
Louis V. Allen.... McLeansboro
John M. Boyd....

Second Lieutenants.
Joseph Coker.... McLeansboro
James H. Dailey.... Mt. Vernon.
Louis V. Allen.... McLeansboro
John M. Boyd....

First Sergeant.
Sam'l H. J. Proctor.... McLeansboro

Co. Q. M. Sergeant.
William B. Allen.... McLeansboro

Sergeants.

James M. Branson	Benton
Sidney A. Boster	McLeansboro
James H. Dailey	"
Thomas W. Marsh	"

Corporals.

Armstead Hurst	McLeansboro
Charles R. Coker	"
George W. Stephens	"
Thomas B. Wright	"
John M. Boyd	"
Harvey C. Miten	"
Samuel Mann	"
John S. Coker	"

Buglers.

Jabiel R. Craig	McLeansboro
William Jones	"

Farrier.

William Medon	Franklin co

Blacksmith.

William Denney	McLeansboro

Saddler.

David Denmon	McLeansboro

Wagoner.

Joseph H. Denny	McLeansboro

Privates.

Allen, James	McLeansboro
Allen, Louis	Mt. Vernon
Boyd, William J	McLeansboro
Betts, John	"
Betts, William	"
Boyer, George	"
Balis, John M	"
Brinkley, George	Benton
Carrel, Henry	McLeansboro
Cox, John	"
Campbell, Joseph	"
Cleveland, Jesse	"
Coker, Abram B	"
Coker, James	Benton
Cravens, Jesse	"
Dial, James	"
Dial, William	"
Dilland, George W	Benton
Darley, Wesley	"
Daily, Landa	"
Faulkner, Leonard	Benton
Foster, Abner	"
Foster, William	Benton
Fann, Philip	"
Flint, John	"
Fann, Benton	"
Ghornley, Jesse	"
Hunt, Wooldig	"
Huffstatler, Solomon	"
Hendrix, William	"
Harrelson, William	"
Hall, William	"
Ingram, Hezekiah	"
Ingram, Milton	"
Ingram, Sewel	"
Johnson, John W	"
Jackson, William M	Benton
Knight, James	McLeansboro
Lay, Jesse	"
Mendon, Moses	"
More, Martin	McLeansboro
Merell, Thomas	"
Mangus, William	"
Mangus, Andrew	"
McLean, William	Benton
Matheny, Calaway	McLeansboro
Nation, Thomas	"
Nunley, William W	"
Nelson, William	"
Oglesby, Jesse	"
O'Neal, Henry	Benton
Pierce, Joseph	McLeansboro
Pettigrew, James M	"
Proctor, Benjamin	"
Putnam, Henry M	"
Putnam, James A	"
Presely, Robert	"
Pitman, John M	"
Robinson, Abram	Benton
Richardson, David	McLeansboro
Redpaten, David L	"
Roundtree, John	Benton
Riley, John	McLeansboro
Randolph, Matthew	"
Smith, Larkin	"
Summers, Houston	Benton
Standerfer, Anders'n T	McLeansboro
Sullivan, Thomas	Benton
Shields, John	McLeansboro
Troit, Hardemoe	"
Williford, William	Massac

VETERANS.

Sergeants.

Joseph S. Williams	McLeansboro
John M. Boyd	"
Andrew F. Stadler	"
Landy C. Dailey	"

Buglers.

Jesse C. Ghornley	McLeansboro

Privates.

Allen, James K	McLeansboro
Betts, William	"
Betts, John	"
Boyer, George W	"
Cleveland, Jesse	"
Coker, James R	"
Coker, Charles R	"
Cox, John	"
Coker, A. B	"
Dillon, George W	Benton
Dwyre, Michael	Metropolis
Dial, William	McLeansboro
Fann, Benton	Melonville
Flint, John	"
Harrelson, William	"
Ingram, Hezekiah	McLeansboro
McLain, William	Benton
Nelson, William	McLeansboro
Nunley, William	"
Robinson, Abraham	Mt. Vernon
Shields, John	Metropolis
Sullivan, Thomas	Mt. Vernon
Williford, William	Metropolis

COMPANY E.

Captain.

Isaac Gibson	Olney

First Lieutenants.

John Lynch	Olney
Edward Ball	"
Harvey W. Stewart	Olney

Second Lieutenants.

Elijah G. Tarplay	Olney
Harvey W. Stewart	Olney
Sylvanus Gird	Albion
Thomas M. Shield	Olney

First Sergeant.

Arthur St. Clair	Albion

Q. M. Sergeant.

Joseph Frazier	Albion

Sergeants.

Jefferson Spray	Albion
John H. McBride	Flora
John McSmith	Albion
Edward Ball	Olney

Corporals.

William Stewart	Olney
James K. Shields	"

Buglers.

Franklin P. Wooden	Albion
James Curtis	Olney
Jackson Gardner	Olney

Farrier.

Jonathan N. Bullard	
David Greathouse	Albion
Sylvanus Gird	

Saddler.

Charles E. Marks	Mt. Carmel

Blacksmith.

Emanuel Compton	Flora

Wagoner.

Lancaster Williams	Louisville

Privates.

William V. Clark	Olney
Asa, James	Albion
Aldridge, Henry	Olney
Brock, William H	Albion
Bates, David	Flora
Blakely, Thomas	Albion
Blakely, James A	Flora
Ballard, William	Albion
Ballard, William H. H	Olney
Byford, John H	Flora
Bradshaw, John	Albion
Bratton, James M	Mt. Carmel
Bond, Leonard C	Olney
Bond, Martin	
Busick, Matthias K	Olney

Captains.

Name	Residence
Cressa K. Davis	Harrisburg
William G. Sloan	
James H. Pierce	Saline co.

First Lieutenants.

Name	Residence
William G. Sloan	Harrisburg
William H. Dove.	
William L. Mitchell	Saline co.

Second Lieutenants.

Name	Residence
James A. Roark.	Harrisburg
G. W. Newell	

First Sergeant.

Name	Residence
James H. Pierce.	Saline co.
Alexander Barnes.	Harrisburg

Q. M. Sergeant.

Name	Residence
Alfred Pease.	Williamson co.
Jarvis Pierce	Harrisburg

Sergeants.

Name	Residence
William Holt	Gallatin co
Theodore Kowalsky	Harrisburg
Geo. Wm. Newell	
Axel Nyburg.	

Corporals.

Name	Residence
William H. Dove.	Harrisburg
Samuel F. Drake.	Wabash co
Alexander Barnes.	Harrisburg
Noah Willliford.	Saline co.
George W. Blackman.	Gallatin co
Andrew P. Pattis.	Saline co.
William O. Tate	
James Pierce.	

Buglers.

Name	Residence
John Carson.	Equality
William A. Combs.	Saline co.

Farrier.

Name	Residence
Lofton Price.	Saline co.

Blacksmith.

Name	Residence
Ephraim Combs.	Gallatin co

Saddler.

Name	Residence
Laton Glover.	Gallatin co

Wagoner.

Name	Residence
Thomas Stiff	Saline co.

Privates.

Name	Residence
Ashby, Charles	Saline co
Ashby, John H.	
Allen, James C.	
Bainbridge, Joseph.	Gallatin co
Bush, William.	
Brown, John M	
Bilee, William.	
Barnes, William.	
Barnett, Ezra	Gallatin co
Barnett, Joseph.	
Blake, Howell.	
Barnett, Samuel W	Saline co.
Baker, James.	
Carson, Charles T.	Equality
Cremeens, Asa.	Gallatin co
Cook, Wesley.	Saline co.
Cook, Granville P.	
Carson, Samuel T.	Gallatin co.
Dejarnatt, John B.	Saline co.
Dayton, Green B.	Gallatin co.
Dillon, James.	
Dillon, Joseph.	Saline co.
Dunning, John M	Gallatin co.
Dew, William A.	Saline co.
Evans, Jacob.	Gallatin co.
Evans, William.	
Empson, Gregory 1	Saline co.
Farmer, Jacob, Jr.	
Feazel, John.	
Farmer, John	
Graves, Joseph.	Gallatin co
Gailord, James.	
Gaskins, William.	
Hinds, Samuel.	Saline co.
Hinds, Leonidas.	
Hays, Thomas.	
Hargraves, John.	
Hale, James.	
Howell, Henry.	
Hartman, George	
Holliday, Joel J	
Jones, John.	
Kramer, John	Gallatin co
Keish, Elijah.	
Morris, John C.	Gallatin co
Morris, Henry M.	Saline co.
Malladay, William E.	Gallatin co
McGill, David.	Saline co.
Mitchell, William L.	
McDermot, James.	
Nunn, John.	

VETERANS.

Co. Q. M. Sergeant.

Name	Residence
Sylvanus Gard.	Albion

Sergeants.

Name	Residence
Joseph Frazier.	Albion
Thomas M. Shields.	Olney

Corporals.

Name	Residence
Marquis Martin.	Olney
John W. Shields.	
William H. H. Ballard.	

Wagoner.

Name	Residence
Lovel E. Cropper.	Albion

Privates.

Name	Residence
Auldridge, Henry	Olney
Bullard, William J	
Busick, Mathias K	
Betebenner, Benton E	Mt. Carmel
Bond, Leonard C.	Albion.
Calegrove, Byran.	Olney.
Clodfelter, George.	N. Salem.
Curtis, James.	Albion
Dayjohn, Joseph	Olney
Ealy, Daniel	Albion
Field, James P.	Olney
Gaddy, James E.	Olney
Gaddy, Lion.	Lawrenceville
Hoyt, William H	Olney
Ingraham, John	Flora.
Lewis, Jarius K.	Olney
Loback, C. A. F.	
Lutinger, Christian	Flora.
Mounts, Hiram	Albion
Niglas, Ignatz.	Peoria
Park, Presley.	Galesburg
Price, John C.	Albion
Steward, Alfred J	Olney
Steward, William	
St. Clair, Arthur.	Albion
Spray, Jefferson	Flora.
Steward, Isaac B.	Olney
Terry, John A.	Albion
Thorn, James T.	

Name	Residence
Vaughn, Samuel H.	Albion
Whitaker, Aquilla.	
White, William.	
Walker, George W.	Olney

COMPANY F.

Name	Residence
Biehl, Daniel.	Albion.
Betebenner, Benton E	Mt. Carmel
Cropper, Lovel E.	Albion.
Curtis, Henry.	
Calegrove, Byron.	Olney.
Davis, Charles.	Flora.
Dunford, Andrew J.	Olney.
Dayjohn, Joseph.	
Ealey, Daniel	Albion.
Floyd, Simon	Olney.
Floyd, Richard.	
Field, James P.	
Gaddy, Lion, a	Lawrenceville.
Greathouse, Isaac.	Albion.
George, Thomas.	Lawrenceville.
Gardner, William D.	Olney.
Gaddy, George M.	Lawrenceville.
Gaddy, James E.	
Guyot, Adam.	Albion.
Hill Sterling M.	
Hicks, Jasper.	Olney.
Hoyt, William H	
Heather, Felix.	
Ingraham, John	Flora.
Irwin, William.	Olney.
Lewis, Jarius K	Lawrenceville.
Lewis, Stephen C.	Olney.
Loback, Christian A. T.	Flora.
Lutinger, Christian	Olney.
Martin, Marquis	Albion.
Mount, Thomas.	Olney.
Mount, Hiram	Albion.
Mulliney, William.	Lawrenceville.
Mangren, Ephraim C.	Shawneetown.
Niglas, Ignatz.	Peoria.
Nadding, Romus E.	Olney.
Nadding, George.	
Price, John C	
Park, Presley.	Galesburg
Park, Elsberry	Albion.
Shields, John W.	Olney.
Shields, Thomas M	
Stotts, William H.	Flora.
Steward, Charles T.	Olney.
Steward, Alfred J	
Stansbury, William N.	Clay City.
Shine, James	Flora.
Shelby, George C.	Albion.
Sapp, Leander	Flora.
Thread, John F.	Albion.
Terry, John A.	
Thorne, James T.	
Turner, Jesse.	Mt. Carmel.

Powell, Robert W .... Gallatin co.
Price, David .... Saline co.
Price, James ....
Priest, Thomas ....
Perkins, John ....
Reed, David W ....
Rogers, John W ....
Slaton, John W .... Saline co.
Stenson, Alexander ....
Schallenger, Lemon M ....
Sherwood, Thomas .... Saline co.
Thomas, Thomas ....
Vineyard, Joshua ....
Waddle, James ....
Ward, John ....
Wilson, James M .... Gallatin co.
Watkins, Lewis B .... Saline co.
Ward, James ....
Weber, Elijah ....
Williford, John W ....

VETERANS:

First Sergeant,
Gregory J. Empson .... Hartford.

Q. M. Sergeant,
Alexander Barnes .... Harrisburg.

Sergeants,
William L. Mitchell .... Mitchellville.
James A. Combs .... New Market.
James Peerce .... Harrisburg.
Robert W. Powell .... Shawneetown.

Corporals,
Lofton Price .... Harrisburg.
Alexander Stenson .... ''

Bugler,
John Kraemer .... Harrisburg.

Privates,
Ashby, Charles .... Harrisburg.
Allen, James C .... ''
Bambridge, Joseph .... ''
Creemeens, Asa .... Shawneetown.
Dayton, Green B .... Equality.
Dillon, James .... ''
Dunning, John M .... Harrisburg.
Dew, William A .... ''
Evans, William .... ''
Farmer, Jacob, Jr .... Equality.
Holliday, Joel J .... Harrisburg.

Howell, Henry .... Eldorado.
Hargraves, John R .... Cottage Grove.
Morris, John C .... Equality.
Mallady, William E .... Harrisburg.
Priest, Thomas .... ''
Schellenger, Lemon M .... Shawneetown.
Sherwood, Thomas .... Harrisburg.
Widdle, James .... ''
Wilson, James M .... Equality.
Ward, John .... Harrisburg.

COMPANY G.

Captains,
John M. Baicourt .... Golconda.
William D. Glass, ...
William P. Foreman. ....

First Lieutenants,
Elijah L. Trovillion .... Golconda.
Nathl B. Cunningham .... Metropolis.

Second Lieutenants,
William D. Glass, ... Golconda.
Samuel L. Woodward. .... Shawneetown.
Hugh F. Patterson. .... Golconda.
John S. Finney. .... ''

First Sergeant,
William P. Foreman. .... Golconda.

Co. Q. M. Sergeant,
James D. Angely .... Golconda.

Sergeants,
Henry Freeman .... Golconda.
Hugh B. Glass, ...
George M. Gilliam. .... Golconda.
William W. Digirman. .... ''

Corporals,
Green B Floyd .... Golconda.
Ezra Hastings ....
David McMurphy ....
Samuel H. Prior ....
Isaac N. Conley ....
Elijah S. Renshaw ....
John M. Parker ....
William F. Hancock ....

Buglers,
William H. Sawyer .... Golconda.
William Hamilton. ....

Farrier,
James McDonald .... Golconda.

Blacksmith,
Charles S. Christman .... Golconda.

Wagoner,
William James .... Golconda.

Privates,
Abbott, Thomas .... Golconda.
Abbott, James M ....
Abbott, Jonathan ....
Baker, John C ....
Austin, Thomas J ....
Austin, Daniel ....
Anderson, William C ....
Anderson, James ....
Adamson, John ....
Baker, Wilson W ....
Brady, Wiley M ....
Bartholon, Zachariah ......
Biggs, William B, L ....
Belford, Benjamin F ....
Belford, Andrew J ....
Brush, Gilbert B ....
Conley, William L ....
Conley, James W ....
Cunningham Henry ....
Chaney, William C ....
Chambliss, William F ......
Curtis, Alexander ....
Calhoun, William B ....
Collins, Thomas P ....
Cossey, James H ....
Cates, David A ....
Cowsert, James ....
Cowsert, George W ....
Coats, Jesse ....
Dills, Wesley Brunford ....
Estus, Elisha ....
Fry, William ....
Finney, James L ....
Ferguson, James ....
Golightly, Charles ....
Glass, John A ....
Glass, Andrew ....
Glass, Robert F ....
Garner, Leander B ....
Garner, Stephen H ....
Gray, Thomas S ....
Hancock, Clark ....

Hopkins, William T .... Golconda.
Henly, William A ....
Hannah, John M ....
Jennings, Daniel ....
Joiner, William ....
King, William ....
Keef, Benjamin F ....
Logan, Peter A ....
Logan, John M ....
Lore, John M ....
Murphy, William H ....
Murphy, Solomon C ....
McGee, John B ....
Marks, Benjamin F ....
Porter, William ....
Robbs, James ....
Robertson, Isaac ....
Randolph, Jasper H ....
Shadown, Morris ....
Slankard, Thomas J ....
Smith, Martin E ....
Sawyer, John ....
Shufflebarger, Elias ......
Scott, Martin V .... Golconda.
Thompson, Jacob A ....
Thompson, Thos. P ....
Trovillion, Daniel F ......
White, James L ....
Yewell, Harvey ....

VETERANS.

First Sergeant,
William P. Foreman .... Golconda.

Q. M. Sergeant,
Samuel H. Pryor .... New Liberty.

Sergeants,
Robert F. Glass .... Golconda.
George W. Cowsett .... Elizabeth.

Corporals,
David McMurphy .... Golconda.
James S. Finney .... Metropolis.

Buglers,
Martin F. Smith .... Golconda.

Saddler,
Isaac M. Robertson .... Golconda.

Privates,
Abbott, Thomas .... Golconda.
Anderson, William C ....
Baker, William W ....

Baker, John C.
Bartholow, Zach'r'h P.
Biggs, William B. L. .... Frankfort
Clark, Charles W. .... Golconda
Calhoun, William B.
Cates, David A.
Farman, James.

Fry, William P. .... Johnson co.
Glass, Andrew.
Garner, Leander B. .... Golconda
Hancock, Clark.
Jennings, Daniel.
Lore, John M.

Sawyers, John M.
Thompson, Jacob A.
Robbs, James.

COMPANY H.

Captains
John J. Ritchey .... McLeansboro
Samuel L. Marshall .... "
Daniel M. Maulding .... "
Samuel P. Maxey .... Olney

First Lieutenants.
James M. Blades .... McLeansboro
Samuel L. Marshall .... "
Daniel M. Maulding .... "
John N. Wilson .... "
Walter B. Maulding .... "

Second Lieutenants.
Samuel L. Marshall .... McLeansboro
Daniel M. Maulding .... "
John N. Wilson .... "
Samuel P. Maxey .... Olney
John T. Wright .... McLeansboro

First Sergeant.
Daniel M. Maulding .... McLeansboro

Co. Q. M. Sergeant.
John Webb .... McLeansboro

Sergeants.
Walter B. Maulding .... McLeansboro
John N. Wilson .... "
John T. Wright .... "
Henry M. Wilson ....

Corporals.
George Epworth .... McLeansboro

John T. Hall
John H. Heard
John W. Echols
John H. Young
John A. Jones
Shelby Echols
Benjamin F. Tennison

Buglers.
Louis L. Biggerstaff .... McLeansboro
Alexander Hart ....

Farrier.
William Bryant .... McLeansboro

Blacksmith.
John Stubbs .... McLeansboro

Saddler.
Henry T. Jones .... McLeansboro

Wagoner.
Fields Trammer .... McLeansboro

Privates.
Brinley, Austin .... McLeansboro
Barron, John
Cook, Thomas
Crisel, George W.
Campbell, Alfred
Campbell, John
Cravens, Henry P.
Bailey, William W.
Easley, Abner
Durham, Peter C.
Digby, Thomas
Dugin, Harvey H.
Dugin, Francis M.
Dilds, John
Echolds, Henry C
Echolds, Moses
Echolds, James F.
Edwards, Presley
Frazier, William .... McLeansboro
Frazier, Charles
Faulkner, Bumsel
Fitzgerald, Davis
Farmer, John
Gillman, John
Ghormley, Lafayette
Galliher, James F.
Galliher, Salmond S.
Goins, Elisha
Hagin, John .... Nashville

Hammontree, John K. .... McLeansboro
Jackson, Wiley N. .... Carmi
Lechner, John .... McLeansboro
Morris, Charles.
Manning, Jonathan
Moore, Jesse A.
Newman, Geo. W. W.
Nelson, Arthur.
Oliver, Charles.
Oliver, John. .... Roland
Oliver, Edward. .... McLeansboro
Oliver, Thomas .... Roland
O'Neal, Samuel D .... McLeansboro
Porter, William
Pearson, William
Richards, William.
Rice, William J.
Sanders, John.
Smith, John S.
Smith, John.
Taylor, John.
Todd, Benjamin.
Vaughn, Alb't or Isaac
Wheeler, John .... McLeansboro
Wheeler, Solomon
Wheeler, William.
Warton, William.
Wright, Thompson
Williams, Elisha.
Williams, Jarvis J
Williams, George W
Williams, John C.
Woodruff, Andrew J
Williams, James.

VETERANS.

First Sergeant.
Walter B. Maulding .... McLeansboro

Q. M. Sergeant.
John T. Wright .... Eldorado.

Sergeant.
Henry M. Wilson .... McLeansboro

Corporals.
John W. Echols .... McLeansboro
William J. Rice
John Riley
Louis L. Biggerstaff
Charles Morris

Saddler.
Henry T. Jones .... McLeansboro

Privates.
Barron, John. .... McLeansboro

Cravens, Henry P.
Cummings, Andrew.
Dailey, William M
Echols, Henry C
Echols, James F.
Frazier, Charles
Faulkner, Bumsel J.
Hagan, John.
Lechmer, John H. .... Sacramento
Moore, Jesse A .... McLeansboro
Mansley, John H.

McCarty, Micheal.
Oliver, John.
Riley, William.
Richards, William
Smith, John S.

COMPANY I.

Captain.
Reuben Loomis .... DuQuoin
Charles W. Whitsit.
Lucius B. Skinner
Thomas W. Lippincott
Wesley F. Fallon .... Pinckneyville

First Lieutenants.
James H. Gordon .... DuQuoin
Charles W. Whitsit.
Lucius B. Skinner.
Benjamin F. Guiteau.
Thomas W. Lippincott
Wesley F. Fallon .... Pinckneyville
Frederick Marlow

Second Lieutenants.
Charles W. Whitsit .... DuQuoin
Lucius B. Skinner.
Benjamin F. Guiteau.
Wesley F. Fallon .... Pinckneyville
Frederick Marlow
Nathan C. Steblins .... Ava

First Sergeant.
Lucius B. Skinner .... DuQuoin

Q. M. Sergeant.
Benjamin F. Guiteau .... DuQuoin

Sergeants.
Caleb H. Throop .... DuQuoin
Jonathan G. Clark ....
Isaac N. East ....
John G. Fulton ....

Corporals.
George W. Clark .... DuQuoin
Wesley J. Fallon .... Pinckneyville
George Ellison .... DuQuoin
Lawrence D. Throop ....
Judson A. Wells .... Memento
Nathan C. Stebbins .... Ava

Hiram P. Skinner .... DuQuoin
Collin Turner .... Worthington

Farrier.
Robert Fallon .... Pinckneyville

Blacksmith.
Calvin Bramley .... DuQuoin

Saddler.
David M. Fligor .... Jones' Mills

Wagoner.
Christian Ulrici .... St. Charles, Mo.

Privates.
Atkins, James R. .... Osage
Adams, Isaac B. .... DuQuoin
Arndell, Phineas ....
Bailey, William .... Vergennes
Bell, Daniel .... DuQuoin
Blackburn Joseph ....
Brandon, Martin V. B ....
Buckley, William ....
Borew, Ira Oliver .... Vergennes
Buckles, Samuel .... DuQuoin
Campbell, John ....
Clark, George D. ....
Cumberland, Chas ....
Denson, Leonard .... Ava
Dye, William M .... Shawneetown
Etherton, William A .... Tamaroa
Emmerson, John .... Ava
Fagg, John W. .... Attila
Fliger, James K. .... DuQuoin
Gwyn, Thomas C. .... Elm Point
Gwyn, Lycurgus B ....
Gwyn, John A ....
Gwyn, Albert F .... 'us,
Hatfield, Christoph'r B .... Vergennes

Henckley, George E. .... DuQuoin
Hickman, Thomas J ....
Hill, John G ....
Hill, Richard ....
Horn, Charles ....
Hodges, David A ....
Hodges, Elves M. ....
Joubert, Lewis ....
Kellogg, Charles ....
Lacey, John ....
Lee, Lafayette J. .... Mt. Vernon
Lippencott, Thos. W .... DuQuoin
McHenry, John R .... Pinckneyville
Moore, Hugh .... DuQuoin
Marlow, Frederick .... Pinckneyville
McKinney, John F. G. .... DuQuoin
Moore, Samuel ....
Morgan, William H ....
Murphy, John .... Ava
Pyle, Thomas .... Osage
Parker, Joseph C .... DuQuoin
Peck, Joseph E .... Benton
Porter, Laurew R. .... DuQuoin
Robertson, George H ....
Renfrow, Enoch ....
Speers, William H ....
Stebbins, John A .... Virginia
Slenger, Lewis .... DuQuoin
Szirkowsky, Ferdin'd ....
Smith, Samuel L .... Greenville
Stephens, Marq's DeL. .... DuQuoin
Throop, Jasper J .... Elm Point
Throop, Newton A. .... DuQuoin
Travillion, James ....
Turner, Benton ....
Webb, James M ....
Wells, George ....
Wilson, Daniel ....
Woolridge, Borne .... Momence
Webb, Jacob .... Pinckneyville

VETERANS.

First Sergeant.
Thos. W. Lippencott. .... DuQuoin

Commis. Sergeant.
John J. Clark .... DuQuoin

Sergeants.
Jonathan G, Clark .... DuQuoin
Wesley F. Fallon. .... Pinckneyville
Nathan C. Stebbins .... Jackson co.

Corporals.
William A. Clark .... DuQuoin
Frederick Marlow .... Pinckneyville
Samuel Moore .... Perry co.
Albert F. Gwyn .... Elm Point

Wagoner.
Phineas Arndell .... Vergennes

Blacksmith.
John R. McHenry .... Pinckneyville

Privates.
Bell, Daniel .... Pinckneyville
Blackburn, Joseph N. .... DuQuoin
Buckles, Samuel ....
Clark, James F .... DuQuoin
Denson, Leonard ....
Dye, Thomas .... DuQuoin
Filgor, James K. ....
Filgor, David N. ....
Hickman, Thomas J ....
Joubert, Louis .... Pinckneyville
Moore, Hugh .... Jackson co.
Parrent, George. .... Perry co.
Pyle, Thomas .... DuQuoin
Robinson, George H ....
Stebbins, John A .... Jackson co.
Stenger, Louis .... DuQuoin
Szirkowsky, Ferdin'd. ....
Throop, Newton A. .... Chester
Ulrici, Christian .... DuQuoin
Wells, George W. ....
Wilson, Daniel M .... DuQuoin
Woolridge, Coone .... DuQuoin

Captains.
Edward Dawes .... Rectorville.
Dorastus L. Grimes .... Saline co.
James M. Banes. .... Hamilton co.

First Lieutenant.
Jesse B. Wilson .... Harrisburg.
James M. Banes. .... Saline co.
Thomas W. H. Miller. .... Hamilton co.

Second Lieutenants.
Cornelius Baker .... Harrisburg.
Dorastus L. Grimes .... Saline co.
Thomas W. H. Miller. .... Cairo.
Richard E. Oliver. .... Saline co.

COMPANY K.

First Sergeant.
John M. Baker .... Harrisburg.

Q. M. Sergeant.
Dorastus L. Grimes .... Saline co.

Sergeants.
Richard Allen .... Hamilton co.
Jhn C. Gregg ....
Amos Gibson ....
Christoph'r Hurdestry ....

Corporals.
Robert L. Lansdale .... Saline co.
Paul G. Thrasher .... Hamilton co.
Francis P. Wilson ....
James H. Gaines ....
James M. Banes ....
George T. Ritchey ....
John D. Riley .... Saline co.
William D. Cook. .... Hamilton co.

Buglers.
Gottweith Allenston .... Hamilton co.
Thomas C. Wright ....

Farrier.
William C. Richey .... Hamilton co.

Blacksmith.
Thomas H. Gentry. .... Saline co.

Saddler.
Allen D. Grimes .... Hamilton co.

Wagoner.
Amos Dailey. .... Saline co.

Privates.
Allen, Zack W .... Hamilton co.
Barker, Thomas. ....
Brown, William. .... Saline co.
Beck, William .... Hamilton co.
Belvin, Reuben A ....
Brown, Thomas. ....
Cleveland, John T .... Saline co.
Cleveland, William J. ....
Cade, John C .... Hamilton co.
Call, John ....
Cannon, James H. .... Saline co.
Campbell, William L .... Hamilton co.
Crawford, George N ....
Donahue, Edward. .... Saline co.
Douglas, James. .... Hamilton co.
Davis, Simeon M ....
Eaton, George W .... Saline co.

Veterans.

Name	Residence
Etherton, Reuben F.	Gallatin co.
Gibson, James	Hamilton co.
Gregg, James G.	"
Glenn, Levi	"
Garey, Jerome B.	Gallatin co.
Homer, William	Saline co.
Hutcheson, Daniel	Hamilton co.
Hutcheson, William	"
Hardestry, John	"
Hardestry, William	"
Hampton, William B.	"
Hudgeons, John	Saline co.
Hudgeons, Asa	"
Hemphill, Samuel A.	"
Harwood, James	Gallatin co.
Hughs, John	Hamilton co.
Hall, James W.	"
Jennings, David H.	"
Kanady, John A.	Gallatin co.
Lanham, Joseph G.	"
Lanham, James J.	Hamilton co
Lanham, John S.	"
Lamb, Zophar B.	Saline co.
Minor, James M.	Hamilton co.
Mayberry, Fred'k S.	"
Mitchell, James W.	Saline co.
Oliver, Richard E.	"
Pennell, Guilbert L.	Hamilton co
Perry, Wade H.	"
Parsons, William S.	Saline co.
Parker, Henry H.	Hamilton co.
Rodgers, James W.	Gallatin co.
Rolman, John.	Saline co.
Rude, William A.	Hamilton co.
Sloan, Henry C.	"
Sommers, William.	"
Schoolcraft, John.	"
Slater, Jackson	
Trousdale, Flavious J	Saline co.
Trout, John.	Hamilton co.
Thrasher, Frederick.	"
Trout, George H.	"
Trout, Henry	"
Wright, William J.	Saline co.
Wilkinson, Silas N.	Harrisburg.
Wise, William H	Gallatin co.
White, William.	Hamilton co.
Wheeler, William T.	"
Wheeler, William T.	Eldora o..
Whisnaut, William	Gallatin co.
Wilson, David C. A.	Gallatin co.
Wisecut, Jacob.	Osage.
Yates, Jonathan H.	Gallatin co.

Veterans.

Name	Residence
Belvin, Reuben A.	McLeansboro
Cook, William D.	"
Cades, John C.	"
Cleveland, Job.	Harrisburg.
Cleveland, John 'T'.	"
Cleveland, William J.	"
Connard, Elias S.	Marion. Ky
Domaine, Edmon.	Harrisburg.
Douglas, James.	"
Duer, William A.	Shawneetown
Etherton, Reuben F	McLeansboro
Ellenstein, Gottwerth	"
Gibson, Amos.	"
Gibson, James.	"
Hutcheson, Daniel	Harrisburg.
Huggins, John.	McLeansboro
Hughs, John.	"
Jennings, David N.	"
Lawrence, Willis.	Pinckneyville
Mayberry, Fred'k S.	McLeansboro
Mitchell, James W.	"
Nall, Rufus R	Morganfield
Oliver, Richard E	Harrisburg.
Parker, Henry H	McLeansboro
Perry, Wade H	"
Rude, William A	McLeansboro
Riley, John D.	"
Robinson, Daniel.	"
Ritchey, George T	"
Slater, Jackson.	Murphysboro.
Trout, Henry.	Shawneetown
Wisecup, Jacob.	McLeansboro
White, William.	"
Wheeler, Willis A.	Harrisburg.
Wheeler, William T.	McLeansboro
Whisnaut, William.	Harrisburg

COMPANY L.

John J. Clark

Captains.

Name	Residence
Thomas G. S. Herod.	Shawneetown
Mathew H. Starr.	
Firth Charlesworth.	
Wade W. McCoy.	Shawneetown

Second Lieutenants.

Name	Residence
Henry Stout.	Shawneetown
Samuel A. Armstrong.	
Mathew H. Starr.	
Firth Charlesworth.	Pope co.
John W. Hughes.	Shawneetown
Joseph A. Davenport.	

First Lieutenants.

Name	Residence
Benedict Crandle.	Shawneetown
Samuel A. Armstrong.	
Mathew H. Starr.	
Firth Charlesworth.	
John W. Hughes.	Shawneetown
Wade W. McCoy.	"
Willibald Yehle.	Alexander

First Sergeant.

Daniel Thorn Hazen	Shawneetown

Q. M. Sergeant.

Aaron Lambert.	Shawneetown

Sergeants. [Idon

T. B. Fogsdden or Logs-	Shawneetown
Omster B. Patte.	
James Adams.	
John W. Hughes.	"

Corporals.

Asa Decker.	Shawneetown
William I. Stinneth.	
Joseph A. Davenport.	
John Reebinacker.	"
Robert Peebles.	
John Pellham.	
Jonathan Wallace.	Golconda

Buglers.

Tipton B. Thomas.	Shawneetown
Marion or Morris Hold er	"

Farrier.

Forquer Morrow.	Shawneetown

Blacksmith.

Granville Winters	Shawneetown

Saddler.

John Gregg.	Shawneetown

Privates.

Name	Residence
Abbott, Sterling H.	Shawneetown
Andrews, John M.	"
Albert, Robert B.	
Allen, Samuel.	
Anderson, George W.	Camp Butler.
Bradford, William A.	Mt. Vernon.
Bush, James A.	
Barnes, Thomas.	Gallatin.
Baker, Benjamin F.	Shawneetown
Blackard, Thomas A.	Roland.
Brooks, James.	Shawneetown
Barnes, Thomas P.	Cave-in-Rock.
Caldwell, Jefferson.	Roland.
Campbell, Robert.	Shawneetown
Collins, Andrew.	McLeansboro
Corwin, James.	
Crank, John M.	Golconda.
Claghorn, Charles.	Mt. Vernon.
Cowsert, John.	Elizabethtown.
Curtis, Commodore D.	Mt. Vernon.
Claghorn, Robert A.	Gallatin co.
Davidson, William.	
Dickerson, David.	Elizabeth
Davis, Andrew J.	Shawneetown
Dennis, Isaac N.	Springfield.
Edmondson, William	Shawneetown
Eakle or Yahle, W.	
Frier, Noah.	
Fogsdon or Logsdon, G A.]	
Fowler, Jesse.	
Folkerson, Thos. or Chas.T.]	Cave-in-Rock.
Goble, Ross.	
Goble, Samuel.	Shawneetown
Hines, Joseph.	"
Hicks, John R. [ard	Olney
Johnson, Robt. or Rich-	Shawneetown
Kingston, John.	Equality
Lastur or Sarten, John.	Springfield.
Lombart, Harvey.	Shawneetown
Morrow, Thomas.	
McKee, John.	
Martin, Benjamin F.	
McCoy, W. W.	
Pate, James.	
Perryman, James C.	McLeansboro
Pohd, Charles.	Shawneetown
Randle, Charles T.	Springfield.
Railing John W.	Shawneetown
Richardson, Theodore.	Elizabethtown.
Rose, John C.	
Sivels, George.	Shawneetown
Smith, Daniel W.	Cave-in-Rock.
Smock, James M.	
Smith, Shadrack J.	Roland.
Stinnett, William.	Shawneetown
Sivells, Warren.	Golconda.
Smith, Charles.	Roland.
Satterfield, John.	Marion.
Stacy, Isaac...	
Shelby, Filbert.	Golconda.
Smith, William C.	Shawneetown
Thacker, Benjamin M.	Harrisburg.
Tucker, Green B.	

[Roster continued]

Name	Residence
Thompson, John	Shawneetown
Wagoner, James	
Wagner, Jesse	Golconda
Webb, Moses	Shawneetown
Wilson, William B.	
Whittaker, H.	
Webb, James A.	Golconda
Whitten, Hugh W.	
Whitmore, Frank G.	Shawneetown

VETERANS.

Q. M. Sergeants,

Name	Residence
Willebald Yuhle	Bloomington
Wade H. McCoy	Roseclaire

Sergeants,

Name	Residence
John Reehmacker	McLeansboro
Charles T. Randell	Springfield

Corporal.

Name	Residence
John C. Rose	Elizabethtown

Privates,

Name	Residence
Allen, Samuel	Shawneetown
Bean, George W.	
Bradford, William A.	Mt. Vernon
Bush, James	Shawneetown
Curtis, Commodore D.	
Dennis, Isaac N.	
Davidson, William	N. Liberty
Davenport, Joseph A.	Shawneetown
Edmunson, William	
Globe, Samuel	Cave-in-Rock
Hines, Joseph	Shawneetown
Harden, George D.	
Hueston, Samuel	
Filsey, William	
Martin, Benjamin F.	
Morrow, Forqua	Tamaroa
Pelam, John	
Richardson, Theodore	St. Louis, Mo.
Railings, John W.	Shawneetown
Smith, William C.	
Satterfield, John	
Sivells, Warren	
Smock, James	Cave-in-Rock
Whitten, Henry W.	
Winters, Granville	Shawneetown

COMPANY M.

Captains,

Name	Residence
Isaiah M. Sperry	South Pass
Elijah T. Phillips	Cairo
Frank W. Babcock	Jackson co.

First Lieutenants,

Name	Residence
Abraham Cover	Saratoga
John T. Coover	Cairo

Second Lieutenants,

Name	Residence
Charles A. Rixlebin	Jonesboro
Edgar A. Finch	Anna.

First Sergeant.

Name	Residence
Robert G. Ayres	Caledonia

Q. M. Sergeant.

Name	Residence
William H. Corbin	Saratoga

Sergeants,

Name	Residence
John E. Masel	Alexander
Billington Taylor	Williamson co.

Corporals,

Name	Residence
John F. Cover	Union co.
Frank W. Babcock	Jackson co.
Benjamin F. Tress	Jonesboro

Privates,

Name	Residence
Adams, Joseph	Alexander co.
Benson, Bryant	Union co.
Brown, John F	Union co.
Brown, Henry	Alexander co.
Ballard, John	Tamaroa
Barrett, Thomas S.	DuQuoin
Bryant, Chesterfield	Union co.
Bays, James B.	
Bivens, Thomas P.	
Caraker, James	
Cover, William A.	
Corbin, William H	Union co.
Chapman, Joseph	Johnson co.
Cline, Thomas M	Union co.
Conf, Michael	"
Dailey, Thomas	Jonesboro
Davis, William	Johnson co
Dorrell, James	
Demsey, Geo, L. W	Union co.
Dills, Austin V.	
Donahue, James	"
Doriss, Thomas	Johnson co.
Eason, Elbert	Franklin co
Floyd, Nicholas	Union co.
Fenil, Thomas J.	Alexander co.
Fouch, George	Union co.
Grantum, John T	"
Hartley, Rufus B	
Henderson, Elijah W.	Johnson co.
Henderson, Gillis V	
Huston, Samuel	Union co.
Hicks, Lucian B.	Massac co.
Hilton, Lionel V.	Williamson co.
Hammonds, Henry T	Alexander co.
Helms, Thomas	Jackson co.
Jones, William T	Louisville, Ky.
Jackson, Harrison	Union co.
Kelley, John P	
King, George	Tamaroa
Lane, Francis D	Alexander co.
Looney, Stephen	Union co.
Looney, Benjamin	
Looney, William	Alexander co.
Lewis, Thomas S	
Maxon, Wesley A.	Massac co.
Murphy, John	Franklin co.
McDaniel, Jackson	Alexander co.
McGinnis, John	Anna.
Medlin, James G. W	Union co.
Medlin, Clark A.	"
Mason, Calvin	
Noyes, Benjamin F	Alexander co.
Oller, George W	
Patterson, William H	Washington co.
Pennington, Stewart	Union co.
Pulley, Braxton	Perry co.
Ritchey, Van Buren	Union co.
Royster, Benjamin F.	Perry co.
Riggs, Charles T	Alexander co.
Stevens, Archibald.	Tamaroa.
Sitter, Marion J	Alexander co.
Skelton, John	Union co.
Slives, John R	Alexander co.
Sjrence, Thomas A	Jackson co.
Vaughn, James W.	Washington co.
Waddington, Joseph.	Jackson co.
Walker, Andrew T.	Union co
Walker, George W	
Webster, John B.	
White, Jackson	
Weaver, Andrew J.	
Yates, Enos T. A. T	

VETERANS.

Q. M. Sergeant,

Name	Residence
Lionel V. Hilton.	Williamson co.

Sergeant,

Name	Residence
Marion J. Sitter	Union co.

Corporals,

Name	Residence
Stephen Looney.	Union co.
John Donley.	Perry co.

Saddler.

Name	Residence
Stilts Goldham.	Perry co.

Privates,

Name	Residence
Adams, Joseph	Alexander co.
Brown, John F.	Union co.
Brown, Henry	Alexander co.
Balard, John	Perry co.
Bryan, Chesterfield	Perry co.
Coover, William A.	Union co.
Chapman, Joseph	Johnson co.
Kelley, John P	Union co.
Looney,	"
Mason, William C.	
Mullen, Clark A.	Alexander co.
Riggs, Charles T	
Shires, John R	
Yates, Enos T.	Union co.

178

SEVENTH CAVALRY REGIMENT.

FIELD AND STAFF.

Name and Rank.	Residence.
Colonels.	
Wm. Pitt Kellogg.....	Canton.......
Edward Prince........	Quincy.......
John M. Graham.......	New Harmony, I
Lieutenant Colonels.	
Edward Prince........	Quincy.......
Wm. D. Blackburn.....	Paris........
George W. Trafton....	New Haven....
Henry C. Forbes......	Freeport.....
Majors.	
Cyrus Hall...........	Shelbyville..
Jonas Rawalt.........	Canton.......
Zenas Applington.....	Polo, Ill....
Henry Case...........	Winchester...
Horatio C. Nelson....	Canton.......
Antrim P. Koehler....	Otega........
Wm. D. Blackburn.....	Paris........
Henry C. Forbes......	Freeport.....
John M. Graham.......	New Harmony, I
Asa R. McDonald......	Vandalia.....
George A. Root.......	Lanark.......
Miles G. Wiley.......	New Harmony, I
Adjutants.	
Sidney Stockdale.....	Canton.......
George A. Root.......	Lanark.......
Allen W. Heald.......	Canton.......
Battalion Adjutants.	
Allen W. Heald.......	Canton.......
George Bestor........	
Charles W. Willis....	
Quartermasters.	
Wm. A. Dickerman.....	
Jas. R. W. Hinchman..	Quincy.......
Battalion Quarter- masters.	
Josiah T. Noyes......	Lightsville..

Name and Rank.	Residence.		
John W. Reisor......		Erasmus D. Chandler.	Lightsville..
Surgeons.		Samuel W. Rode......	Vandalia.....
Clark D. Rankin.....	Peoria.....	Thomas Upton........	
Daniel Stahl........	Quincy.....	*Commis. Sergeants.*	
Thomas J. Riggs.....	Chicago....	Benjamin F. Bartlett.	Sublette.....
First Ass't Surgeons.		Daniel E. Robbins...	Abingdon.....
Thomas J. Riggs.....	Chicago....	Henry F. Barker.....	Vandalia.....
Charles H. Norred...	Dawson.....	Lovel G. Hamlin.....	Canton.......
Second Ass't Surgeons.		David B. Spencer....	Germantown, T
Alson J. Gilbert....	Troy Grove.	Byron H. Tuller.....	Decatur......
Milton W. Nesmith...	Manchester.	Charles Hemingway...	Lightsville..
Chaplain.		Arthur V. Ray.......	Canton.......
Simon G. Miner......	Decatur....	*Hospital Stewards.*	
Commissaries.		Henry Jayne.........	Springfield..
Henry F. Barker.....	Freeport...	Daniel C. Jones.....	
Daniel E. Robbins...	Vandalia...	Charles H. Hunting..	Paris........
	Abingdon...	John M. Mahr........	Lagrange, Tenn
NON-COMMISSIONED STAFF.		DeConcrey O'Grady...	Knoxville....
		Charles R. Hall.....	Grayville....
Sergeant Majors.		Richard R. Surby....	Paris........
George M. Tunnison..	Springfield	*Principal Musicians.*	
William O. Yarvan...	Knoxville..	Matthias Erickson...	Germantown, T
Augustus Leseure....	Paris......	Davis T. King.......	Decatur......
		Thomas J. Ellis.....	Canton.......
Henry Voris.........	Shelbyville	Edward M. Gibbs.....	Decatur......
Henry P. Heald......	Canton.....	*Saddler Sergeants.*	
Marshall A. Hartley.	Paris......	Valentine Smith.....	Grayville....
William A. Waterbury.	Lightsville	Daniel R. Pruitt....	Springfield..
James K. Moller.....	Mendota....	Caleb R. McKinney...	
Veterinary Surgeon.		Peter B. Small......	Germantown, T
Albert G. Livings...	Grayville..	Joseph B. Maloney...	Canton.......
Q. M. Sergeants.		*Farrier Sergeants.*	
John A. Woolsey.....		DeWitt C. Rexford...	Sublette.....
Augustus C. Tyler...	Germantown	William Seary.......	Cape Girardeau
Samuel Nutt.........	Galesburg..		

BAND.

Band Leader.	
Henry G. Smith......	Mt. Carroll..
Band.	
Brissenden, John....	Grayville....
Bedford, Winfield S..	Kensalaer, Ind.
Clark, A. M. S......	Grayville....
Clark, Angelo A. B...	Paris........
Chaffee, Gustavus...	Polo.........
Foltz, Edward J.....	Paris........
Fisher, Harvey G....	Mt. Carroll..
Finfrock, Samuel....	Polo.........
Moore, Samuel.......	Mt. Carroll..
Simmons, Harvey B...	Pecatonica...
Strong, Joseph J....	Decatur......
Strecher, Samuel....	Mt. Carroll..
Waterbury, Fordyce R	Buffalo......
Waterbury, John, Jr.	
Whitney, Silas D....	

COMPANY A.

Captains.	
William D. Blackburn.	Paris........
Charles Hunting.....	''
First Lieutenants.	
Charles Hunting.....	Paris........
Jacob J. Lagrange...	''
David V. Rhea......	''
Second Lieutenants.	
James R. Morrison...	Paris........
Jacob J. Lagrange...	''
David V. Rhea......	''
Marshall A. Hartley.	
First Sergeant.	
James Loughead......	Paris........

Q. M. Sergeant.
John Henderson...... Paris

Sergeants.
Daniel C. Jones......
Richard W. Surby...... Paris
Marshall A. Hartley......

Augustus Leseure......

Corporals.
John Ross...... Paris
Colonel P. Burns......
John Ditto......
John A. Minor......
Henry Wilson......

Cornelius B. Griffin......
David V. Rhea......
Eli Thayer......

Farrier.
Henry Faith...... Paris

Blacksmith.
Michael Wagoner...... Paris

Saddler.
John W. Heck...... Paris

Buglers.
Jeremiah Y. Antrim...... Paris
Oliver A. Keys......

Wagoner.
John L. Craig...... Paris

Privates.
Burns, George W...... Paris

Barber, Henry B......
Bishop, Richard......
Battershell, Sanford......
Bell, Samuel......
Bledsoe, Levi......
Burton, Hugh F......
Clever, John W......
Casteel, Joseph W......
Carver, William Jr......
Denham, James W......
Denham, Frank......
Duck, Daniel M......
Duck, James M......
Douglas, George W......
Dewey, Isaac M......
Dailey, Michael......

Leason, William H......
Fox, George W......
Fox, Seth R......
Fults, Edward J......
Faith, Thomas J......
Gillespie, William A......
Gibbens, William......
Gibbens, James......
Green, Lindley......
Housam, Adam......
Helt, Franklin S......
Helt, Jesse P......
Henderson, John O. F......
James, John......
Johnston, Joseph......

Johnson, John B......
Kelch, Leonard S......
LaGrange, Jacob J......
Light, Samuel H......
Mathis, Thomas......
Maddox, William R......
McComas, James......
McDonald, Mark......
McFerren, Reynolds......
Miller, John B......

Miller, William W...... Paris
Moyer, Elias F......
Moriety, John......
Mann, Levi......
Newlon, Wireman......
Post, James H......
Phipps, Horace V......
Ray, Isaac N......
Ransdell, Daniel......
Smith, Francis M......
Smith, Hiram B......
Stewart, Elias......
Thomas, Alva B...... Paris
Taylor, Aaron......
Tyler, Milton......
Tweedy, Amander G......
Vanhouten, William E......
Vanhouten, James......
Wolverton, George W......
Wyeth, Erasmus J......
Wyeth, John M......
Wright, Robert......
Willis, Ammiel K......
Wilds, Samuel N......
Whelan, Thomas R......

VETERANS.

First Sergeant.
Marshall A. Hartley...... Paris

Augustus Leseure...... Paris
Richard W. Surby......

Sergeants.
Reynold B. McFerren...... Paris
George W. Douglas......

Hiram B. Smith......

Saddler.
John W. Heck...... Paris

Privates.
Buckingham, Samuel...... Vandalia.

Battershell, Sanford A...... Paris

Bishop, Richard......
Fox, Seth R......
Light, Samuel H......
Mathis, Thomas......
Moriety, John......
Smith, Francis M......

Stewart, Elias......
Tyler, Milton......
Tucker, Dillard B......
Wright, Robert A......

COMPANY B.

Captains.
Zenas Applington...... Polo.
Henry C. Forbes...... Ridott.
William McCausland......
Stephen A. Forbes......

First Lieutenants.
Henry C. Forbes...... Ridott.
William McCausland......
Joseph O'Kane...... Elkhorn Grove
Charles Cross......

Second Lieutenants.
Oscar V. Sammis...... Polo.

Captains.
George A. Root...... Milledgeville.
Joseph O'Kane...... Elkhorn Grove
Stephen A. Van Epps...... Ridott.
Herman A. Van Epps...... Elkhorn.

First Sergeant.
Josiah T. Noyes...... Ridott.

Q. M. Sergeant.
Erasmus D. Chandler...... Wysox.

Sergeants.
George A. Root...... Milledgeville.
William McCausland...... Ridott.
Charles E. Welty...... Warren.
Francis E. Bassett...... Buffalo.

Corporals.
William R. Waterbury...... Brookville.
John N. Worden...... Buffalo.
Abram V. Campbell...... Polo.
David D. Johnston......
John J. Elliott...... Lysander.
W. M. Sturdivant...... Rock Creek.
Edwin N. Turner...... Durand.

Buglers.
Fordyce H. Waterb'ry......
Gustavus Chaffee......

Blacksmith.
Richard V. Jones...... Byron.

Wagoner.
Soloman Shafer...... Buffalo

Privates.
Addler, Charles...... Ridott.
Avery, Sylvester S...... Polo.
Allen, Charles......
Burrll, William J......
Buffington, Wm...... Rock Creek.

Bair, Samuel...... Polo.

Barnes, George H...... Ridott.

Bennett, Charles H...... Elkhorn.
Combs, Henry D...... Freeport.
Corwin, John H...... Lysander.
Crampton, Martin......
Campbell, George W...... Elkhorn.

Curtis, Henry R...... Durand
Cross, Edwin...... Rock Creek.

Coffen, Warren .... Polo
Davis, Theodore D .... Milledgeville
Davis, Thaddeus H .... Ridott
Dennis, Cornell A .... Rock Creek
Forbes, Stephen A .... Ridott
Fraker, John W .... Elkhorn
Furlong, William .... Durand

Groom, George .... Polo
Goddard, Samuel N .... Lena
Gill, Daniel .... Wawega, Wis
Higby, Thomas A .... Ridott
Hughes, Enoch .... Lysander
Hughes, Levi .... Rock Creek

Hallowell, Francis .... Wysox
Hemmingway, Ch's.F. .... Rock Creek
Hall, George S ....

COMPANY C.

Captains.
Jenkins, George J .... Lena
Johnston, James H .... Polo
Lockhart, Joseph C .... Elkhorn
Longenecker, Benj. F. .... Polo
Lewis, John H .... Wysox
Martin, Charles E .... Durand
McCausland, Seth A .... Ridott

Myers, Charles .... Durand
Miller, William H .... "
Maxwell, James H .... Polo
Maxwell, Calvin A ....

Moulding, John .... Elkhorn
Noyes, Lucius A .... Ridott

Noble, Charles B .... Elkhorn
Overholtzer, Jacob A .... Polo
O'Kane, Joseph .... Elkhorn
Pattee, Truman .... Forreston
Prindle, Hiram M .... Durand

Porter, Ira A .... Baileyville
Robb, William S .... Durand

Robinson, Isaac E .... Elkhorn
Reis, Peter .... Buffalo
Sharp, Andrew .... Mt. Morris

Smith, Henry H .... Polo
Simmons, Harvey B ....
Thorpe, Andrew .... Elkhorn

Van Epps, Austin H .... "
Wood, Arthur S .... Wysox

Captains.
Prescott Bartlett
David S. Porter .... Mendota

First Lieutenants.
John H. Shaw
David S. Porter .... Mendota
Robert D. McCord .... "

Second Lieutenants.
Benjamin F. Berkley
Stephen H. Richardson
Elmore W. Hunt .... Franklin Grove

First Sergeant.
Stephen H. Richardson

Q. M. Sergeant.
James Henderson

Sergeants.
David S. Porter
Edgar N. Bird
Robert D. McCord
William A. Statia

Corporals.
Cyrus T. Ames
George W. Rexford
Andrew J. Phillips
Franklin McKennett
Walter H. Norton
Elmer N. Hunt
Charles H. Evitt
George Bentley

Woodward, Wm. N. .... Eagle Point
White, George .... Wysox

Veterans.
Allen, Charles
Corwin, John H .... Polo / Pecatonica

Dennis, Connelly A .... Lightsville
Elsey, Henry .... Polo
Fraker, John A .... Ridott
Forbes, Stephen A .... Elkhorn
Moulding, John .... Ridott
Myers, Charles .... Ridott
Porter, Ira A .... Baileyville
Sien, Frederick .... Quincy
Van Epps, Herman A .... Elkhorn

Butler.
George H. Chadwick

Farrier.
Dewitt C. Rexford

Blacksmith.
Edward M. Scank

Saddler.
Francis M. Avery

Wagoner.
Oscar A. Dewey

Privates.
Allen, Crofford

Blake, James
Boddenhogen, Fred'k.
Buchan, William

Butler, George B
Bosworth, Harvey
Brumfield, Charles T
Beard, Calvin

Burnett, Herman
Clark, Thomas
Clark, Andrew J
Clark, Chetal
Cass, Parker L.
Christopher, Wm. H.
Clink, Jackson S.
Clapp, Henry
Collins, Owen N
Douglas, Alex'r.
Davis, George L
Eby, Henry H
Eddy, Washington
Eddy, Levi
Eddy, Joseph
Fuller, Franklin
Greerhart, Peter
Grier, Absalom
Hellain, Benjamin
Hemstock, Cornelius
Helmestine, Augustus
Houston, John W
Hoges, Giles
Hamblin, Eli
Hay, Michael
Huff, Charles V
Hare, John
Hublitz, Phillip C

Hublitz, William T.
Hublitz, Michael
Hood, Mahlon T
Laycock, William
Lasinan, Henry

Lind, Andrew
Mayers, Peter C
Moller, James K
Maxwell, Andrew
Munger, Reed
Moultroup, Lemuel
McCloud, John.
McKeen, George.
McCall, John

Nickles, George
Orris, William G
Penfield, Charles T

Penfield, Harrison
Phillip, Albert J
Pierce, James M.
Pierce, Henry
Pair, Joseph
Pifer, Anton
Robinson, Milo P
Ross, Richard M

Rhybert, Levi

Stewart, Alfred
Scudder, Albert E
Springer, Richard
Steadman, George W
Scott, Samuel
Thornton, Ellery C
Tredwell, Burton
Wright, William A
Westgate, George W
Weldon, James
Williams, George M

Veterans.
Ames, Cyrus T .... Lee Centre

Bird, Edgar A .... Sublette
Boddenhogen, Fred. ....
Butler, George B .... Lamoille

Christopher, Wm. H. .... Sublette
Clink, Jackson L .... Bradford
Clark, Thomas .... Sublette
Clark, Chetal ....
Clark, Andrew J. .... Dixon
Douglas, Alexander. .... Abingdon

Eddy, Washington......... Sublette
Eddy, Levi.................. Mendota
Fuller, Franklin........... Mendota
Helmestine, Augustus..... Sublette
Hunt, Elmore W...........
Houston, John W.......... Amboy
Hellain, Benjamin......... Mendota
Hublitz, William.......... Bradford
Laycock, William......... Sublette
Maxwell, Andrew.........
McCord, Robert D........
Meyers, Peter C.......... Mendota
McKeen, George C........ Sublette
Norton, Walter H......... Bradford
Orris, William G.......... Amboy
Porter, David S........... Bradford
Phillips, Andrew J........ Sublette
Pair, Joseph.............. Mendota
Pierce, James M.......... Sublette
Thornton, Ellery C........

COMPANY D.

Captains.
Wright Wolsey........... Orange.
Levi Hodge.............. Knox.
William H. Reynolds..... Orange.
David W. Bradshaw...... Brunswick

First Lieutenants,
William H. Reynolds.....
David W. Bradshaw...... Orange.
Franklin Mount.......... Brunswick
.... Ceda.

Second Lieutenants.
Levi Hodge.............. Knox.
William O. Yaryan....... Orange.
David W. Bradshaw...... Brunswick
James S. McCool........ Sparta.
Samuel M. Reynolds..... Berwick.

First Sergeant,
Stephen E. Olmsted...... Victoria.

Q. M. Sergeant,
Charles W. Olmsted...... Orange.

Sergeants,
David W. Bradshaw...... Warren co.
Thomas D. Smith........ Orange.

Corporals,
James S. McCool........ Sparta.
Charles N. Morris....... Orange.

Davis Vulgimore........ Maquon.
Samuel M. Reynolds..... Berwick.
Abiel H. P. Griffin..... Floyd.
Freeman T. Garrison.... Chestnut.
John B. Hendricks.......
Allen M. Davis..........
Joshua Potts............

James P. Reed.......... Berwick

Buglers,
James Lawrence......... Knox co.
Henry P. Mosier........ Young Hickory.

Farrier,
Daniel McCray.......... Knox co.

Blacksmith,
John Wilson............ Gainesburg

Saddler.
John Roscum............ Knox co.

Wagoner.
Eli Cover.............. Knox co.

Privates,
Ackley, DeWitt C....... Cedar
Allen, John H.......... Maquon.
Barthleman Geo. C...... Chestnut

Baldwin, Ed ard........ Indian Point.
Betterton, John........ Chestnut
Betterton, George R.... Orange
Barnett, Alexander.....
Bone, Wallace G........ Floyd.
Bloom, James M......... Knox.
Belden, George.........
Craver, Charles P...... Cedar
Crary, Emmet J.........
Cunningham, John....... Orange
Coe, Joseph W.......... Orange
Dagget, Nealy.......... Kelly.
Dennis, William H...... Orange

Davis, George W........ Maquon
Denean, Daniel......... Cedar.
Earl, George........... Sparta.
Elwell, James A........ Orange

Eastes, James A........ ''
Errick, Charles........ Knox
Erickson, Mathias...... Galesburg
Edrington, George E.... ''
Fields, Francis P...... Knox
Gibbs, Francis A.......
Gallentine, William P.. Orange
Garrett, John H........ Farmington
Gallentine, Charles W.. Farmington

Hubbard, Uri........... Chestnut
Humiston, Cyrus J...... Cedar
Henderson, George H.... Maquon
Jones, Safford......... Cedar
Jones, John L.......... Indian Point.
Jones, Charles......... Cedar
Lawrence, George F..... Orange
Lavelle, William N..... Bond co.
Mather, Joseph......... Orange

Maholan, Andrew........ Indian Point.
Mullis, Samuel.........
Massey, Isaac J........ Orange
Milam, William......... Maquon
Meadow, Jacob.......... Floyd
Mott, John C........... Victoria
Mount, Franklin........
Marsh, Alden B......... Cedar
Morey, James K.........
Messenger, Leonard G... Victoria.
Morrison, George G..... Cedar
Mote, Edward M......... Galesburg

Newgent, Thomas........ Knox
O'Grady, DeCourcy......
Peters, Jacob..........
Potts, Noah............ Chestnut
Reynolds, Leonard J.... Cedar
Raines, Peter R........ Floyd
Rictschey, Anthony..... Floyd
Rutledge, Isaac........ Galesburg

Rodgers, David G....... Indian Point.
Short, Harvey T........ Chestnut
Shumaker, John H....... Cedar
Stephens, Robert....... Cedar

Staley, Abraham O...... Kelly
Terry, Isaac C......... Ontario
Vulgimore, Joseph...... Maquon
Whip, Charles.......... Galesburg
Woods, Nealy C.........

Veterans,
Betterton, George R.... Knoxville
Barnett, Alexander.....

Bloom, James M......... Knox
Baldwin, Edward........ ''
Craver, Charles P...... ''

Crary, Emmet J......... ''
Coe, Joseph W.......... ''
Elwell, James A........ Knoxville
Erickson, Mathias...... Knoxville
Earl, George........... Knox

Griffin, Abel H. L.....
Hubbard, Uri...........
Henderson, George......
Jones, Charles.........
Lawrence, James........
Lawrence, George F.....

Morris, Charles N...... Knox
Morrison, George G..... ''
Mount, Franklin........
Massey, Isaac J........ ''
Messenger, Leonard G...

Mott, John C........... Knoxville
Reynolds, Samuel M..... Knox
Reynolds, Leonard J.... ''
Reed, James D.......... Knoxville
Roscum, John........... Knox

Short, Harvey T........ ''
Terry, Isaac C......... ''

Vulgimore, Davis....... Knoxville
Whip, Charles.......... Knoxville
Woolsey, John A........ Knox
Way, Samuel............
Wallick, Martin L......

Wallick, Martin L...... Orange
Way, Samuel............ Chestnut
Wahlgrane, Axle F...... Knox
Wilcox, Thomas J....... Galesburg
Yaryan, William O...... Orange

Wahlgrane, Axle F...... ''

COMPANY E.

Captains.
John M. Graham........ Phillipstown....
Miles G. Wiley........ New Harmony, I
John Etheridge........ Grayville........

First Lieutenants.
Daniel Heasty......... Phillipstown....
Miles G. Wiley........ N. Harm'ny, Ind
James M. Caldwell..... Grayville........
John Etheridge........   ''
Albert McKnight.......   ''

Second Lieutenants.
James M. Caldwell..... Grayville........
John Etheridge........   ''
Albert McKnight.......   ''
Ernest Wiley.......... N. Harm'ny, Ind

First Sergeant.
Miles G. Wiley........ N. Harm'ny, Ind

Q. M. Sergeant.
Robert Stanley........ Grayville........

Sergeants.
John H. Gush.......... Phillipstown....

Corporals.
Charles R. Hall....... Grayville........
Earnest Wiley......... N. Harm'ny, Ind
John Etheridge........ Grayville........
Bradford R. Gilbert... Grayville........
Stroder Nance......... Enfield..........
Butler Enlow.......... Grayville........
Licurgus K. Kelly.....
Joseph Noble.......... Mt. Carmel......
William A. Stanley.... Phillipstown....
Daniel B. How......... Grayville........
Wm. H. H. Shaptaugh.. Phillipstown....

Buglers.
William Shultz........ Maple Grove.....
John G. Mathers....... West Salem......

Farrier.
Albert G. Livings..... Grayville........

Blacksmith.
John Cougan........... Grayville........

Saddler.
Valentine Smith....... Grayville........

Wagoner.
John Ward............. Phillipstown....

Privates.
Aldridge, William J... Owensville, Ind
Arbaugh, Jesse........ Phillipstown....
Brissenden, John...... Grayville........
Basket, John W........
Brown, John........... White co........
Bouser, Smith......... Sciota co. O....
Bender, Frederick..... Edwards co......
Clarke, A. M. S....... Grayville........
Clarke, Angelo B......
Crawford, Henry W.....
Connor, Benjamin F....
Chandler, Thomas......
Coozan, Patrick.......
Compton, Noah.........
Calkins, David........
Driggers, Thomas...... Phillipstown....
Davis, Franklin N..... Grayville.......
Etheridge, Job D......
Etheridge, Michael....
Enlow, James W........

Folks, Augustus....... Maple Grove.....
Fowler, Wilson L...... Grayville........
Gray, Elnathan S...... Phillipstown....

Helck, John G......... Edwards co......
Hersum, George H...... Grayville........
Hubbard, Regdan....... Phillipstown....
Hay, Alfred...........
Heady, Thomas J....... Stuartsville, Ind
Howell, George W...... Kirk's Mills, Ind
James, R. D........... Phillipstown....
Jackson, Julius C..... Grayville........
Lucas, John........... Owensville, Ind
Livingston, Cyrus M...
Lovil, James.......... Carmi...........
Lischer, Samuel B..... Mt. Carmel......
McCrary, Joseph S..... Grayville........
Magors, Reuben........ Phillipstown....
Morris, George W...... Carmi...........

Maxwell, George R..... Grayville........
Magors, John W........ Phillipstown....
Melrose, Sydney....... Grayville........
McKnight, Albert......
McCracken, N. P....... Greenville......
Nance, Richard........ Enfield.........
Nance, Jesse..........   ''
Oren, Charles F.......
Ruff, Augustus........ Albion..........
Rose, William R....... Carmi...........
Rose, David........... Phillipstown....

Reno, Ezra............ Grayville.......
Smith, Stephen B......   ''
Sears, Jordan......... Stuartsville, Ind
Sirwell, Richard G.... Grayville.......
Spencer, Henry........   ''
Taylor, John..........   ''
Tedrer, George W...... Carmi...........
Tanquirry, Jacob R.... Albion..........
Webber, Mathias....... Phillipstown....
Williams, Martin...... N. Harmony, Ia..
Wiley, Morris......... Cedarville, O...
White, William........ Crayville.......
Weed, John............ Cincinnati, O...
Walkendrof, Isaac..... Cincinnati, O...
Ward, George B........ William's Ferry

Williams, John........ Phillipstown....
Way, Shubal J. T......
Webster, John L....... Grayville.......

VETERANS.

Sergeants.
Albert McKnight....... Grayville.......
Earnest Wiley.........   ''
William A. Stanley....   ''

Corporals.
Henry E. Spencer...... Grayville.......
Charles F. Orin.......

Privates.
Arbaugh, Jesse........ State of Tenn..
Bender, Frederick..... Grayville.......
Clark, George W....... State of Mo....
Folks, Augustus....... Grayville.......
Hubbard, Rigden....... White co.......
Helck, John G......... Grayville.......
Hersum, George H......   ''
Kelly, Licurgus K..... White co.......

Lucas, John........... Grayville.......
Lischer, Samuel B..... Camp Butler....
Livings, Albert G..... Grayville.......
Melrose, Sydney.......
Rose, William R....... White co.......
Shultz, William...... Grayville.......
Taylor, John A........
Williams, Martin.....   ''
Wiley, Morris B....... Grayville.......
White, George W....... Bird's Point, Mo
Weed, John............ Grayville.......

COMPANY F.

Captains.
Antrin P. Kockler...... Otego.
Asa W. McDonald...... Bowling Green.
Joseph M. Chase...... Shabonier.

First Lieutenant.
Charles F. Lee...... Bowling Green.
Joseph M. Chase...... Shabonier.
Solomon Goodbrake...... Vandalia.

Second Lieutenants.
Jacob Sloop...... Howard.
James Breeze...... Vandalia.
Samuel W. Rode......

First Sergeant.
Asa W. McDonald...... Bowling Green.

O. M. Sergeant.
George W. Haley...... Vandalia.

Sergeants.
James M. Vaughan...... Vandalia.
Robert L. Guy......
William R. Beele...... Howard's Point.

Corporals.
William A. Smith...... Salem.
Frederick Trieble...... Howard's Point.
Joseph M. Chase...... Shabonier.
Jabez W. Smith...... Loudon City.

Buglers.
Robert F. Young...... Howard's Point.
John Goodbrake...... Sefton.
Wilson C. Warner...... Vandalia.
Samuel J. Moore...... Howard's Point.

Buglers.
John Wheeler......
Henry F. Stahl...... Vandalia.

Farrier.
August Hoardt...... Belleville.

Blacksmith.
William J. Becannon...... Howard's Point.

Saddler.
Alex. J. Urquehart...... Vandalia.

Wagoner.
W. Lemuel McCord...... Greenville.

Privates.
Arnold, William...... Fosterburg.
Arnold, Felix W......
Allen, William A...... Vandalia.
Bowning, George......
Becannon, John......
Barker, H. F...... Hurricane.
Clow, John...... Alma.
Clow, Allen...... Effingham.
Castor, Lorenzo D...... Wheatland.
Clark, Thomas N...... Clinton.
Coldron, Nathan C...... Vandalia.
Carson, James......
Cunningham, Andrew...... Greenland.
Cochran, Abraham...... Vandalia.
Dowd, Patrick...... Bowling Green.
Doyle, James M...... Vandalia.
Daniels, Edward H...... Loudon City.
Dearduff, Simon...... Fayette co.
Englar, Casper...... Vandalia.
Eyestone, John W......
Ellison, James......
Foster, Phillibert...... Bowling Green.
Foster, Andrew J...... Salem.
Foster, Henry C......
German, Lewis...... Vandalia.
Gable, George......
Grandfield, Thomas......
George, Matthew......
Griffith, William H...... Howard's Point
Goodbrake, Solomon F.. Vandalia.

Hadley, Thomas C...... Williamsburg
Harris, Isaac, Jr...... Vandalia.
Harris, Isaac Sr......
Hendrickson, Wm. H...... Otego.
Hubbawacks, Conrad...... Patoka.
Hamilton, John N...... Vandalia.
Heusinkveld, George......
Jacoby, John...... Salem.
Jones, Eldridge......
Kreight, Charles...... Vandalia.
Knight, John...... Salem.
Knight, William......
Kepner, Elijah...... Vandalia.
Lafrance, Jeff......
McConkey, Lotham A...... Springfield.
Moon, Amos...... Fosterburg.
Myres, George...... Howard's Point.
Milton, Bennett B...... Salem.
Miller, Thomas...... Vandalia.
Moon, Thomas Foster.. Fosterburg.
Phifer, John...... Vandalia.
Parker, Samuel A...... Howard's Point.
Pickarski, Joseph...... Greenville, Mo.
Paton, James M...... Vandalia.
Parkinson, Isaac L......
Radcliff, Edward......
Rose, Samuel W......
Sidwell, John......
Sullivan, John......
Sims, James B...... Williamsville
Smith, Thomas...... Vandalia.
Savage, George W......
Sage, John......
Sholtz, Andrew...... Salem.
Tilly, Jesse......
Upton, Thomas...... Vandalia.
Victor, Henry W...... Bowling Green.
Wren, Gideon B...... Fosterburg.
Wall, John......

Veterans.
Arnold, William M...... Fosterburg.
Carson, James...... Vandalia.

Herman, John V......

Harris, Isaac...... Loudon City.
Jones, Eldridge...... Fosterburg.
Knight, William...... Vandalia.
Knight, John......
LaFrance, Jeff......
Melton, Thomas......
Miller, Thomas......
Miller, Bennett B......
Pikarski, Joseph N......
Radcliff, Edward......
Rode, Samuel W......
Sage, George W......
Savage, George W......

Sim, James B......

Wall, John W...... Kinmundy.
Young, Robert F...... Howard's Point

COMPANY G.

Captains.
George W. Trafton...... New Haven.
William H. Stiles...... Newmarket.
Davis V. Ugamore......

First Lieutenants.
Richard Hardin...... New Haven.
James M. Gaston...... Butler.
Thomas Slinger......

Second Lieutenants.
William H. Stiles...... Newmarket.
Samuel Way...... Hennon.

Chase, Joseph M...... Shabonier.
Clow, Allen B...... Alma.
Cochran, Abraham...... Vandalia.
Daniels, Edward H...... Loudon City.
Davis, John W...... Bowling Green,
Dearduff, Simon...... VanBurensburg
Ellison, James...... Vandalia.
Foster, Andrew J...... Patoka.
Fournier, Phillibert...... Bowling Breen.
Foster, Henry C...... Patoka.
Goodbrake, Solomon F.. Vandalia.
Grandfield, Thomas...... Sefton.

First Sergeant.
Edwin W. Gaston .... White co.

Q. M. Sergeant.
Horace C. Catlin .... New Haven

Sergeants.
John J. Powell .... Roland
William H. Stone .... New Haven
Jasper N. Robinson .... Carmi
William J. Smith .... White co.

Corporals.
James W. Powell .... Roland
Robert McGhee ....
James M. Gaston .... Butler
Samuel Nelson .... New Haven
David N. Pool .... "

William W. Black .... "

Elias R. Goad .... "
George T. Pool .... Roland

Buglers.
William Roy .... New Haven
George W. Mills .... State of N.Y.

Farrier.
John W. Miller .... New Haven

Wagoner.
Isaac York .... Elm Grove

Blacksmith.
Horace T. Dort .... Butler

Privates.
Adams, Stephen .... New Haven
Adams, Alexander .... "
Allen, Joseph H .... "
Boyer, Samuel .... Butler
Brooks, Leonard D .... New Haven
Boyer Calvin .... Mt.Vernon, Ind
Bishop, Jesse .... White co.
Bryant, Henry A .... "
Black, Thomas ....
Blazier, William .... New Haven
Coats, Berry .... "

Chester, Joseph T .... Roland
Cowen, Wesley .... New Haven
Cowen, James .... "

Colbert, William .... Elm Grove
Campbell, James .... Roland
Campbell, John M .... Elm Grove
Duncan, William .... New Haven
Dorris, John .... Roland
Dorris, William .... New Haven
Epley, George W .... "
Farley, James .... "
Glover, Daniel .... Carmi
Gaston, James .... "

Hendricks, Samuel .... New Haven

Hensen, Dennis .... "
Hughes, Rees M .... Carmi

Hanagan, Michael .... Sacramento
Hughes, John .... Carmi
Ives, Richard F .... Butler
Liddikie, Henry C .... "

Ledbetter, Wm. Wash. .... New Haven
Lightfoot, Walker F ....
Morris, R. C .... Butler
Montgomery, Samuel .... White co.
McMullen, Francis M .... Emma
Marglin, Eli .... New Haven
Martin, George W .... Chambersb'g, M
Morris, Jordan .... New Haven
McCalister, Jerrold .... White co.
McCalister, Edward ....
Maugrim, Levi .... Shawneetown
McMullen, Nathaniel .... New Haven
McGhee, Andrew .... Roland
Pain, William ....
Palmore, Thomas J .... Hardin co.
Pearce, Horace J .... Roland
Pool, Thomas .... Carmi
Phipps, John W ....

Palmore, Calvin H .... Hardin co.
Rodman, William .... Hew Haven
Robinson, William H .... Roland
Robinson, James .... New Haven

Rinehold, George .... Shawneetown

Sherer, William .... Butler
Sturgill, Fielding .... New Haven
Smith, David R ....
Timmons, Samuel .... Emma
Taylor, John H .... New Haven
Vinson, Levi D .... Cottonwood

Venters, John .... New Haven
Vines, Thomas ....
Webb, Samuel ....
Webb, James ....

Wilson, John B .... Mt.Vernon, Ind
Wall, Thomas .... Emma

Veterans.
Acord, Hiram .... Sacramento
Allen, Joseph H .... McLeansburgh
Boyer, Samuel .... New Haven
Bryant, Henry A .... "
Corder, Abraham C .... Roland
Campbell, James .... Carmi
Duncan, William ....
Hughes, John .... Roland
Holland, John W .... Butler
Ives, Richard F .... Hardin co.
Ledbetter, William W .... New Haven
Martin, George W .... Roland
Pool, George T ....

Robinson, William H .... New Haven
Smith, David R .... Butler
Sherer, William J .... Carmi
Smith, William J .... New Haven
Watson, John ....

COMPANY H.

Captains.
Milton L. Webster .... Shelbyville

Uriah Brant .... "

First Lieutenants.
Isaac V. D. Moore .... Shelbyville
Jacob C. Miller .... Mattoon
Henry Voris .... Shelbyville
Uriah Brant .... Windsor
Samuel F. Gammell ....

Second Lieutenants.
Jacob C. Miller .... Shelbyville
Uriah Brant .... "
Samuel A. Kitch ....
Michael Freybarger ....

First Sergeant.
Samuel A. Kitch .... Shelbyville

Q. M. Sergeant.
Leonidas Crawford .... Windsor

Sergeants.
Uriah Brant .... New Haven .... Shelbyville
Michael Freybarger .... "
Charles W. Brown .... Cottonwood
Jesse W. Miller .... Greenland

Corporals.
Josua P. Judkins .... Mt.Vernon, Ind .... Shelbyville
Clark Thomas .... Emma
Peter Emrick .... Allensville, O
John Randall .... Sacramento .... Greenland
James Hotz .... McLeansburgh

Samuel F. Gammel .... New Haven .... Windsor
Matthew Stotts .... " .... Shelbyville
Wm. W. Whitehead .... Roland .... Jersey, Ohio
Carmi

Buglers.
Caleb R. McKinney .... Roland .... Sullivan, Ind
William J. Hartman .... Butler .... Shelbyville
Hardin co.

Farrier.
William T. Stotts .... New Haven .... Shelbyville
Roland

Blacksmith.
John Weiry .... Shelbyville

Saddler.
Martin Heffron .... Shelbyville

Wagoner.
George A. Kashner .... Shelbyville

Privates.
Armstrong, Levi .... Greenland
Aichel, George .... Shelbyville
Aichel, George C ....
Aichel, Adam .... "
Aichel, Philip .... Ostend, Ohio
Brownfield, Henry .... Bunker Hill, O
Bresler, Mathias .... Carey, Ohio
Brechtel, Andrew .... Shelbyville
Carnes, James ....

Churchfield, James .... "

Cook, William A .... Mt. Eaton, O
Craven, Samuel ....

Churchfield, Thomas .... Shelbyville
Earnest, Samuel .... Greenland
Ensign, George G .... Shelbyville
Fancher, Henry ....
Far, John ....

Name	Residence
Fowler, Uriah	
Hantry, John	Mattoon
Harrison, John	Greenland
Hildebrand, Henry	
Justice, Harvey	Lacon
Johnson, John	Shelbyville
Jones, Richard	West Bedford, O.
Leathers, William	Shelbyville
Light, Henry	
McFadden, Philem'n B	Logan, Ohio.
Morgan, Thomas E.	Shelbyville
Myers, Joseph	Greenland
McLain, David L.	Shelbyville
Miller, Peter	Vandalia
Martin, William	Shelbyville
Olinger, William H	Greenland
Patrick, James W	Mt. Auburn
Phillips, William C	Mt. Auburn

Captains.
Poltorff, Samuel F.	Warren co., Ia.
Paul, Ralph	Vienna, Md.
Patrick, Americus	Mt. Auburn.
Ray, James	Harrisburg

First Lieutenants.
Root, Walker G.	Shelbyville.
Richardson, David F.	Greenland.
Ruse, George W.	Shelbyville.
Sheley, Ansel D	Bennett
Scott, Edwin R.	

Second Lieutenants.
Stegmire, Charles.	Sugar Grove, O.
Shull, Jacob F.	Mt. Auburn.
Tabler, William.	Shelbyville.
Thompson, George M.	

First Sergeant.
Turney, James W.	Cold Spring
Turner, William C.	Mattoon
Valentine, William.	Shelbyville.
Voris, Henry	Shelbyville.
Webster, Lovinas	Windsor.
Waller, Alfred J.	
Winson, Francis	
Winters, Milton A.	

Veterans.
Aichel, George	Shelbyville.
Aichel, Adam.	
Bechtel, Andrew.	
Bressler, Mathias	
Brown, Charles W.	
Cook, William A	
Emrick, Peter	
Freyburger, Michael	
Gaumel, Samuel F.	Effingham.
Harrison, John.	Shelbyville.
Hefron, Martin.	
Hartman, William T.	Argyle
Hautry, John	
Johnson, John	

Blacksmith.
George Fornof....

Wagoner.
William Deal....

Judkins, Joshua P	Springfield
Jones, Richard H	Shelbyville.
Miller, Jesse W.	
Miller, Peter	
Morgan, Thomas E.	
Patrick, James E.	
Petters, William H	
Ruse, George W	
Shull, Jacob F.	
Stotts, William J.	
Stegmire, Charles.	
Sheley, Ansel D.	
Thompson, Gen. M.	
Turner, William C.	
Valentine, William.	

COMPANY I.

Captains.
Arthur J Gallagher ... Decatur
William Ashmead.
Byron H. Tuller. ...

First Lieutenants.
William H. Stratton. ... Decatur
Horace K. Rice. ... Mason

Second Lieutenants.
William Ashmead. ... Decatur
Steph'n G. Washburne.
Oliver L. Kendall. ... Wheatland

First Sergeant.
William F. Clark.

Q. M. Sergeant.
George Flattery.

Sergeants.
John W. Haworth.
Matthew W. Ruby.
George H. Gardner.
Steph'n G. Washburne

Corporals.
Archibald Dickson
Daniel H. Dunbar.
George W. Kaylor.
Marion Ashmead.
William D. McCombs.
Abner H. Jordan.
Thaddeus N. Varney.
William Hill.

Buglers.
Davis T. King.
Joseph J. Strong.

Farrier.
Argyle W. Furr....

Privates.
Adams, John Q.
Bowier, John.
Belknap, Cyrus M
Bartlett, Robert.
Beals, Luther.
Calhoun, Webster
Calhoun, David
Cornwell, Isaac P
Clark, George
Dugan, Charles.
Dugger, William A.
Douer, William A.
Dawson, Ebenezer H
Dickson, George.
Earls, Walter.
Fletcher, George W.
Gibbs, Edward M.
Goff, Charles.
Grove, William.
Grady, Henry P.
Hartman, John P.
Hopkins, Charles W.
Hays, John.
Haworth, Frank.
Hafran, James
Jones, James M.
Jones, John S.
Kendall, Oliver L.
Knipple, Henry
Ledbetter, James C.
Martin, William
Martin, Henry
May, Marion.
Myers, Henry C.
McCay, Samuel C.
Melville, Edward.
Miller, Lawrence.
McElroy, James.
McDougal, John R.
McCay, Thomas.
Nicholson, James.
Nicholson, James P.
Powers, John.
Powers, Michael.
Paine, Robert S.
Riley, William.
Ruby, Henry.
Rice, Horace.
Smith, Cyrus B.
Stookey, John A.
Smythe, Charles E.
Sullivan, Michael.

Veterans.
Adams, John Q. ... Decatur
Belknap, Cyrus M.
Cornwell, Isaac P.
Clark, George.
Dickson, Archibald
Doner, William H.
Dugan, Charles.
Grove, William
Knipple, Henry.
Knipple, Henry.
Martin, William.
Miller, Lawrence.
Nicholson, James.
Powers, Michael.
Ruby, Henry C.
Rice, Horace.
Sullivan, Michael.
Tuller, Byron H

Tuller, Byron H
Temple, Pulaski L.
Tooter, Henry....
Taber, Augustus A.

Veterans.
Thomas, John R.
Vancourt, John D.
Weatherby, Warren D
Williams, Charles.
Wood, George W.
Webb, Edward S.
Westfall, Charles.
Walters, James F.
Yopes, Simon.

COMPANY K.

captains.
Horatio C. Nelson. ... Canton.
Joseph R. Herring. ... "
Charles C. Hays.... ... "

First Lieutenants.
Joseph R. Herring. ... Canton.
John W. Maxwell. ... "
John J. Shriner. ... Springfield.

Second Lieutenants.
Andrew B. Hulitt. ... Canton.
Henry Jayne. ... Springfield.

First Sergeant.
John J. Shriner. ... Canton.
William H. Roberts ... Canton.

Q. M. Sergeant.
Philip Slaughter. ... Canton.

First Sergeant.
Peter M. Binnix. ... Canton.

Sergeants.
George B. Baylor..... Canton
Lovel G. Hamlin..... "
John W. Maxwell..... "
Abram B. Garabrant.. "

Corporals.
John Carlton..... Canton
James Seety..... "
John M. Pollison..... "
John J. Shriner..... "
Bernard D. Kimble..... "
David B. Spencer..... "
Joseph Coykendall..... "

Edwin Weed..... "

Bugler.
Thomas J. Ellis..... Canton

Farrier.
John An'on..... Canton

Saddler.
Peter B. Small..... Canton

Privates.
Anderson, Eric..... Canton
Arringdale, Thomas..... "
Ball, Henry..... "

Bell, William P..... "
Berkshire, Jonathan H.. "
Clinton, Bernard..... "
Cockrill, Matthias..... "

Deford, Thomas..... "
Drake, Jerod M..... "
Fitch, George L..... "

Veterans.
Arringdale, Thomas J. Canton
Bell, William T..... "
Brown, Joseph D..... "
Cockrell, Royal..... "

Drake, Jared M.....
Freemole, George W.....
Floyd, John W.....
Fillingham, John F.....
Hays, Charles C.....
Hahn, Henry..... Dover
Kimble, Bernard D..... Canton

Fillingham, John F..... Canton
Floyd, John Wesley..... "
Freemole, George..... "
Fuller, Barney..... "
Greenslit, Eugene G.....
Hall, John D.....
Handley, William H.....
Hamil, David A.....
Harper, James H.....
Harper, John.....
Head, James G.....

Heald, Allen W.....
Hesch, Peter.....
Hill, George H.....

Hornig, Thomas.....
Hornstein, John G.....
Hopwood, Thomas J.....

Jayne, Henry.....
Johnston, John P.....
Knot, James N.....
Malony, Joseph B.....
Messler, Nathan R.....
Metcalf, Thomas.....
McMillen, Walter J.....
Moran, George W.....
Neff, Joseph B.....
Reitch, Alexander.....
Rankin, Ebenezer M.....
Roberts, William H.....
Robison, Henry.....
Robison, James.....

Rooks, Emanuel.....
Rosin, Levi.....
Riegel, Jacob.....
Sanders, Henry C.....

Shackelford, James B..... Canton
Spencer, John W..... McHenry's Mill
Stegr, Henri..... Canton
Stevenson, Edward..... "
Stevenson, Thomas..... "
Stickler, John..... "
Switzer, John..... "
Traphagan, Peter S..... "
Varner, Wilson P..... "
Wilcox, Alex. W..... "
Wycoff, William P..... "

Wilson, James W..... "

Kay, Arthur V.....
Shriner, John J.....
Small, Peter B.....
Spencer, David B.....
Stickler, John.....
Tyler, Augustus C..... Galesburg

Varner, Wilson P..... Canton

COMPANY L.

Captains.
George M. Scott..... Bushnell
Squire N. Fipperson..... "
Daniel M. Wilt..... "

First Lieutenants.
Warren W. Porter..... Johnson
James Price.....

Second Lieutenants.
Squire N. Fipperson..... Bushnell
Daniel M. Wilt..... "
Eliab F. Martin.....
Louis Pickle..... Raritan

First Sergeant.
William M. Morris..... Raritan

Q. M. Sergeant.
Alexander W. Scott..... Bardolph

Sergeants.
Israel Markham..... Bardolph
James W. Laney..... Bushnell
John R. Spurling.....
Eliab Martin..... "

Corporals.
James F. Vance..... Galva

Elijah Jacklin..... Raritan
Lester Husted..... N. Salem
Alexander Lockard.....

Richard C. Smith..... Bishop Hill
John T. Laney..... Bushnell
Henry B. Parvin.....
George A. Stansbury.....

Blacksmith.
Frank Lemon..... Raritan

Privates.
Alpaugh, Sylvanus..... Fairview
Arnold, James F..... Owen co., Ky.
Bates, Moses M..... Burnsville
Bledsoe, Henry T..... Knox co., Mo.
Boyd, Horatio N. B..... Cambridge
Case, Jacob..... Vermont
Clark, Jacob..... Burnsville
Cleland, Thomas..... Cass co., Mich.
Duncan, William L..... Bishop Hill
Dewey, George J..... Prairie City
Davis, Frederick..... Fairview
Francis, Henry H..... Colchester
Gauf, James W..... Bushnell
Hammer, John..... Bardolph
Harris, Alexander.....

Harland, James..... Table Grove

Hopwood, Josephus..... Bardolph
Huffman, William..... Fairview
Harris, William R..... Table Grove
Laney, Zachariah..... Burnsville
Lambert, David W..... Bushnell
Lark, William..... Dauphin co., Pa.
Lair, Daniel..... Bushnell

Longford, Thomas..... Rock Island

Long, Henry..... Bushnell
Meyer, Christian.....

Mathewson, Theophi's.. Broomfield
Meyers, Frederick..... Bardolph
Parks, David..... Bishop Hill
Price, James..... Johnston
Pickle, Louis..... Raritan
Post, George K..... Fairview

Pugh, Hiram H..... Cambridge
Powelson, Simon P..... Fairview
Quick, Peter V..... Allonia
Rogers, David G..... Fairview
Rodorner, George..... Bishop Hill
Smith, John B..... E. Cambridge

Schoffstoll, Samuel..... Raritan
Sholl, Samuel S..... Macomb

Thompson, Lemuel..... Allonia
Thompson, George P.....

Thompson, Abram P.....
Thompson, John.....

COMPANY (continued)

Vandyne, Emory D ... Bishop Hill
Wilt, Daniel M ... Bushnell
Wilson, Daniel M ... Bushnell
Wilson, James N ... Bardolph
Wilson, James ... Bushnell
Wilt, Solomon ... Fulton co., Pa.
Waters, Edward ... Table Grove

Veterans.
Adcock, Joseph E ... Bushnell
Bledsoe, Henry T ... Galva
Boyd, Horatio N. B ... Galva
Dewey, George J ... Bushnell
Francis, Henry H ... Galva
Hammer, John ...

Long, Henry ... Bushnell

Lark, William ...
Lambert, David W ...

Martin, Eliab ...

Price, James ... Galva
Pickle, Louis ... Bushnell
Rodgers, David G ... Knoxville

Scott, Alex. W ... Bushnell

Smith, Richard C ... Galva
Schotfstoll, Samuel ... Bushnell
Thompson, Abram P ... Galva

Thompson, John ...
Taylor, Leroy ... Bushnell
Wells, Andrew ... Lamoille
Wilt, Solomon ... Bushnell

COMPANY M.

Captains,
John P. Ludwig ... Red Bud
Bernard C. F. Janssen ...
Charles Stoll ...

First Lieutenants,
Bernard C. F. Janssen ... Red Bud
Charles Stoll ...
John Nicholson ...

Second Lieutenants,
John H. Meyer ... Red Bud
Henry Nicholson ...
Charles Valier ...
John Nicholson ...
Augustus Lesure ... Paris

First Sergeant,
... C. S. Bel ... Red Bud

Sergeants,
John W. Eppens ... Red Bud
Henry Klemmer ...

Q. M. Sergeant,
John N. Reitz ... Red Bud

Charles Stoll ... Red Bud
Henry Neuber ...

Corporals,
Jacob Zimpelman ... Red Bud
Charles Rathert
William H. Foley
Philip Thon
William Beckmeier
Charles Weking
Henry Ideker
Jacob Koenigstein

Buglers,
Daniel Fickies
Henry Dankenbring ... Red Bud

Farrier,
Henry Ritter ... Red Bud

Blacksmith,
Louis VanColten ... Red Bud

Saddler,
Herman Mueller ... Red Bud

Privates,
Allen, Miner E ... Red Bud
Andermann, George
Blattner, Samuel
Besse, Lorenz
Baer, Daniel
Brockmeier, Henry
Buhrmeister, Christ'n
Butz, John
Blatter, Randolph
Ducker, Casper
Ducker, Conrad

Emo, Niemrod

Egle, Frederick
Ennich, Jacob
Ellner, John
Fischer, Charles
Gubert, Charles
Gummel, Henry
Haestel, Hermann
Hitzemann, Ernst
Jannet, David
Joseph, John
Kroemer, Frederick C
Killerman, William
Kruger, Hermann
Kruse, Henry C
Koenigstein, Michael
Koch, William
Klopfer, Christian
Nimholz, Henry
Manderfeld, John
Murke, Henry

Norris, William
Nicholson, Henry
Nicholson, John
Paust, Melchior
Paust, Casper
Rice, George ... Red Bud
Rathert, Cort
Rathert, H. William
Rathert, Henry
Rathert, Frederic
Rosenmeir, Frederic
Schurhart, Charles
Sippel, Henry
Stock, Charles
Schaeffer, Stephen
Schlicher, John
Strackbein, Louis
Starr, Joseph
Selbert, Henry C

Schimeigall, Frederick

Schwartz, Joseph
Schwartz, Andrew

Schnett, Adam
Schneider, Jacob
Thurn, Gottlieb
Tillmann, George
Valleur, Charles

Veiht, Dr. Franz L ... Red Bud
Weber, Jacob
Wichel, John
Wagner, Henry
Weber, Michael
Wilhelms, August
Wither, Frederic

Wilson, Frederick
Wiele, Frederick

Veterans.
Andermann, George ... Red Bud
Buhrmeister, Christ'n

BATTERY K.*

Captains,
Angzean, Franklin ... Vienna
Jason B. Smith ... Vienna
Isaac W. Curtis ... Metropolis

First Lieutenants,
Jason B. Smith ... Vienna
Joseph P. Shelton ... Vienna
Isaac W. Curtis ... Metropolis

Second Lieutenants,
Wm. O. Stephenson ... Vienna
James G. Helm ... Metropolis

First Sergeant,
Isaac W. Curtis ... Metropolis

Q. M. Sergeant,
Joseph W. Franklin ... Vienna

Sergeants,
William H. Hower ... Metropolis
John B. Wilbourne ... Marion, Ky.
Elijah B. Franklin ...
Samuel Cummins ...

Corporals,
George W. Rice ... Metropolis
William H. Mick ... Golconda
George W. Leach ... Vienna
Wm. P. Whittenburg ...
Jeremiah Cummins ...
Robert A. Holm ...
Wm. H. Richardson ...
Alexander E. Wasson ... Golconda

Bugler,
Jasper N. Cross ... Vienna

Farrier,
William I. Marberey ... Vienna

Blacksmith,
Ambrose H. Smith ... Vienna

Wagoner,
George Clark ... Metropolis

Privates,
Butler, Allen ... Golconda
Benard, James
Beaze, John D ... Marion, Ky.
Bynum, Samuel M ... Vienna
Busby, James H
Bynum, Martin V
Birklow, William J ... Golconda
Bridges, Benjamin F ... Vienna
Boss, James H
Boales, William J ... Metropolis
Crowell, David M ... Vienna
Cummings, Martin A
Conger, John K
Carr, William G ... Metropolis
Cox, Alfred H ... Marion, Ky.
Canfield, Scott ... Vienna
Davidson, John S ... Vienna

Veterans.
George Clark ... Red Bud

		Veterans.	
Monday, John R	Golconda	Benard, James	Golconda
Mick, Charles		Burklow, James W	
McDonald, John	Marion, Ky	Crowell, David M	Vienna
Mick, Cornelius R ... Harrisburg	Golconda	Dixon, Francis M	Shawneetown
Mick, George W	New Columbia	Felps, Ezekiel	Metropolis
Pullen, Thomas F	Golconda	Frasier, William	
Presgrove, George W	Vienna	Farmer, James J	
Renfro, Stephen C	Golconda	Goddard, James	Golconda
Renfro, Francis A		Grisham, William H	Vienna
Robertson, Martin A		Harper, Matthew	Golconda
Rose, Francis M		Handley, James M	
Simpson, John P		Jaco, John	
Sweeney, William		Leverett, David	Vienna
Shufflebarger, Ellis		Lauderdale, Francis M	Golconda
Saylors, Lafayette		Miller, William W	
Thompson, Charles W		Modglin, James M	Metropolis
Tiley, James	Marion, Ky	Mick, William H	
Thomas, Charles	Shawneetown	Robertson, John A	Vienna
Virag, Frank	Vienna	Robertson, Martin A	Golconda
Whitesides, James A	New Columbia	Walker, Nathan G	Marion, Ky
Wilson, Henry G	Golconda	Williams, Jasper M	Vienna
Wallace, Hiram, Sr.		Wasson, Alexander E	Golconda
Wyatt, David L		*Recruits.*	
Walker, J. L. ... Vienna		Alford, William M	Golconda
		Anderson, Daniel W	Metropolis
		Black, William H	Vienna
		Belcher, Benjamin	Golconda
		Brewer, William H	
		Beard, Franklin	Vienna
		Bailey, George F	Golconda
		Cummins, George W	
		Clark, Wiley	Vienna
		Cross, William H	
		Caldwell, Edward	
		Chauncey, Oliver	
		Cross, James M	
		Dean, Samuel L	
		Fairfield, Hiram C	
		Fisher, Franklin A	
		Fisher, Robert W	Golconda
		Green, Enoch J	Metropolis
		Horn, John	Vienna
		Harris, John W	Golconda
		Harris, James T	Metropolis
		Hopkins, Anderson	Vienna
		Hard, Jacob	Vienna
		Hendley, James M	
		Irby, John H	Vienna
		Johnson, Jacob F	Metropolis
		Jackson, J. W.	Vienna
		Knight, John	Golconda
		Lacey, John	Vienna
		Lauderdale, David O	Golconda
		Lauderdale, Jasper N	Vienna
		Marberry, Leonard F	Golconda
		McCorkle, George W	

Dixon, Francis M	Golconda
Fulgham, James	
Farmer, Harrison	Vienna
Felps, Ezekiel	
Frasier, William	Shawneetown
Farmer, Jefferson Jas.	Metropolis
Farley, Nathaniel	
Gosage, James W	Golconda
Godard, Casper	Vienna
Grissom, John D	Golconda
Grissom, William	
Girtley, James	Vienna
Harper, Matthew	Golconda
Harper, James A	
Harper, William R	
Helm, James G	Metropolis
Harris, William D	
Irby, James	Vienna
Johnson, James H	Golconda
Johnson, John C	
Jaco, John	Marion, Ky
Kilpatrick, Wm. H	Vienna
Lacy, John W	Golconda
Lloyd, William J	
Leverett, David	
Lockeby, Elias	
Lodderdel, Francis M	Golconda
Modglin, James A	
McCorkle, Thomas G	Vienna
Morris, John C	Golconda
Miller, William W	
Nickelson, Thomas E	Vienna
Robberson, John	
Renfro, Samuel C	
Renfro, Francis M	
Scott, James	
Smith, Jasper F	
Smith, Hiram	
Skelton, Joseph P	
Scufflebarger, Wm. L	Golconda
Taylor, George W	Metropolis
White, John F	Vienna
Whitesides, Abram	Golconda
Warson, John F	
Walker, Thomas H	Metropolis
Williams, James	Vienna
Williams, William	
Walker, Wesley A	
Walker, Nathan G	Metropolis
Williams, Jasper M	Vienna
Williams, Abram D	Golconda
Williams, William J	
Williams, Thomas B	Vienna
Williams, Thomas	Vienna
Wallace, Hiram	Golconda
Wallace, James	

NOTE: More accurate individual records of those men listed above are available from:

National Archives (GSA)
Military Records
Room 13W
Seventh & Pennsylvania
Washington, D.C. 20408

The National Archives requires that their form be filled out with name of veteran, name of regiment number, company, etc. They will send the military records of the individual for a reasonable fee.

Index

Other Books by Larry Underwood

The Custer Fight and Other Tales of the Old West
Love and Glory: Women of the Old West
Guns, Gold and Glory
Geronimo and the Chiricahua Apaches